THE RAILWAY WORKSHOPS OF BRITAIN, 1823–1986

Also by Edgar J. Larkin

WORKS ORGANIZATION AND MANAGEMENT
THE ELEMENTS OF WORKSHOP TRAINING
MEMOIRS OF A RAILWAY ENGINEER

The Railway Workshops of Britain, 1823–1986

Edgar J. Larkin, OBE, CEng, FIMechE
and
John G. Larkin, MA, LLM (Cantab.), Barrister

MACMILLAN
PRESS

First published 1988

Published by
THE MACMILLAN PRESS LTD
Houndmills, Basingstoke, Hampshire RG21 2XS
and London
Companies and representatives
throughout the world

Printed in Hong Kong

British Library Cataloguing in Publication Data
Larkin, Edgar J.
The railway workshops of Britain, 1823–1986.
1. Great Britain. Railway services.
Rolling stock. Maintenance and Repair.
Workshops, to 1986
I. Title   II. Larkin, John G.
625.2'028'8
ISBN 0–333–39431–3

Dedicated to the hundreds of thousands of men and women who for several generations have made history as skilled, semi-skilled and unskilled staff, as workshop supervisors, as managerial staff and as chartered mechanical and electrical engineers, in the railway workshops of Great Britain during the nineteenth and twentieth centuries.

Contents

Preface

An undertaking of the size and complexity of a great national railway network requires the integration of a wide range of engineering and related skills. The story has already been told of the essential contributions of the civil engineers, signal engineers and operating staff: those who design, construct and maintain the permanent way, bridges, tunnels, stations and signalling equipment, and those who daily operate the trains. There can be little doubt that in the industrial revolution the men who made Great Britain great were the engineers, and in their forefront the railway engineers who not only designed, built and operated the railways and the vehicles but also pressed through Parliament the legislation which made their activities legitimate. Today, with a much greater range of technology affecting the development of the country, the influence of the railway engineer is comparatively less, but the standard of engineering in the railway workshops remains as high as ever.

It is no exaggeration to state that the history of the railways of Britain is in large measure the history of the main railway workshops of Britain. At the outset the railways created the need for the workshops, but without the workshops there could have been no railways. Once the workshops had been created, however, the way was open for them to provide the impetus and the means for the creation of more railways as the network expanded, a process which also fostered the propagation of more workshops. This book narrates the story of those workshops and of the people who have helped to make them the powerhouses of the railways. The development of the railway workshops has mirrored the growth and development of the railways themselves, and their history has often reflected advances and changes in the economic and social development of the nation.

This book meets the need for an authoritative and well-documented history of the railway workshops of Britain, which have been and continue to be involved with the various types of locomotives and power units as well as all the passenger and freight rolling stock, and also of the mechanical and electrical engineers and their skilled artisan staff who have constructed and efficiently maintained them for over one and a half centuries. The story is one of wide-ranging mechanical and electrical engineering interest and it is a story which has never previously been published. Many scores of good railway books have been written over the years, but this is the first time that the principal features of all the main workshops have been fully described. This omission can readily be ascribed to the fact that railway engineers are seldom inclined to put pen to paper in order to explain their work and achievements. The authors have benefited from the support of British Rail in all aspects of the project and from access to a wealth of resources which have been brought together to record a great deal of fascinating railway history. A special feature of this publication is the extensive Appendix, which contains tables giving valuable statistical information, much of it never before published. Their compilation, involving many hundreds of hours of research, puts on record information which could otherwise have been lost for ever.

The main workshops are the home of British Rail's new manufacture, major modifications and heavy repairs of locomotives, carriages and wagons. A main works on British Rail is defined as one in which the new manufacture of locomotives, carriages and/or wagons, and/or any type of heavy repair, is undertaken. Work undertaken in the separate workshops of the Civil Engineering Department, the Signal and Telecommunications Department, the Motive Power Running Depots, the Electric Car Service Depots and Carriage and Wagon Depots for day to day maintenance and the Outdoor Machinery Department has been excluded to keep the scope of the book within reasonable bounds. Private contractors' workshops have also been excluded from detailed consideration. Design aspects have largely been omitted because design was not an integrated railway workshop function until 1984.

It was resolved at an early stage that the main railway workshops to be highlighted in this history should be those in operation at the time that the amalgamation of the railways under the Railways Act 1921 came into effect, on Vesting Day, 1 January 1923, when the four autonomous main-line railway companies were formed. It was also resolved that the individual histories of each works should be arranged under each of the four railway companies formed in 1923. Chapters 2, 3, 4 and 5 collectively describe the origins of the forty-two main works of the four group railway companies which came into existence at that date. The main preoccupation of all these works was locomotive, carriage and wagon construction and repairs. Since that time most of the works have been closed and the workload involved concentrated in the continuing works. Irrespective of whether the works are still functioning or have been closed, and irrespective of size, they are arranged in chronological order of date built, to facilitate appreciation of the historical development of the works and their indispensable place in the development of British Rail from its earliest forerunners onwards.

This is a concise yet substantial work which traces the story from George Stephenson and the early days of steam, through the subsequent expansion of the railways during the nineteenth century, through amalgamation in 1923 and nationalisation in 1948, through adaptation from steam to diesel and electric traction, and through subsequent contraction. It is indeed a unique story which will appeal to all who share an interest in the influence of the railways on the history of our national life. Such an illuminating and comprehensive story could only be written by one or more long-serving railway engineers who had attained to top-level management positions in the workshops. Some retired senior engineers discussed the project and agreed to go ahead for the sake of posterity before it was too late. The most senior was R.C. Bond (1903–80), formerly Chief Mechanical Engineer of British Rail, later General Manager of BR Workshops Division, a Past President and Fellow of the Institution of Mechanical Engineers, a Fellow of the Institution of Civil Engineers and Companion of Engineering; he assisted at the outset in determining the overall scope and titles of the various chapters in conjunction with a few of his colleagues.

Acknowledgements

A comprehensive work of this kind, which has taken five years to put together, could not have been so authoritative without the able assistance of many friends and colleagues, and the authors express their grateful thanks to all those who have assisted in giving answers to specific enquiries.

At the outset of the project considerable assistance was provided by Ian D. Gardiner, BSc, CEng, FIMechE, Director of Engineering, British Rail, and formerly Chairman of the Railway Division of the Institution of Mechanical Engineers (1982–3). In his former capacity as Managing Director of BREL he kindly requested all senior management located at BREL Headquarters in Derby, and all the Works Managers of the main works, to co-operate fully. He also kindly arranged for Alastair Brown, BA, to undertake a wide range of historical research work on our behalf and for which assignment the latter proved to have a special ability. These arrangements were a splendid gesture and added enormously to the wealth of valuable information which we received.

We are also grateful to Philip A. Norman, CEng, FIMechE, Chairman and Managing Director of BREL, for his support of the project in its final stages. Our thanks are due to two retired long-serving senior railway officers formerly at BREL Headquarters, R. C. S. Low, MC, BSc, CEng, FIMechE, Engineering Director, and S. A. S. Smith, CEng, FIMechE, Technical Manager. The former provided some useful material for Chapters 6 and 13, and the latter undertook research and prepared material for Chapters 10, 11 and 12.

We are indebted to British Rail for providing many of the photographs and illustrations in the book, and to Buckingham Palace for permission to use a photograph of HM the Queen and HRH the Duke of Edinburgh. We are grateful to the Department of Transport for the provision of and permission to reproduce valuable statistical information concerning road transport. We benefited greatly from the assistance of two prominent librarians in the build-up of material. These were C. P. Atkins, Librarian at the National Railway Museum, York, and S. G. Morrison, Librarian at the Institution of Mechanical Engineers, London.

The names of the following contributors will be recognised as including former General Managers and Chief Officers and former and present senior management staff within the railway organisation; they provided relevant material for different chapters. Several former and present Works Managers also provided information concerning the works they have controlled. The authors express their sincere appreciation to all the undermentioned for their willing co-operation and for the valuable information which they supplied: J. J. C. Barker-Wyatt; D. S. M. Barrie, OBE, OStJ, FCIT; A. E. Bates, CEng, FIMechE; Dr M. R. Bonavia; G. Brecknell; J. B. Campbell; B. Carmichael; M. V. Casey, BSc(Eng), CEng, FIMechE; F. G. Clements, MBE, CEng, FIMechE; F. Coles; P. Corbishley, BSc(Econ); Joan Cox;

Acknowledgements

W. J. Currie; G. R. Curry; A. G. Dunkley; N. Dytham; A. H. Emerson, CEng, FIMechE, FIEE; J. D. Forster; G. H. Foulk; C. H. Garratt; D. Gibbons; Frances Heckler; D. Hitchings; P. Holmes; J. A. Horton; N. J. Hunter; G. A. Hutcheson, MSc(Eng); F. B. Illston, CEng, FIMechE; G. M. James, CEng, MIMechE; J. Jarvis, CEng MIMechE; J. Jennings; H. J. Johnson; H. E. Kemp, MBE, CEng, MIMechE; A. G. Kentridge, BSc (ChemEng); Janet A. Kierton; E. A. Langridge, CEng, MIMechE; the Rev. Peter J. Larkin; D. J. Lees, BSc; J. I. MacDonald; G. H. D. Mackie, OBE; T. Matthewson-Dick, CEng, FIMechE, FIEE, ACIT; R. Meads; H. W. Mear; T. C. B. Miller, MBE, OStJ, CEng, FIMechE; F. O. de Nobriga; Kathleen Odell; Sir Peter Parker, MVO; Clare Patchett; A. S. Peck, CEng, FIMechE; S. R. D. Power, MBE, MA, BAI, CEng, FIMechE, FIEE, MICE; M. C. Purbrick, CEng, FICE; B. Reed; R. T. Ribbons, CEng, FIMechE; S. Ridgway, CEng, FIMechE; H. R. Roberts; A. E. Robson, OBE, CEng, FIMechE; A. D. Roche; C. F. Rose; L. I. Sanders, CEng, FIMechE; C. F. Saunders; F. W. Sidders; G. T. Smithyman, CEng, FIMechE; J. R. Stables, CEng, FIMechE; G. C. Stevens, MBE; D. R. Taylor; G. H. Taylor; R. H. Wilcox; S. Wise; C. R. Wood; L. N. S. Wooler.

Useful information was contributed by various local authorities and railway societies. These included: for Chapter 2, *Caerphilly:* R. Douglas Scobie, MIPR, Public Relations Officer, Rhymney Valley District Council; County Councillor H. P. Richards, Caerphilly Historical Society; *Swindon:* Borough of Thamesdown; *Wolverhampton:* Miss Elizabeth A. Rees, Archivist, Public Libraries Department, Metropolitan Borough of Wolverhampton; for Chapter 3, *Barrow-in-Furness:* R. Smith, Local History Librarian, Barrow-in-Furness Library, Cumbria County Council; *Bromsgrove:* R. B. Brotherton, Estate Agent, Bromsgrove; J. M. C. Pugh, Solicitor, Bromsgrove; D. A. Stokes, District Secretary, Bromsgrove District Council; *Crewe:* David H. Arnold, Public Relations Dept, and J. Greenwood, Chief Planning Officer's Dept, Borough of Crewe and Nantwich; *Derby:* City of Derby; *Horwich:* T. K. Campbell, Archivist, Arts Department, Bolton Metropolitan Borough; *Kilmarnock:* Kilmarnock and Loudoun District Council; *Stoke-on-Trent:* J. H. Kelly, Keeper of Social History, City Museum and Art Gallery, City of Stoke-on-Trent; for Chapter 4, Peter Holmes, Hon. Secretary, The Gresley Society; *Cowlairs:* Dr Ian Grant, Assistant Keeper, Scottish Record Office; *Darlington:* Mrs F. M. Layfield, District Librarian, Darlington Branch, Durham County Library; *Doncaster:* Doncaster Metropolitan Borough; *Walkergate:* City of Newcastle-upon-Tyne; for Chapter 5, *Ashford:* Mrs J. I. Tindall, FLA, Divisional Librarian, and Mrs Janet Adamson, Deputy Divisional Librarian, Kent County Council, County Library, Ashford Division.

We are also indebted to Roland C. Bond's son, Robin, who kindly gave access to his father's unique collection of BR workshop history before it was transferred to the National Railway Museum, York.

To all concerned we tender our warmest thanks.

List of Plates

The plates are numbered according to the chapters to which they correspond.

List of Figures

List of Figures

1 Railway History Affecting the Workshops

BEFORE THE 1923 AMALGAMATION

The nineteenth century in Britain, a period of momentous and exciting change, was the era when the railway workshops appeared on the industrial scene in which they were to play a decisive role. The spread of the 'iron way' across the country, the development of locomotives and rolling stock, the story of the railway founding fathers, all conjure up a romantic picture closely associated with Britain's industrial progress. Once the idea of the railway had been conceived, there had to be a place where rails were cast and iron plates and castings made to produce the component parts of the locomotives, carriages and wagons, and where they could be assembled, aided only by the simplest equipment and powered largely by human muscle.

The introduction of steam engines enabled Richard Trevithick to design a locomotive which was built in 1804 at Penydarren ironworks, South Wales. The undeveloped concept of railways had come to the mines of northern England from the continent in the sixteenth century, and this locomotive was designed to operate on colliery tramways. Early locomotive development owes much to the genius of men like Trevithick, Blenkinsop, William Hedley and Timothy Hackworth. Many were friends of the great George Stephenson, who was essentially a practical engineer. He is said to have had a faith which was to tunnel the earth and bridge the sea to smite a path for the iron child of his dreams. Pioneers like him and his son Robert planned, designed, built, maintained and operated the emerging railways and fought the Railway Bills through Parliament. The first locomotive works in Britain was Robert Stephenson's Forth Street works at Newcastle-upon-Tyne, established in 1823 as a contract workshop associated with the Stockton & Darlington Railway. As the railway boom swept the country, the Stephensons became increasingly involved in the expanding network, and there can be no doubt of the profound effect which they had upon the industrial and social history of Britain and the world.

Other contract works emerged in the north of England as the demand for railway vehicles increased, including Mather & Dixon of Liverpool (1827); Edward Bury of Liverpool (1830); R. & W. Hawthorn of Newcastle (1831); Sharp Roberts of Manchester (1833); and Charles Tayleur, Vulcan Foundry, Newton-le-Willows (1833). Many had originally supplied machinery to the cotton industry and stationary steam engines for a range of industries. Their entry into the locomotive business was undoubtedly stimulated by the opening of the two pioneer railways, the Stockton & Darlington (1825) and the Liverpool & Manchester (1830). The history of these early locomotive works provides little evidence of where carriages and wagons were built, but from their design they must have been produced by builders of horse-drawn carriages, who adapted their product for mounting on sturdy frames and running on flanged iron wheels. The need soon arose for maintenance facilities. Engineers were regularly confronted by the failure of parts requiring replacement, and most running repairs were carried out on the line side. As railways became operational rather than experimental, a place was needed where heavier engineering work could be performed and where equipment could be housed. The first railway repair workshop was opened at New Shildon in Durham under the direction of Hackworth to handle heavy repairs following the opening of the Stockton & Darlington Railway.

More railways connecting two cities or industrial towns began to appear, both in the south (Canterbury & Whitstable, 1830; London & Birmingham, 1833) and in the north (Glasgow & Coatbridge, 1831; Dundee & Newtyle, 1833). The rolling stock continued to be built in the contract works in the north of England. Repair facilities were rudimentary and help was sought from local engineering firms and millwrights, including ironworks and forges. The lack of experienced engineers placed heavy demands on men like George Stephenson and Edward Bury, who acted as engineering superintendents for these railways. No railway works started in the 1830s was initially equipped to build vehicles; they existed solely to carry out repairs.

A new phase began in the 1840s with the linking of several city-to-city railways to form some of the major pre-amalgamation railways, and eleven main works were established. This decade saw the appointment of locomotive superintendents on a number of railways: men such as Daniel Gooch at Swindon, with the ability to design and build their own locomotives. By the middle of the century railway mania was still in full swing. The only competition came from horse-drawn transport, and although the roads had steadily improved, the financial justification for a railway was readily made. Smaller railways continued to obtain their rolling stock from contract works, but wherever an engineer of experience and initiative was appointed he soon put his ideas to the test and built his own locomotives. The demand for rolling stock was so great that the contract works were still fully occupied. By the second half of the century most of the larger firms were producing locomotives and other equipment for overseas railways, particularly in India and Africa, and were seldom involved in maintenance work for the larger railway groups. Gradually the whole country was covered by a railway network, through routes were established operating over the tracks of adjoining companies, and numerous small railways amalgamated to form larger, more viable companies.

Workshop development is necessarily an ever-changing process, with flexibility required to meet changing commitments and available resources. Throughout the century technology not only advanced the development of railway operation, but also made a great contribution to general mechanical engineering. It was no coincidence that in 1847 George Stephenson became the first President of the Institution of Mechanical Engineers, at a time when the skill and achievement of Britain's engineers were contributing to her development as a leading world power. The main workshops became the engineering centre of each railway, where locomotives and rolling stock were designed, built and repaired, and this helped to encourage the emergence of outstanding personalities. The Locomotive Superintendent, or Chief Mechanical Engineer (CME) as the senior engineer was known on some railways, held sway uninhibited by departmental organisation, and some of the chiefs of those days – such as F. W. Webb of Crewe – were powerful and autocratic characters.

With growing expertise came a desire for self-sufficiency. Most larger works had their own iron and brass foundries, forge, and press, boiler, machine, smith's and erecting shops. At Swindon and Crewe the machinery included rolling mills producing steel billets for the heavy forge and press shops and even the running rails. The expansion of the railways exerted an enormous effect on the social structure of the country, and the establishment of a railway works in an area often had profound consequences. When the railways were at their zenith whole towns grew up around railway works, and they provided services now undertaken by local or central government.

The end of the century came with the railways financially sound. Table 1.1 shows the number of staff employed by private contractors at the time. Expansion had given way to consolidation and improvement of services. After the first world war, during which little capital investment was channelled into railway requirements, the companies were in financial difficulties and also beginning to encounter a new competitive form of transport, the road motor vehicle: never again would the railway have a monopoly. Even before 1923 individual railways saw the need to join together to improve their chances of survival; for example, the London & North Western Railway

TABLE 1.1   *No. of staff employed in the British locomotive industry in 1900*

Name of company	No. of staff employed
Neilson & Co.	3 275
Dübs & Co.	2 017
Beyer Peacock	1 866
Sharp Stewart	1 561
Kitson	1 440
Robert Stephenson	1 047
Vulcan	820
Manning Wardle	590
Nasmyth Wilson	526
Hunslet Engine Co.	300
Total	13 442

joined with the London & Yorkshire, and the Midland Railway absorbed the London, Tilbury & Southend and the Somerset & Dorset Railways. The stage was set for a far-reaching reappraisal of the railway transportation of the country.

1923 AMALGAMATION TO 1947

The quarter of a century from 1 January 1923 to 31 December 1947 was the era of the four autonomous railway companies: the Great Western (GWR), the London Midland & Scottish (LMS), the London & North-Eastern (LNER) and the Southern (SR). It was during this period that Britain's railways reached their peak in overall efficiency. The influence of road transport was still only marginal, but following the first world war there was a need to rationalise in order to complete and to obtain Government support for re-equipment. The Railways Act 1921 provided for the amalgamation of 120 companies into the four great main-line companies (see Appendix). Under the new companies some subsidiary works were closed and certain specialised activities were concentrated in the main works as part of the process of rationalisation.

Between 1923 and the second world war the railway companies were able to follow stable policies, but although by 1939 they had reached a peak of technical and operating efficiency, profitability declined. This was, however, the heyday of the steam locomotive. Substantial progress was made towards a programme of new locomotive and rolling stock construction as well as the provision of modern workshop equipment to make up for the lean years of the first world war. Significantly, each company developed its own headquarters and workshops organisation and introduced its own designs of locomotives and rolling stock. A limited number of design and running standards, such as the profile of wheel tyres, were agreed by the four CMEs at their regular CMEs' Committee. In addition to their control of the main works, CMEs' considerable responsibilities included the design, installation and maintenance of all mechanical and electrical equipment and lighting throughout the company. The main exception was the low voltage requirements of the signal and telecommunications engineers, who had their own workshops. The CME's department was the largest technical department on each railway, and his wide responsibilities accounted for a high proportion of all the professional, technical, supervisory, clerical and artisan staff employed by his company (see Figure 1.1).

The four new 'group' companies – as they were officially termed – established firm individual characteristics. Each of the constituent companies had enjoyed its independence over a long period and had developed an organisation which best suited it. From 1923 they all needed to conform to a co-ordinated pattern of organisation adopted by their amalgamated company.

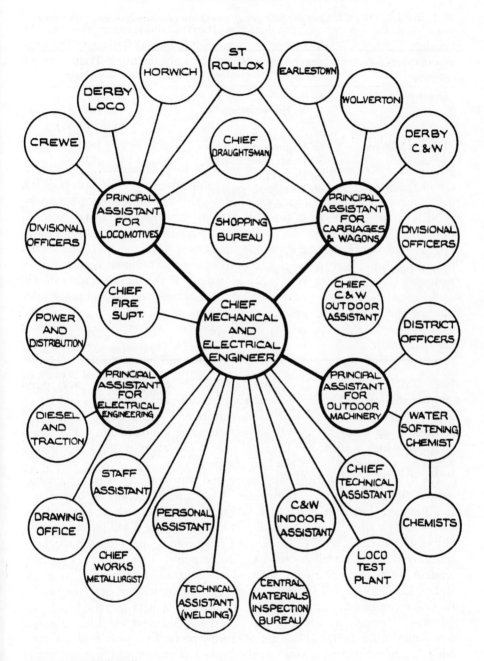

SOURCE British Rail

FIGURE 1.1 *Pre-nationalisation functions of the CM&EE of the LMS, illustrative of the extensive responsibilities of the four CM&EEs. Those of the GWR and LNER had additional responsibility for the motive power department.*

TABLE 1.2   *The CMEs of the four group companies on amalgamation and their successors*

Railway company	Chief Mechanical Engineer	Year appointed
Great Western	C. B. Collett	1923
	F. W. Hawkesworth	1941
		(retired 1949)
London Midland & Scottish	G. Hughes	1923
	Sir Henry Fowler, KBE	1925
	Sir Ernest Lemon	1931
	Sir William A. Stanier, FRS	1932
	C. E. Fairburn	1944
	H. G. Ivatt	1945
		(retired 1952)
London & North-Eastern	Sir Nigel Gresley, CBE	1923
	E. Thompson, OBE	1941
	A. H. Peppercorn	1946
		(retired 1950)
Southern	R. E. L. Maunsell	1923
	O. V. S. Bulleid, CBE	1937
		(retired 1951)

Each CME (see Table 1.2) was naturally influenced by his own background and experience, and hence the four adopted different approaches and set up different organisations at their headquarters and in the works under their control. Each main works was subject to some control from CME head-quarters, which was the fundamental reason for many of the differences in works organisation between the four companies.

The GWR retained its original name and was less influenced by amalga-mation than the other three companies. A unique feature was the disparity in size between Swindon and other GWR main works, which adapted the Swindon-style organisation to local conditions. On the LMS authority initi-ally vested in Mechanical Engineers at Crewe, Derby and Horwich was later transferred to CME headquarters, and the responsibilities of a works superin-tendent were confined to the internal administration of his works. At St Rollox Locomotive and Carriage Works the responsibilities of a Mechanical Engineer continued, but with a large measure of control exercised by head-quarters. Through its strongly centralised management the LMS pursued economies in the better utilisation of motive power by a system of diagram-ming, made substantial savings in the main locomotive and carriage works with its standardised form of functional organisation, and rationalised the manufacture of large numbers of components at particular works through its Manufacturing Costs Committee, which operated from CME headquarters. Its first chairman was R.A. Riddles.

The LNER had at its four main locomotive works a Mechanical Engineer who, as well as running the locomotive works and carriage & wagon works, also controlled the functions of the CME's department within his geographical area, including maintenance of outdoor machinery and electrical services and the provision of technical stores. At Cowlairs he was also responsible for Inverurie Works. The LNER system resulted in works retaining greater autonomy than existed on the other three railways. On the Southern Railway the importance of steam traction continued after 1923, owing to the virtual cessation of further electrification. The increase in engine building which resulted from co-ordinating the resources of the three main locomotive works under the detailed direction of CME headquarters had no counterpart on the other railways. Works Managers' authority was confined to the works. The responsibility of the CME for running repairs at the sheds was, however, similar to that of the GWR.

There were thus two fundamental differences in the administration of the main works of the four railways. On the LMS and SR Works Managers were confined to supervising internal works matters, whereas on the GWR and LNER (where they were called Mechanical Engineers) they also had responsibilities away from the works. By 1923 many settled features of workshop organisation had emerged. The need was clearly recognised for close collaboration at all levels between those who designed, built and maintained locomotives and rolling stock and those who used them. Works were not normally concerned with design, except perhaps to advise on modifications to reduce the cost of production: design responsibility and quality assurance control traditionally rested with the CME.

On the LMS and SR motive power arrangements were broadly similar in principle: the motive power section was an integral part of the operating department, its superintendent being responsible to the Chief Operating Manager for non-technical aspects of his work and to the CME for locomotive maintenance in the motive power depots. The LNER motive power section (called the Locomotive Running Department) was more independent. The LNER had no all-line officer in charge of the department as a whole. Instead it had a divisional Locomotive Running Superintendent responsible to each of the General Managers of its four administrative areas. Locomotive maintenance at the running sheds, however, as well as in the main works, had to conform to standards laid down by the CME. The GWR differed from the other companies in that locomotive running was the CME's responsibility, through a Locomotive Running Assistant. Locomotive maintenance in the running sheds was thus under his direct control. The dual nature of motive power work should always be recognised: its essence is to maintain at all times an even balance between the demands of the Operating Department and the requirements of the Mechanical and Electrical Engineer and workshops. The arrangements brought into operation from 1923 were not standardised until after nationalisation in 1948.

A feature distinguishing British railway workshops from those of most countries was their involvement in work arising from activities other than running trains – docks, shipping services, hotels – but their principal function has always been the manufacture and maintenance of most of the locomotives and rolling stock, despite the existence of a well-established locomotive, carriage and wagon building industry, which has largely manufactured for export. In the main workshops new manufacture has always been sporadic, whereas maintenance, the ever-present problem, has consistently represented a high proportion – if not all – of the workload. New manufacture has normally provided a balancing load to keep expensive machine tools and equipment fully utilised, often on a double shift. Outside contracts for new locomotives have only been made when spare capacity has temporarily been fully absorbed.

AFTER NATIONALISATION

The Transport Act 1947 set up the British Transport Commission on 1 January 1948 to take over the nation's principal transport undertakings, and provided for a Railway Executive to administer British Railways. In 1948 the four companies were divided into six regions, each with a Chief Regional Officer, over whom the Railway Executive exercised direct functional control (see Fig. 1.2). Robert Riddles, formerly Technical Vice-President of the LMS, was appointed as the railway executive member responsible for Mechanical, Electrical and Road Motor Engineering, exercising supreme control over the regional CMEs. His five senior officers at headquarters were: R.C. Bond, Chief Officer (Locomotive Construction and Maintenance); C.M. Cock, Chief Electrical Engineer; E. Pugson, Chief Officer (Carriage and Wagon Construction and Maintenance); E.S. Cox, Executive Officer (Design); and A.E.C. Dent, Road Motor Engineer. As the four former CMEs retired (see Table 1.2) Riddles split up their modified departments, appointing in their place a Mechanical and Electrical Engineer and a Carriage and Wagon Engineer in each region (see Table 1.3).

The workshops' regional organisation was now subjected to the most comprehensive investigation in its history. Riddles set up two policy committees within a week of nationalisation, followed by several more. The first, the Locomotive Repairs Policy Committee (chaired by J. F. Harrison, Assistant CME, Eastern and North-Eastern Region), was to examine the methods the companies had used to decide when locomotives should be sent for repair and to recommend a system for universal adoption. Its remit was based upon five principles:

(1) The decision as to whether or not a locomotive should be agreed for shop repairs would be made by the Regional Mechanical Engineer's department;

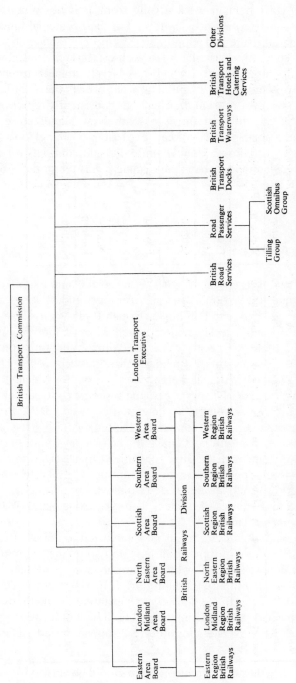

NOTE.—" Other Divisions " include Pullman Car Co., Thos. Cook and Son Ltd., and certain other organisations controlled by the Commission.

SOURCE   British Rail

FIGURE 1.2   *British Transport Commission: outline organisation of divisions, 1948. Total staff approximately 750 000 of which 450 000 BR employees.*

TABLE 1.3   *The four CMEs at nationalisation in 1948 and their immediate successors in the six new regions of British Railways*

Railway company	Last Chief Mechanical Engineer	Replaced by		Region	Regional HQ	Departmental HQ
		Mechanical & Electrical Engineer	Carriage & Wagon Engineer			
Great Western	F. W. Hawkesworth	K. J. Cook	H. Randle	Western	Paddington, London	Swindon
London Midland & Scottish	H. G. Ivatt	J. F. Harrison	H. Randle	London Midland	Euston, London	Derby
		M. S. Hatchell	J. Blair	Scottish	Glasgow	Glasgow
London & North-Eastern	A. H. Peppercorn	J. F. Harrison	A. E. Robson	Eastern	Liverpool St Station, London	Doncaster
				North-Eastern	York	Doncaster
Southern	O. V. S. Bulleid	S. B. Warder	F. Munns	Southern	Waterloo Station, London	Brighton & Eastleigh

(2) Such a decision would be based only on the actual condition of each individual locomotive;

(3) The stock of locomotives would at all times be maintained in first-class mechanical condition;

(4) The expenditure incurred on the maintenance of locomotives would be the minimum consistent with principle (3) above;

(5) The resources of all works in each region and between the various regions would be used to the best advantage.

The second committee, the Locomotive Works Organisation Committee (chaired by E. J. Larkin, Assistant to the CME, London Midland Region) included representatives of the CMEs of Eastern, Southern and Western Regions. Its remit commented that whilst the work done at the main locomotive works was generally the same in all regions, the forms of organisation differed. There was probably one form which, having regard to the size of the works and other local factors, was the most efficient. If so it should be applied to all regions. The committee was therefore required to:

report in full detail upon the organisation of the main locomotive works in all regions, showing up in chart form the lines of responsibility and duties of the various assistants and supervisory grades employed, with particular reference to:

(1) the organisation for controlling the progressing of locomotive repairs; and

(2) the control of new manufacturing activities, e.g. new locomotives and boilers, and spare parts required for locomotive maintenance.

The committee's report (December 1948) – a wide review of the organisation at the eighteen locomotive works, including costs, output and methods of control of construction and repairs – highlighted strong general grounds for introducing tighter control and co-ordination between the various sections. A standardised, clearly-defined organisation would improve efficiency; full-scale production planning should be introduced, and the most economical methods laid down in precise terms; there should be means of collecting reliable production data so that operating efficiency could be improved. It recommended a functional type of organisation, with clear lines of demarcation between the duties of the various managers and supervisors.

In September 1949 Larkin chaired a committee of senior carriage and wagon officers with a similar remit relating to carriage and wagon works, which also recommended (December 1950) a functional type of organisation. These two reports played a significant role in the decision on the management pattern adopted in the subsequent reorganisations. The most important of the other committees was the Design Committee, chaired by E.S. Cox, which investigated motive power requirements. Riddles decided on twelve standard types of steam locomotive, of which 999 were built, and a 350 hp diesel-electric shunting locomotive designed to meet all BR requirements.

TABLE 1.4   *Number of steam locomotives*
of company design built following
nationalisation in 1948

Former company	Steam locomotives built
GWR	452
LMSR	640
LNER	396
SR	50
Total	1 538

TABLE 1.5   *Number of BR steam locomotives*
of new Standard designs built 1951–60

Wheel classification	Power classification	Number built
4–6–2	8	1
4–6–2	7	55
4–6–2	6	10
4–6–0	5	172
4–6–0	4	80
2–6–0	4	115
2–6–0	3	20
2–6–0	2	65
2–6–4	4	155
2–6–2	3	45
2–6–2	2	30
2–10–0	9	251
Total		999

(Previously there were in operation about 20 000 steam locomotives of 448 types, many of which were gradually phased out.)

Riddles retired in 1953, having achieved a major pioneering task. The Transport Act 1953 disbanded the Railway Executive and set up a Railway Division under the Transport Commission; the BR Central Staff now came into being. The Chief Regional Officers became Chief Regional Managers and in 1955, when functional control reverted to the regions and Area Boards were appointed, were redesignated General Managers. Sir Brian (later Lord) Robertson was chairman of the commission when the Government authorised a plan for the modernisation and re-equipment of British Railways, to be implemented within fifteen years. The pre-nationalisation companies had not had the financial resources for main-line electrification, or to replace the outdated freight fleet, and at nationalisation in 1948 the Government had been unable to allocate finance to make good the arrears of wartime maintenance, still less to assist modernisation. After the war the railways paid their way until 1952, but then became increasingly unprofitable.

Under the plan steam was gradually to be replaced by electric or diesel traction. This involved electrifying many miles of track and introducing thousands of electric or diesel locomotives. All steam-drawn passenger rolling stock had to be replaced, largely by multiple-unit electric or diesel trains; the remainder, to be drawn by electric, diesel or steam locomotives, had to be modernised; and the principal passenger stations and parcel depots required considerable expenditure.

The commission proposed to authorise no new passenger or suburban steam locomotives after 1956, and to end all steam locomotive building within a few years. It was envisaged that the initial programme of diesel shunting units to replace steam locomotives would be completed in 1957, and another was being prepared. The elimination of shunting and trip working by steam locomotives – some 1500 of them being replaced by about 1200 diesel locomotives, additional to those already authorised – was to be achieved over fifteen years, by which time it was envisaged that about 2500 main-line diesel locomotives would be in use, and some 31 000 new passenger carriages. Between 1948 and 1954, 258 diesel shunting units were built; under the plan a further 1780 were built between 1955 and 1964, as well as 2251 main-line diesel (electric and hydraulic) locomotives (see Table 1.6).

The modernisation centred around new equipment: continuous brakes fitted to all freight wagons to bring about faster, smoother freight traffic operation; resited and modernised goods terminal facilities and marshalling yards (the latter to be reduced in number); larger wagons, particularly for mineral traffic; and extensive modernisation of loading and unloading appliances (see Fig. 1.3). There would also be track and signalling improvements

TABLE 1.6   *1954 estimate of BR fleet size by 1967*

Type of stock	Number	Totals
Locomotives		
Diesel main-line	3 570	
Electric main-line	358	
Diesel shunting	2 011	
Steam	4 000	9 939
Coaching stock		
Locomotive-hauled passenger-carrying	15 000	
Diesel multiple unit	2 500	
Electric multiple unit	7 500	
Non-passenger-carrying	8 000	33 000
Wagons (all types)		500 000

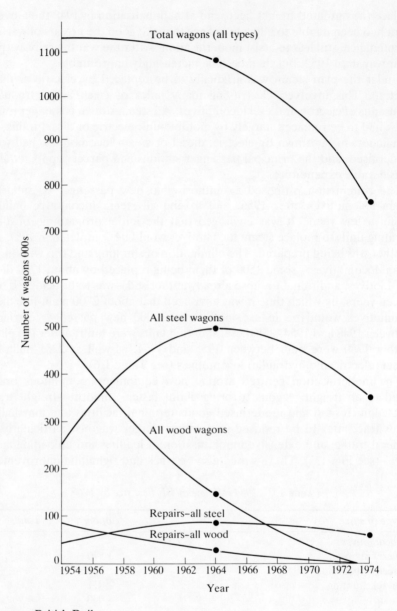

Source   British Rail
Notes:
(a) Figures are based on a heavy repair every 6 years.
(b) Reduction in total wagon numbers reflects increased carrying capacity and reduced train timings due to the introduction of continuous brakes.

Figure 1.3   *Twenty-year forecast of BR wagon stock trends, 1954.*

to make higher speeds possible over trunk routes and to make better use of the physical assets; an extended use of colour-light signalling, track circuits, automatic train control and modern telecommunications services; more power-operated signal boxes; and the installation of centralised traffic control where conditions were suitable. This involved the expenditure of £1240 million (later increased to £1500 million), an unprecedented amount to spend on the railways in a single package. The plan made no direct reference to the effect on the main works, but they clearly played a major role in providing and maintaining the developing forms of motive power and rolling stock. It was apparent that diesel-engined units and electrical control equipment would have to be purchased from the trade, thereby reducing the staff in some large works. Dr Beeching commented in 1963:

> It was a plan to modernise equipment, but it did not envisage any basic changes in the scope of railway services or in the general mode of operation of the railway system. It was expected that the substitution of electric and diesel haulage for steam, concentration of marshalling yards, reduction in number and increased mechanisation of goods depots, resignalling, and the introduction of other modern equipment, would make the railways pay by reducing costs and attracting more traffic.

Many of the schemes envisaged by the modernisation plan were in progress when, on 31 December 1961, the Transport Commission was disbanded, each of its divisions being empowered to have its own board. Robertson retired and Dr Richard Beeching was appointed Chairman of the new British Railways Board, which first met on 6 December 1961. Beeching never regarded the plan as viable; he endorsed the electrification, permanent way and signalling schemes and some other major improvements, but was outspoken in saying that there had been no fundamental reappraisal of the shape and form of the railway system and that the commercial outlook was too superficial. He was particularly conscious of the effects of increased road transport on both freight and passenger traffic, especially on branch lines. For many years freight receipts had far exceeded passenger receipts, but then the situation had reversed, with a much smaller total in real money terms, whilst duplication and unprofitable services had continued. Beeching advocated a critical examination to ascertain the volume of railway traffic which was potentially worthwhile and to identify which parts of the network should be discarded, before deciding on modern methods of conducting the system on the basis that a nationalised railway should have no duplication of main-line services (such as Paddington to Birmingham *and* Euston to Birmingham). In 1963 he produced his historic report *The Re-Shaping of British Railways*, which outlined large-scale economies and substantial reduction in route miles.

In 1961 the first Regional Chief Mechanical and Electrical Engineers were appointed with overall control of both locomotive and carriage and wagon workshops, but the 1962 Transport Act transferred control of the main works from the regions to the new board. The new centralised organisation, called

British Railways Workshops Division, had its headquarters in Derby and was regarded as of equal status with the six (later five) regions. A new feature was the establishment within the division of Accountants' and Supplies Departments, both previously under separate departments. In addition each Works Manager had a Works Accountant and a Supplies Officer.

The 1962 reorganisation was based on a radical workshops plan produced by Sir Steuart Mitchell, a board member, who became Deputy Chairman in 1963. This involved closing twenty-one main works and a sweeping rationalisation of the workload. The plan was based on a number of fundamental principles:

(1) The greatest economy was to be obtained by maintaining the smallest number of works compatible with satisfying the needs of the Railway Operating Department;

(2) The workshops to be retained should be the most efficient and productive, subject to geographical factors being taken into account to avoid excessive light-running to and from the workshops;

(3) The main functions of the works should be to carry out repairs, with an economic margin to be taken up by new construction;

(4) The predominant factor in deciding which workshops to retain should be the provision of efficient and reliable service to the regions.

After approval by the Minister of Transport the plan was conveyed to the trade unions at a meeting of the Railway Shopmen's National Council in London on 19 September 1962, chaired by Mitchell. No main works had been closed for more than thirty years and there was considerable unrest and ill-feeling amongst the staff following the announcement that many would have to be closed and others reduced in area and personnel.

The Department of Applied Economics at Cambridge University became interested in the plan, and once the unions had been advised of it the board gave the department access to all its reasoning and intentions. The university produced two extremely informative reports on the plan: *Railway Workshops: the problem of contraction*, by Dr P. Lesley Cook, and *Redundancy and the Railwaymen*, by Professor Dorothy Wedderburn. As a result of the plan only sixteen of the main works were retained, these being subjected to a well-considered rationalisation programme and improvements worth £18 million (see Fig. 1.4). Staff numbers were reduced by some 40 per cent.

TABLE 1.7   *Staff employed in the main works*

Staff	1962	1967
Salaried staff	7 300	5 800
Wages grades	58 700	34 200
Total	66 000	40 000

Key

Horwich .... works continuing

Gorton ....works closing down

C ....activity on carriages

L ....activity on locomotives

W ....activity on wagons

An encircled letter indicates that
activity is to be discontinued

①.......one works where there
           were previously two

②...............2 works closing

2............2 works continuing

SOURCE   E. J. Larkin, *Memoirs of a Railway Engineer* (Mechanical Engineering Publications, 1979)

FIGURE 1.4   *The reorganisation of BR's main works*

Each of the continuing works developed its own modernisation and re-organisation plan, thus avoiding a large central planning team and ensuring that full account was taken of local factors. There was now a unique opportunity to replan to meet the needs of the existing workload most economically. Shops were enlarged and resited to improve locomotive and vehicle flow through the works. Individual works projects embraced civil engineering work (new buildings; improved heating, lighting and staff amenities), alterations in shop layouts and repair arrangements to reduce unit costs, and recommendations for modern machine tools and other plant and equipment. The board authorised all the schemes between May and October 1964 and completion was achieved commendably near to the target date by the end of 1966.

The 1962 Transport Act provided for the workshops to manufacture and repair any product for the use of the BR Board or the other boards which had been part of the Transport Commission, but not for outside parties. In November 1965 it was announced that legislation would be introduced to remove limitations on the use of the manufacturing resources of the nationalised industries. This was welcomed by the workshops management, because production demands – for maintenance and new construction – were subject to wide fluctuations which it would do much to eliminate.

Under the Transport Act 1968 the Workshops Division became a separate but wholly-owned subsidiary company of the board, named British Rail Engineering Ltd (BREL), with freedom to undertake outside work to fill periods of slack internal demand. The first Managing Director was A. E. Robson, who was appointed in 1970, having previously been General Manager of the Workshops Division. Later the same year a Commercial Department was added to the organisation for the first time. There was no requirement for BREL to enter industry on a wider scale or to provide additional capacity over and above that needed for railway purposes. In 1971 a joint export sales company, BRE-Metro Ltd, was formed with Metropolitan Cammell Ltd, and BREL joined the Railway Industry Association as part of a policy of co-operation with the private sector, with particular emphasis on exports.

During the 1970s many large contracts were undertaken, including wagons for Malaysian Railways, Sweden, Yugoslavia and Bangladesh; coaches for the Northern Ireland Railway and Coras Iompair Eireann; iron ore tipplers for the British Steel Corporation; passenger and freight vehicles for Tanzania; diesel-electric shunting locomotives and wagons for Kenya; electric multiple-unit trains for Taiwan; and containers for UK and overseas customers. This spread of activities, developed in a relatively short period, made a useful contribution to the British balance of payments and reflected great credit on BREL. British Rail is one of the few railways in the world with its own facilities for the manufacture and heavy repair of locomotives and rolling stock, and BREL constitutes its workshop organisation.

TABLE 1.8 *Stock of locomotives on British railways at historical turning points*

Amalgamation 1923	Steam	Battery	Electric	Petrol
LMS	10 313	1		3
LNER	7 392		13	1
GWR	3 901			
SR	2 281			
Total locomotives vested in 'big four'	23 887	1	13	4

Nationalisation 1948	Steam	Diesel	Electric	Petrol
LMS	7 805	45		
LNER	6 525	4	14	2
GWR	3 856	1		
SR	1 838	3	2	
Total locomotives vested in BR	20 024	53	16	2

Modernisation 1954–9	1954	1955	1956	1957	1958	1959
Steam	18 425	17 960	17 527	16 959	16 108	14 457
Diesel	318	454	609	823	1 201	1 800
Electric	71	71	71	71	72	85
Diesel cars	62	116	271	791	1 399	1 933
Electric cars	2 150	2 177	2 262	2 290	2 404	2 601
Total locomotives	21 026	20 778	20 740	20 934	21 184	20 876

Completion of diesel programme 1965	Steam	Diesel	Electric
Total BR locomotive stock	2 989	4 811	277

2 The Main Works of the Former GWR

The Great Western Railway (GWR), the third in size of the four group companies, was unlike the others in retaining its original name at amalgamation – mainly because it absorbed relatively few other companies. From its inception in 1833 the GWR was always held in high esteem, and it retained its prestige and reputation for good service throughout the years. It was blessed with an almost legendary Chief Civil Engineer, the pioneering Isambard Kingdom Brunel.

An important characteristic of the GWR was the great disparity in size between Swindon Locomotive and Carriage and Wagon Works and the other main works. The unbroken existence of the GWR for over a century resulted in the concentration of locomotive construction and repair at Swindon, other works adapting the Swindon-style organisation to suit local conditions. A unique feature was that the smaller locomotive works were answerable to the CME at Swindon and also locally to a Divisional Superintendent who, like the mechanical engineers on the LNER, had wide CME's departmental responsibilities embracing traffic commitments. Running repairs at the motive power sheds were also the CME's responsibility.

SWINDON LOCOMOTIVE WORKS

The locomotive works at Swindon always enjoyed the highest reputation, both within and outside the railway organisation, and was pre-eminent among the many British railway workshops. In 1840 Swindon was a market town with a population of less than 2000. In 1836 Brunel had begun enquiries for locomotives and soon ordered twenty from various manufacturers, but considerable troubles were experienced. Daniel Gooch was asked to report on the best site to build a large works for repairing stock, and he recommended Swindon. The works was built by the GWR in 1842, and by 1843 over 400 men were employed, of whom 72 were skilled craftsmen. The works was extended in 1848 to enable locomotive building to develop in addition to repairs. Further extensions were built in 1853 and the rolling mill added in 1861. The total area grew to 140 acres including the running shed.

It was GWR policy to ensure the wellbeing of its workforce, and the many amenities introduced at Swindon anticipated by over half a century the standards generally provided for British workers. The rapid growth of Swindon's population in the 1840s made housing the main priority. The railway village designed by Matthew Digby Wyatt, architect of Paddington Station in London, is one of the earliest examples in Britain of an estate comprehensively planned

TABLE 2.1   *The main works of the former GWR at amalgamation in 1923*

Works	Date built	Railway Co. for which built	Total acreage	Covered acreage	Principal activities following amalgamation
Swindon Locomotive	1842	Great Western	140	35	Locomotive building and repairing; new boiler building; laminated & coil springs for locomotives, carriages & wagons; rolling mill for steel sections & bars; iron & brass castings for entire railway system; chair castings and points & crossing manufacture for Civil Engineering Dept; outdoor machinery maintenance (except Northern Division) and dock maintenance for GWR docks.
Wolverhampton Locomotive	1855	Great Western	14	5	Repairing all types of tank locomotives and smaller tender locomotives; outdoor machinery maintenance for Northern Division.
Swindon Carriage & Wagon	1869	Great Western	137	39	Building and repairing carriages, wagons & containers; timber conversion; drop stampings & heavy forgings for all GWR carriage & wagon requirements; manufacturing carriage & wagon wheel sets for all GWR requirements; building & repairing road vehicles.
Caerphilly Locomotive	1899	Rhymney	9	6	Repairing tank locomotives of types allocated to South Wales and components for South Wales outstation depots.
Caerphilly Carriage	1901	Rhymney	7	2	Repairing carriages, the Locomotive Works providing smithing and machining assistance.

and built by an industrial undertaking. Each house had a small garden fronting on to a wide street, and a minimum of two bedrooms and a toilet. Of an advanced design for the period, they were far superior to colliery and similar houses being built in northern England. The Bath stone used in their construction, and much of the building of the workshops, came from the excavations for the main line at Box Tunnel.

The enlightened 'family provider' attitude came to be synonymous with the GWR. Many Welshmen came to Swindon to find work, and in view of their strong chapel orientation a place of worship was provided in a building which began as a railway workers' lodging house. After 90 years as a Wesleyan Chapel the local authority acquired it and converted it into the present

Railway Museum. The directors also provided a school for the workers' children. This and the church, both opened in 1845, were built with funds subscribed by company shareholders. The Mechanics' Institute, built in 1844 to encourage adult technical education, provided evening classes (in mathematics, engineering and English for men; arithmetic, dictation and domestic subjects for women), a reading room and lending library, lectures, drama and other entertainment, and facilities for washing and baths. Swindon was the only railway works with its own swimming baths, built in 1866 on land east of the Cheltenham branch and administered by the GWR Medical Fund Society.

The Medical Fund Society and hospital was an outstanding example of industrial welfare work. Developed in 1847 when the directors recognised the need to provide medical care for the railway families, it eventually became the model for the National Health Scheme. Extensive premises provided for eight resident medical officers, a consultant surgeon, three dental surgeons, an ophthalmic surgeon, pharmacists, three physiotherapists and a chiropodist. Washing, Turkish and Russian baths were installed, and later the swimming baths.

The historical growth of the town and the railway works were always inseparable and interdependent. In 1844 the GWR purchased land which later became the 'GWR Park' for use by public and railwaymen alike; this was given to the local authority in 1925 in exchange for land which the company used for additional carriage and wagon workshops. Water was pumped from a well at Kemble (inaugurated 1903) for the houses and the works; gas was provided to the town from the company's own plant, then the largest in Europe; coal came from the company's Welsh mines; a specialist workshop in the village undertook property repairs. When Swindon became a borough it elected as its first mayor G. J. Churchward, the eminent locomotive engineer who was Locomotive, Carriage and Wagon Superintendent (1902–16) and later CME. With some 14 000 on the payroll by 1925, the works was by far the largest employer in the town, other local businesses depending upon the works for economic stability. Since the second world war several other industries developed in Swindon, influenced by the local authority's offer to build houses for employees.

The history of the development of railway engineering at Swindon is as impressive as the town's railway-based social history. The company was making its own locomotives in increasing numbers after 1846. The early success of its broad-gauge (7'-0") locomotives was an incentive to the narrow-gauge (4'-8½") railways to make their locomotives more powerful; meanwhile the GWR sought to maintain the superiority of broad gauge by instructing Gooch in 1846 to build a 'colossal locomotive working with all speed' which after thirteen weeks' intensive effort emerged as Swindon's first passenger locomotive, 'Great Western', to be followed by six similar engines. In 1846 the Gauge Commissioners reported in favour of the narrow gauge, but paid tribute to Brunel's genius and the liberality of the GWR in introducing higher speeds and increased accommodation in railway carriages. Both gauges were pursued until the great disadvantages of mixing gauges over the broad-gauge sections became apparent, and in 1869 an Act of Parliament adopted a policy of gradual conversion to the 4'-8½" gauge.

The building of 'single-wheelers' was a feature of locomotive production at Swindon until the end of the century, but locomotives with four wheels coupled had been introduced as early as 1849, when Gooch designed the first of the so-called 'bogie' class passenger engines – saddle tank 4–4–0 locomotives with six-foot diameter driving wheels for negotiating the severe gradients of the South Devon Railway. Churchward's periods of office – as Assistant Chief Superintendent from 1897 and as Locomotive Superintendent from 1902 – witnessed an increase in the size and cost of locomotives. In 1903 he produced the famous City class of 4–4–0 tender engines with 6'-8½" driving wheels, followed in 1904 by the Counties; 1906 saw the first four-cylinder 4–6–0 engine, 'North Star', built originally as a 4–4–2. Later four-cylinder engines were all 4–6–0 wheel arrangements, the first with 14½" diameter by 26" cylinders, enlarged to 15" diameter in subsequent engines, commencing with the 'Prince of Wales'. The first Pacific type (4–6–2) locomotive built in Britain, where it was the only one of its type for 14 years, was designed and constructed at Swindon in 1908; named 'Great Bear', it was later rebuilt as a 4–6–0 and renamed 'Viscount Churchill'.

On 28 April 1924 a visit was made by King George V and Queen Mary, when a commemorative casting was made in their presence in the engine repair shop. In another royal visit on 15 November 1950 Princess Elizabeth named the last Castle class locomotive 'Swindon' in honour of the town and in commemoration of her visit. In 1927 the most powerful locomotive yet built, the King class, was created, of which 'King George V' took pride of place, representing Britain (together with a model of the 'North Star') at the Baltimore and Ohio Railways Fair of the Iron Horse in the USA. Swindon also saw the appearance in 1928 of the down-to-earth workhorse Hall locomotives.

Swindon Works was always noted for its high-quality craftsmanship, not least in the boiler shops. C. B. Collett (CME 1921–41) took steps to bring precision into boiler manufacture, but his appointment of a fitter, F. R. Higgs, as chief boiler foreman caused consternation among the boilermakers. Collett was determined to retain the appointment, saying that if necessary he would make Higgs boiler shop manager; boilermaker foremen in charge of individual shops would instruct their men, but under Higgs' direction and working to his instructions. Higgs was chief boiler foreman for some 25 years, doing excellent work, particularly in improving the equipment of the shops, their heavy flanging and plate-forming equipment and tools generally.

The works' output in 1947 was 717 heavy and 287 light classified repairs, plus 60 new locomotives; 3946 locomotives were maintained. The average number of working days on the works was 21.9 and the overall time 23.9. Additionally, 85 boilers were under repair off the frames. The weekly output of boilers was 16.2, averaging 25.8 working days. In 1954, before the modernisation and re-equipment plan affected the workload, the works completed

417 general and 241 intermediate classified repairs, plus 226 casual and non-classified repairs, a total of 884. Some 2824 artisan staff were engaged on this work. In the same year 42 new locomotives were built, employing 604 artisan staff.

Between 1949 and 1960 nearly 200 of the twelve BR standard designs of steam locomotives introduced by the Railway Executive were built at Swindon, culminating in the completion on 18 March 1968 of the last steam locomotive built for BR, 'Evening Star' (No. 92220), a BR Standard 9F 2–10–0. In 1957 the first diesel-hydraulic main-line locomotive on British Railways was built at Swindon.

Under the 1962 rationalisation scheme the new building of locomotives and rolling stock at Swindon was transferred to other main works. Locomotive repairs and all carriage and wagon work for Western Region were to be undertaken in Swindon Locomotive Works, and the site of the carriage and wagon works was sold to Swindon Corporation. This integration, at a cost of

TABLE 2.2   *Swindon Works: output from principal spheres of activity year ended 31 December 1981*

Major modifications and conversions

Life extension – Kent Coast EMUs	128
Refurbishing DMUs	28
Replacement of 150 HP AEC engines – DMUs	3
High-impact glass cab windows	18

Repair work	*General*	*Intermediate*	*Light*	*Total classified*	*Unclassified*
Diesel shunting locos	26	13	—	39	42

	Armature	*Carcase*
Traction motors	—	—
Main generators	45	45

	C1R	*C1/C2*	*C3*	*C3T*	*C4*	*Total classified*	*C5*
Loco-hauled coaches	—	—	—	—	—	—	3
Loco-hauled coaches (non-passenger-carrying)	—	1	15	—	30	46	7
DMUs	28	11	354	—	17	410	20
EMUs	128	—	—	—	—	128	—

	GR	*IR/L*	*IR/W*	*IR*	*Total*
Traffic wagons	108	3	107	332	550

	Engines	*Gearboxes*	*Torque converters*	*Final drives*
DMU traction components	545	455	—	582

£2.4 million including new equipment, resulted in a modern and compact works. Its repair and manufacturing output in 1981 is shown in Table 2.2. The locomotive works closed in 1986.

WOLVERHAMPTON LOCOMOTIVE WORKS

The Stafford Road Works began in 1849 when the Shrewsbury & Birmingham line reached Wolverhampton, terminating at a temporary station and goods shed (later the site of the coppersmiths' shop) on the lower slope of Dunstall Hill. High stone retaining walls were built bordering the road, and spoil from the side cut in to the hill was used to raise the ground to rail level as far as the Oxley Viaduct. The Shrewsbury & Birmingham Railway was an independent company, but it was operated as one line with the Shrewsbury & Chester Railway, which used its own staff – Joseph Armstrong being in charge of locomotives and rolling stock, with his headquarters at Saltney Works – whereas the Shrewsbury & Birmingham at first used contractors for operating and maintenance.

At amalgamation Joseph Armstrong became Locomotive Superintendent of the Northern Division of the GWR. His father, a friend of George Stephenson and Hackworth, had apprenticed him to Robert Hawthorn (whose sons founded R. & W. Hawthorn of Newcastle) at Walbottle Colliery, where 'Puffing Billy' operated. In 1836 he was an engine driver on the Liverpool & Manchester Railway, then foreman at the Hull & Selby and London & Brighton Railways, before going to Saltney in 1852. When he was promoted to Swindon in 1864 his younger brother, George, succeeded him at Wolverhampton, with William Dean as his assistant and manager of Stafford Road Works. George, who had also been at Walbottle Colliery, Hull and Brighton, and had worked as an engine driver on the Nord Railway in France, continued in charge at Wolverhampton until he retired, aged 75, in 1897.

The Oxford, Worcester & Wolverhampton Railway joined the Grand Junction Railway in 1854, when the first broad-gauge running shed was built at Wolverhampton, the temporary buildings were dismantled and boiler repair shops built. After the GWR was extended to Wolverhampton it was decided to concentrate on locomotive repairs there, and the carriage and wagon repair shops were demolished. Their work was transferred to Saltney in exchange for locomotive repairs.

The GWR policy of building its own locomotives was extended to Wolverhampton to build standard-gauge locomotives independently of Swindon. Because the Shrewsbury & Birmingham had purchased its locomotives and spare parts from private firms, the works were laid out for maintaining rolling stock. Expansion of the works started in 1858. The boiler shop, foundry and Mechanics' Institute were built on the site of the original goods depot. A new running shed was built (demolished c. 1890) near Oxley Viaduct and an erecting shop and wheel shop on the site of the original shed. Behind this was a traverser serving a workshop with a number of roads for locomotive running and general repairs. Alongside the S-curve connecting the Shrewsbury & Birmingham with the GWR and the Oxford, Worcester & Wolverhampton Railway were the forge and smithy with furnaces for tyres and plate-flanging.

The first locomotives built at the works were Nos 7 and 8 of the type 2–2–2, designed by Joseph Armstrong, built in 1859. As the Northern Division grew by absorbing smaller railways – the Birkenhead (jointly with the London & North-Western in 1860) and the West Midland (1863) – a collection of miscellaneous engines resulted, and the extension of mixed gauge led to an increase in standard-gauge engines. A large engine shed was formed to house locomotives displaced by the closure of the West Midland Railway, accommodating some 120 tender and tank engines.

During the reign of the Armstrong brothers (1854–97) Wolverhampton enjoyed virtual independence from Swindon, partly owing to the problems of the two gauges. Joseph's scope was limited by lack of facilities and the problem of maintaining miscellaneous stock. New standard-gauge engines were supplied by Swindon and private firms working to Swindon designs, but after the 1858 and 1863 reorganisations he was able to design and build his own locomotives.

From 1875 locomotive repair work on standard-gauge engines at Swindon was simplified by their being of GWR design. This was not the case at Wolverhampton, where engines of differing design and manufacture meant it was not always possible to obtain spares, particularly if manufacturers had ceased production. A policy of rebuilding was introduced using standard parts such as boilers, cylinders and springs when replacements became necessary. If rebuilding was impossible, the engine was scrapped when it wore out. The appearance of its locomotives showed Stafford Road's independence from Swindon. Each works had its own standard boilers and other parts: for example, Wolverhampton copper chimney caps were of a smaller diameter with a more rounded contour. Sometimes locomotives of the same class emerged from the two works, after rebuilding, looking entirely different, although their overall dimensions remained the same. The most noticeable difference was in livery: Swindon a leaf green above oak-brown frames, Wolverhampton dark blue-green above red-brown frames.

In 1868 Joseph Armstrong called William Dean to Swindon as his Chief Assistant, to the annoyance of brother George. Joseph's death in 1877 and Dean's succession to his post posed a delicate problem – a one-time inferior becoming a superior. Faced with this Dean left George to continue his virtually independent reign for another twenty years. After Gooch's death in 1889 and the abolition of broad gauge, the question arose whether Swindon or Wolverhampton should become the main GWR locomotive building and repair works. The Wolverhampton site had major advantages: proximity to raw and semi-manufactured materials, a good labour market providing a pool of skilled and semi-skilled men; whereas Swindon was isolated from large centres of industry and also had to bring in fuel and materials by rail. But the availability of land was clearly an important factor in the decision. It proved impossible to obtain reasonably-priced land at Dunstall Hill, so Swindon, where cheaper land was more readily available, was chosen. But considerable locomotive construction continued at Stafford Road as well as repairs. Saddle tanks of the 0–4–2 and 0–6–2 types and 0–4–2 and 0–6–0 type side tanks were produced, in addition to the maintenance of the Northern Division locomotive fleet. Tender engines, such as the single-wheeler No. 999 'Sir Alexander', were also rebuilt.

George Armstrong's retirement marked the end of the individuality of Stafford Road, and Swindon influence gradually became dominant. His successor, his former Works Manager W. H. Waister, was himself succeeded later in 1897 by J. A. Robinson, formerly Divisional Locomotive Superintendent at Bristol. When land prices fell at the end of the century, more of Dunstall Hill was purchased, but too late to detract from Swindon's expansion. Work began in 1900: an area was levelled for building a modern self-contained works, and by 1905 site, plans and estimates were ready, but reduced receipts due to a slump meant the plan was shelved. The works declined and the last Wolverhampton locomotive was built in 1908. After this the works was confined to repairs within the plant capacity.

There was no redevelopment until 1930 when, taking advantage of the Developments (Loans, Guarantees and Grants) Act 1929, the GWR reorganised the now obsolete works. It handled all types of locomotives, from the GWR King and Castle classes to smaller types such as the 0–4–2, and later the BR standard steam locomotives. In 1947, the year before nationalisation, there were on average 106 locomotives in the works; they took an average of 28.6 working days to repair and an overall time in and out of works of 30.6 days. The year's output was 178 heavy and 68 light repairs, a total of 246 or one locomotive every working day. The total staff was 664.

In 1959 the total establishment of 520 technical, supervisory, clerical and workshop staff included 198 craftsmen of various trades and 136 semi-skilled and unskilled staff, a total of 334 working on locomotive repairs. In addition some 115 staff were employed for the maintenance of ancillary plant and machinery. In one area boiler tubes no longer usable in locomotives were made into unclimbable fencing. The works finally closed on 1 June 1964 as part of the 1962 rationalisation plan, after existing for over a century and having well and truly played its part throughout the heyday of the steam locomotive.

SWINDON CARRIAGE AND WAGON WORKS

In common with other early railways the first GWR carriages and wagons were supplied by private contractors. The design of the early carriages – even those built all in iron – was similar to horse-drawn vehicles. There was

substantial wagon-building space on the west side of the new Swindon Locomotive Works, which quickly began producing a wide variety of four- and six-
wheeled iron wagons. From 1850 to 1892 a standardised group of wagons was
produced, with capacities from six to twelve tons, and in 1871 some experimental wagons were also built, notably four 21-ton 6-wheel open goods and a
25-ton double bogie vehicle.

By the early 1860s the amassing of rolling stock – there were 5689 broad-
and 8284 narrow-gauge wagons – led the directors to recognise the urgent
need for a central construction and repair complex. The supposed advantages
of Oxford were overshadowed by public protest from its citizens and the flood
potential of the low-lying site. Eventually Swindon was chosen, and the
works, authorised by the directors in October 1867, was completed in 1869.
Almost the whole of the GWR vehicle fleet was worked into Swindon, 13
miles of additional sidings being developed to accommodate the vehicles.

Carriages and wagons were the responsibility of the traffic department until
1864, when Gooch resigned as Locomotive Superintendent and J. Gibson
retired as Carriage and Wagon Superintendent. Joseph Armstrong was
promoted to take over both posts, as the first Locomotive, Carriage and
Wagon Superintendent of the GWR. There were good reasons for the changes
in responsibility; Brunel had been critical of the engineering standards of
design and manufacture of the running gear of coaches, and passenger comfort left much to be desired. One critic wrote, 'The passengers' impression
was one of elegant discomfort.' There is also a coroner's report that 'The
deceased died from cold and exposure from travelling in a second class
carriage on the GWR.'

As the ground level of the new site was lower than the main line, the floor
level was raised, creating valuable under-floor space. The space below the
sawmill was used for machine shafting, with individual belts coming up
through the floor at each machine. One area became a large staff dining room,
another was used by the St John Ambulance for classes. In 1953 spare space
was used for a unique Rehabilitation Centre for staff partially disabled by
accident or illness, who used specially designed machines under the direction
of the Railway Medical Officer. Space heating of all the new shops was
provided by steam produced from the sawmill waste timber. This boiler plant
also heated the water for the swimming bath: a brick-lined tunnel was driven
below the cottage estate southwards, rising to the surface inside the building.
The construction of the famous 'Tunnel Entrance' gave safe access to the
locomotive works beneath the running lines.

Within a few years further development was necessary, to release space in
the locomotive works used for wagon construction. The site was on undeveloped land east of the Cheltenham line and north of the station. With the
move to this new area, the whole of the carriage and wagon function came
under the direct control of an independent Works Manager. The first new
shop, built in 1878 for wagon building, was followed in 1880 by a wagon repair
shop. Many new workshops followed, principally: wagon lifting (repair) 1889;

wheel 1890; carriage lifting (repair) 1894; drop-stamp and forge 1897; machine and carriage brake (repair) and a new central office block 1910. The 1910 extension was largely on the site of two large 'borrow-pits' used until 1903 as settling pits for canal water extracted by the locomotive works, and on which the carriage and wagon works also depended. Once there were facilities for new construction, purchase from private contractors ceased. By the 1880s new construction had also ceased at the Bridgwater, Worcester and Saltney workshops.

The first railway-built Royal Saloon, an 8-wheeled vehicle 43 feet long, was built at Swindon as a broad-gauge vehicle in 1874 but converted to narrow gauge in 1889 and fitted with 'Dean' type swing-link bogies. The first complete corridor train was produced in 1891 and in 1900–1 two such trains with electric lighting, using J. Stone double battery patent, were introduced on the South Wales service. Later the Leitner system was used and after nationalisation the 'Wolverton' lighting system became the BR standard, Swindon making this type whilst continuing to repair the former GWR equipment.

The first experimental sleeping cars introduced in 1877 were on six wheels and had accommodation for 7 gentlemen and 4 ladies, but only one lavatory. Four years later an 8-wheel narrow-gauge sleeper was built as a convertible on a broad-gauge frame and included two lavatories. Steam heating for passenger vehicles appeared in 1892 and a first-class restaurant car four years later. In 1896 trials were carried out using oil-axleboxes on carriages, and in 1897 on wagons. By 1903 the standard length of carriages had become 68 feet minimum and some reached 70 feet over mouldings.

Activity in the new wagon-building shops was intense and varied. An open all-steel 20-ton coal wagon was introduced in 1897, followed in 1905 by a large number of internal user 40-ton open coal wagons to convey locomotive coal from the collieries to the new elevated coal stages throughout the GWR system. Other special freight wagon types included wagons for transporting locomotive boilers to other works; low-loading types up to 60 tons; a special 'gun truck' suitable also for transformers up to 120 tons; refrigerator vans for meat; steam-heated vans for bananas; ventilated vans for Cornish broccoli; and circus vans.

The forge and stamping shop produced several million items for rolling stock, particularly draw hooks and coupling links, notably the 'instanter' type of short or long coupling link. This was used on GWR loose-coupled freight trains from about 1900 and, modified and using higher grade steel, adopted by British Rail after nationalisation.

In the first decade of the twentieth century all the extensions at Swindon, with few exceptions, took place in the carriage works. The carriage lifting and repair shop reached its final stage and a large addition to the wagon lifting shop was concluded. Later additions to the works were the timber drying kilns (1913) and the laundry (1930). By the early 1920s the works had absorbed almost all the land it had purchased and the town had finally hemmed it in. When a new 1800-foot carriage stock shed and shop was built in

1939 to the north of the works it was on land acquired from the local authority in exchange for the GWR Park.

Together the carriage and wagon works and locomotive works formed a unique and impressive complex. The two were separated by the main Paddington to Gloucester line, and the carriage and wagon works was itself divided by the Paddington to Bristol line, with building to the south and maintenance to the north. The conversion mill was some distance from the building shops, on the opposite side of the line. To avoid any confusion, each carriage and wagon shop was known by a number, each locomotive shop by a letter. The total area of the carriage and wagon works was 137 acres (39 covered), approximately equal to the acreage of the locomotive works. Progressive modernisation over the years meant that, unlike the other three companies, there was no change after 1923 in the work undertaken at Swindon. In 1949, following nationalisation, the carriage and wagon works employed 4472 staff, covering all grades.

Early in the 1950s Swindon started building all-steel bodied integral coaches to BR designs, as well as diesel multiple train sets, first class restaurant cars, kitchen cars, open firsts and seconds. They also built the prototype Mark II dual steam/electrically-heated coach. From 1951 until closure in 1964 some 1247 coaches were built. Many other items were also manufactured – containers, road vehicle bodies, platform trucks, furniture and, until the National Health Service started, artificial limbs. In the oil and grease works bulk supplies were purchased and a large amount of oil recovered and cleaned – from these supplies blended lubricants in several grades were produced.

A special disinfecting unit was also erected for passenger vehicles and wagons from all railways. They were put into an 85-foot long steel cylinder 6'-6" in diameter. The entry was sealed, the whole heated by steam coils, a vacuum created and then formalin or other disinfectants admitted to deal with insects or bacteria. In 1954, prior to the influence of the modernisation and re-equipment plan, the works built 166 new carriages (with underframes built at Ashford) and 1439 wagons. The number of classified repairs, representing the main portion of the workload, was well maintained.

When in 1962 the BR Board set up the Workshops Division, the impact on both Swindon works was without parallel in their long history. New manufacture was transferred to other works and the carriage and wagon works was closed. The locomotive works was equipped for the repair of diesel main-line and shunting locomotives and diesel multiple-unit vehicles, including Pullman de-luxe trains, wagons and containers. Manufacture of springs and non-ferrous castings was undertaken, as well as work on civil engineer's plant and equipment and certain outdoor machinery services for the Western Region. In 1970 the Workshops Division became British Rail Engineering Ltd and began to undertake work for outside organisations. This amounted in 1970 to £350 000 in value and was as follows: 170 lumber flats and 5000 end frames for Johnson Line; overhaul of bus and commercial vehicle engines; miscellaneous machining work; manufacturing of testing equipment for Magnaflux. Bus operators had the benefit of Swindon Works expertise, not only for engine work, but for modification to coach body shells and interiors.

A falling workload throughout BR necessitated final closure of Swindon Works in 1986. Its exceptionally high standard of craftsmanship was always recognised throughout the railway world. The local authority, in conjunction with BREL, created an industrial estate and found employment for several hundred employees.

CAERPHILLY LOCOMOTIVE WORKS

Caerphilly Works, the only main works in Wales, was built for the Rhymney Railway Company in 1899 and became part of the GWR in 1923. It formed a compact establishment, repairing tank engines and other items for the South Wales motive power depots. The erecting shop had a traverser with the advantage of a covered avenue. In 1947 a total of 638 staff was employed, the average number of locomotives on the works was 35, the number of working days for each locomotive was 29 and the overall number of days was 31.9. The output in the same year was 184 heavy and 40 light, a total of 224 classified repairs.

The building of the workshops and the expansion of Caerphilly were undoubtedly linked, although the main growth of the area was due to the expansion of the local mining industry. The Census figures for 1891–1971 reflect this development, though it should be noted that the Caerphilly Urban District Council area included several villages.

The Rhymney Railway began operating on the 23-mile Rhymney to Cardiff line on 25 February 1858. The first workshops, opened in 1857 at Cardiff Docks, were initially adequate, but as the locomotive and other stock expanded their repair capacity proved insufficient. Attempts to expand were abandoned owing to the high cost and inadequacy of available land. Negotiations for a new site were undertaken between the General Manager, Cornelius Lundie, and Lord Windsor, who owned land bordering the Caerphilly to Cardiff section of the line. Of the two sites considered – one near the Heath south of Llanishen Station, the other at Wernddu, three-quarters of a mile east of Caerphilly Station – the latter site was chosen. Completed and equipped by December 1901 at a cost of £63 000, this was the largest railway works in Wales in both area and number of staff.

At the beginning of this century older locomotives were reboilered and fitted with cabs, and in 1903 six 0–6–2 tank locomotives were ordered from Robert Stephenson & Co. of Newcastle-upon-Tyne. Experience came from Gorton Works when C. H. Riches became Locomotive Superintendent in 1906 and appointed J. H. Sellars as Chief Works Foreman. Their policy was to modernise and standardise the locomotive stock, and towards the end of 1906 Riches designed a standard boiler and cylinders for the whole range of saddle tank engines. Also in that year he and Sellars designed the first new class of 0–6–2 side tank engine, built by Stephenson & Co. The replacement, rebuilding and repair of old locomotives continued up to the first world war. The average staff throughout the period up to amalgamation in 1923 – including the carriage and wagon shop – was 250. In 1919 Sellars became Works Manager and the post of Chief Works Foreman was abolished.

In the latter part of 1923 a scheme for Caerphilly was prepared which completely changed repair facilities in South Wales. At the beginning of the 1920s Caerphilly repaired only Rhymney locomotives, but by 1922 they were being sent from the Barry Railway and in 1924 the first Swindon-built locomotive came in for a running repair. A works was needed which could cope with various classes of pre-amalgamation as well as standard GWR locomotives. This meant enlarging an existing works rather than building a new one. Only three – Taff Vale Railway West Yard, Caerphilly and Barry – were large enough. Caerphilly was chosen because it had ample yard space for expansion, had direct rail access to South and Central Wales, and was within easy reach of the main centres of Cardiff and Newport. The contract for the new erecting shop went to E. C. Jordan & Son of Newport, and although delayed by the General Strike it was completed in 1926. The old erecting shop was converted into the new boiler shop, the old boiler shop became the new wheel shop and a new five-table weighbridge was installed by Messrs Pooley.

As the expanded works came into full production the closure or reduction of the other Welsh works went ahead: Barry was reduced to dealing with light repairs; Taff Vale Railway West Yard was closed and its staff moved to Caerphilly. Throughout 1927 staff came from all parts of South Wales, from Worcester locomotive repair shops and a few from Swindon at their own request. Considerable activity occurred in 1928 with the rebuilding of constituent locomotives, which were fitted with GWR boilers and in some cases GWR cabs and bunkers. The enlarged works proved its value with greatly increased production, further increased by reorganised working in the erecting shop. Until then an engine was allocated to a chargehand, whose gang carried out the complete repair, involving stripping, despatch of boiler wheels to other shops and re-erection, a time-consuming procedure: a normal heavy repair took 40 to 60 working days. With increasing numbers of GWR standard locomotives a change was needed, and in 1929 a grouping system was introduced. The time allowances depended upon the class under repair. There was not time for heavy boiler repairs, so a stock of spare standard constituent boilers was kept for quicker replacement. This reorganisation led to a considerable reduction in the time spent on repairs.

The works did not escape the severe economic depression of the 1930s and 200 men were discharged. The situation improved and by 1938 the workforce had increased from 600 to nearly 700. Various schemes were inaugurated to alleviate the effects of the depression, including building new carriage repair shops at Caerphilly, making it the principal repair centre for South Wales. Further reorganisation began in 1950, when Caerphilly took over responsibility for Barry locomotive shops and for all outdoor machinery work in South

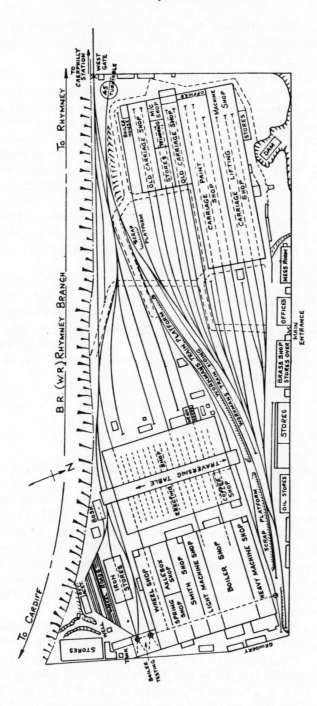

Figure 2.1 *Plan of Caerphilly Works at closure*

and West Wales and became directly responsible to Swindon for locomotive repairs, instead of through the Locomotive Superintendent of the Cardiff Valleys Division as since 1922.

Until 1952 Caerphilly was a tank locomotive repair works, repairing only a few tender engines. From 1952 two-cylinder tender engines were allocated for heavy and light repairs, mainly because the standard of post-war repairs had been consistently high and the time taken low. The relative ease with which these were carried out led to larger locomotives being sent there, the first being 4–6–0 No. 5955, 'Garth Hall'. Changes emerged in the locomotive shops during 1958 and 1959. With Swindon committed to diesel locomotives, Castle class and BR Standard class steam locomotives, particularly the Class 9 2–10–0s, came in for heavy and light repairs. In 1962, 163 Western Region locomotives were maintained at Caerphilly and it was announced that Swindon would take over heavy repairs of all steam locomotives except 5600 class 0–6–2T and 0–6–0PT, two disappearing types. Caerphilly's repair output between 1921 and 1963 is summarised in Table 2.3.

When the locomotive works closed on 29 June 1963 the entire works site, with its 20 workshop buildings and offices (see Fig. 2.1), was sold for £75 000 to Caerphilly Council for conversion into a heavy industrial estate. Some small shops were leased and the erecting shop and 6 acres were bought by South Wales Switchgear Ltd. In January 1964 the new Harold Wilson Industrial Estate was officially opened by Harold Wilson, some months before he became Prime Minister.

CAERPHILLY CARRIAGE AND WAGON WORKS

The original workshop of the Rhymney Railway Company was relatively small when built in 1857 near Cardiff docks. In 1867 the stock was 18 locomotives, 33 passenger vehicles and 101 wagons. As the coalfields to the north developed and suitable rail connections were introduced, traffic along the Rhymney Valley increased, and by 1895 there were difficulties in maintaining 76 locomotives – with more to come. In 1901, when the new works was built at Caerphilly – on the same site as the locomotive works – to supplement the old works, it maintained 100 passenger vehicles and 859 wagons of great variety. The final Rhymney totals were 123 locomotives, 131 passenger vehicles and 1200 wagons.

With an acreage of only 6.5 (2 acres covered) Caerphilly Carriage and Wagon Works became at amalgamation in 1923 the smallest of the GWR main works. It performed normal repairs and built most replacement stock, particularly mineral brake vans and wagons and a small quantity of passenger stock. In 1930 a new wagon shop opened at Cardiff Cathays and two years later Caerphilly's main activity of converting carriages from the Westinghouse air brake to the GWR vacuum brake ended. As a result the staff, which had

TABLE 2.3   *Caerphilly Works: locomotive repair output, 1921–63*

Year	Category of repair			Total repairs	Remarks
	Heavy	Light	Running		
1921	38	30			Old erecting shop ⎫
1922					Old erecting shop ⎪ other figures
1923					Old erecting shop ⎬ not
1924	37	36			Old erecting shop ⎪ available
1925	43	82		125	Old erecting shop ⎭
1926	37	87		124	New erecting shop fully open Aug.
1927	87	74	93	254	1926
1928	153	67	81	301	
1929	213	38	43	294	'Group' system of repairs started
1930	261	53	70	384	13.5.29
1931	257	66	35	358	From 16.3.31 to 25.12.48 heavy
1932	206	89	41	336	repairs subdivided between general
1933	171	122	87	380	and intermediate
1934	201	89	78	369	
1935	193	145	114	452	
1936	191	144	81	416	
1937	282	106	94	482	
1938	268	98	53	419	
1939	218	170	49	437	
1940	212	184	42	438	
1941	194	152	62	408	
1942	225	102	41	368	
1943	227	79	27	333	
1944	238	73	17	328	
1945	198	69	22	289	
1946	196	61	22	279	
1947	183	44	26	253	
1948	197	39	22	258	
1949	226	35	31	292	New classification for repairs started
1950	229	25	42	296	27.12.48
1951	207	37	30	274	H/G Heavy general
1952	197	41	46	284	H/I Heavy intermediate
1953	199	43	44	286	H/C Heavy casual
1954	200	55	17	272	L/I Light intermediate
1955	205	52	22	279	L/C Light casual
1956	206	61	21	288	UN Unclassified
1957	218	59	17	294	
1958	208	56	25	289	
1959	191	53	23	267	
1960	194	59	40	293	
1961	204	45	50	299	
1962	145	76	41	262	
1963	13	26	16	55	Last engine repair 10.4.63

reached about 900 by 1931, was reduced to some 600 and the carriage and wagon work was gradually phased out.

In co-operation with Government schemes to assist the South Wales depressed areas, it was decided to build new carriage shops at Caerphilly and convert the buildings at the west end into the principal repair shops for South Wales. The work (completed 1939) comprised a lift and body shop, 421 feet by 72 feet, with two 20-ton cranes fitted with special twin-armed crabs to lift under the solebar of carriages; and a second shop of a similar size for painting and trimming. These additions trebled the covered area for carriage repairs. The works was now equipped for repairing carriage stock only. At nationalisation it had a total staff of 102, much the smallest of any BR main works: some subsidiary works employed more staff, but were not equipped for heavy classified repairs. During the second world war the locomotive and carriage works employed many women on work then normally done by men, and later in the war Italian POWs were employed on purely railway work.

In 1949 the output was 101 heavy and 228 light repairs, a total of 329, giving a weekly output of 6.6 carriage repairs and an average of 1.3 repairs each working day. In February 1962 it was announced that the carriage shops, apart from diesel railcar work in the lifting shop, would be closed, and despite representations by the Works Committee and Caerphilly Council they were closed that May, after an existence of over 60 years. For two-thirds of that time they were part of the GWR, saving a good deal of light mileage to and from Swindon, where the workload was transferred. The closing of the two Caerphilly works brought to an end the only main works ever established in Wales.

3 The Main Works of the Former LMS

The foundations of the London Midland & Scottish Railway Company (LMS), the largest of the 'great four', date from two events of worldwide repute. The first was the Rainhill trials in 1829, a contest to find the best locomotive for the new Liverpool & Manchester Railway. Four steam engines – George and Robert Stephenson's 'Rocket', Timothy Hackworth's 'Sans Pareil', Braithwaite & Ericsson's 'Novelty' (the first tank engine) and Timothy Burstall's 'Perseverance' – and one horse-powered vehicle, 'Cyclopede', competed for the £500 prize. More than ten thousand people watched the 'Rocket' win by reaching a speed of 32 miles per hour. The second event was the opening of the Liverpool & Manchester Railway by the Prime Minister, the Duke of Wellington, on 15 September 1830. The 'Rocket' pulled the first inter-city train at the opening and provided the world's first steam service for both passengers and freight. Following this the railways expanded rapidly, transforming the landscape and economic structure of Victorian Britain.

The vast LMS network extended from Goole on the English east coast to Donegal Bay on the west coast of Ireland, and from Bournemouth in the south to Thurso in the far north of Scotland. It had 19 000 track miles, 40 per cent of the total route mileage of England, Scotland and Wales, employed 275 000 staff and owned 10 000 locomotives and 300 000 carriages and wagons. In 1939 it carried some 434 million passengers and 125 million tons of freight traffic, the latter amounting to 6750 million ton miles. There were 15 main and 39 subsidiary (8 locomotive, 31 wagon) works, plus outdoor machinery districts and carriage and wagon outstation depots, employing a total of 40 000 staff. The main works carried the major part of the massive workload, which included the maintenance of the 5000 cranes used throughout the system.

WOLVERTON CARRIAGE AND WAGON WORKS

Wolverton strongly resembled Crewe in being a railway colony, whose inhabitants were all engaged in one occupation. The first permanent houses built at New Wolverton, or 'Wolverton Station' as it was known, were in Bury, Gas, Creed, Ledsham and Young Streets and Glyn Square, all named after directors and officials of the railway company except Gas Street, named from the works at its east end. Gas and water were both supplied by the company, and until recently the works fire brigade also served the whole area. The Science and Art Institute, near where the church was to be built, was founded in 1840 at the suggestion of the Locomotive Superintendent,

TABLE 3.1   *The main works of the former LMS at amalgamation in 1923*

Works	Date built	Railway Co. for which built	Total acreage	Covered acreage	Principal activities following amalgamation
Wolverton Carriage	1838	London & Birmingham	89	36	Building and repairing carriages & wagons including Royal Train; timber conversion; drop stampings and heavy forgings for all LMS carriage & wagon works; manufacturing carriage & wagon wheel sets; reclamation of non-ferrous scrap; iron foundry castings; battery manufacture for all train lighting on LMS.
Derby Locomotive	1840	North Midland	47	14	Locomotive building and repairing; maintenance of breakdown cranes.
Bromsgrove Wagon	1840	Birmingham & Gloucester	14	3	Repairing wagons and containers; recovery of used wagon timber and ironwork for use at outstations.
Crewe Locomotive	1843	Grand Junction	137	44	Locomotive building and repairing; steel castings; drop stampings and heavy forgings for all LMS works; chair castings and points & crossing manufacture for Civil Engineer's Dept; manufacture of signals, locking frames and crossing gate work for Signal & Telecommunications Dept.
Barrow-in-Furness	1846	Furness	30	13	Locomotive and carriage & wagon building and repairing.
Bow Locomotive	1850	North London	10	2	Locomotive repairing chiefly for North London Railway and London, Tilbury & Southend section; heavy chain repairing and testing.
Earlestown Carriage & Wagon	1853 (owned by Jones & Potts)	Acquired by London & North-Western 1853	36	14	Repairing of wagons, building and repairing containers & mechanical horse trailers, repairing road vehicles; manufacture of firelighters for Motive Power Dept.
St Rollox Locomotive	1856	Garnkirk & Glasgow (later Caledonian)	15	9	Locomotive repairing.
St Rollox Carriage	1856 (rebuilt 1882)	Garnkirk & Glasgow (later Caledonian)	15	6	Repairing carriages; timber conversion for carriages & wagons; repairing road vehicle bodies.

TABLE 3.1 *Continued*

Works	Date built	Railway Co. for which built	Total acreage	Covered acreage	Principal activities following amalgamation
Kilmarnock Locomotive	1856	Glasgow & South-Western	13	2	Locomotive repairing and breaking up obsolete locomotives.
Stoke Locomotive Carriage & Wagon	1864	North Staffordshire	12	8	Locomotive and carriage & wagon building and repairing.
Derby Carriage & Wagon	1876	Midland	128	36	Carriage & wagon building and repairing.
Newton Heath, Manchester	1876	Lancashire & Yorkshire	n/a	n/a	Carriage & wagon building and repairing.
Horwich Locomotive	1887	Lancashire & Yorkshire	81	17	Locomotive building and repairing; mechanised foundry for chair castings & brake blocks.
Barassie Wagon	1901	Glasgow & South-Western	22	6	Wagons & containers.

Edward Bury. In 1885 the park and recreation ground were given to the town by the LNWR directors.

Wolverton Carriage and Wagon Works, on the northern boundary of Milton Keynes, is the oldest of the LMS main works, built in 1838 as a locomotive repair centre for the London & Birmingham Railway. The site was chosen for its position approximately halfway between London (Euston) and Birmingham. At that time the works covered only 2.27 acres. In July 1846 the London & Birmingham and the Grand Junction Railways amalgamated to form the London & North-Western Railway, and the works became the LNWR Engine Works, Wolverton. In 1849 it manufactured its first locomotive, a 2–2–2 express. Up to 1861–2 three types of 2–2–2 express engines were built, as well as the 0–6–0 'Wolverton Goods' engines and the 0–4–2 'Wolverton Tanks' – the first LNWR tank engines to operate in London. The end of locomotive work at Wolverton came in 1877, following the 1865 decision to centralise locomotive and carriage building. Crewe acquired all locomotive work and Wolverton the new carriage construction and repairs, which for some years had been undertaken at Saltley, Birmingham. Once again the name changed, to the LNWR Carriage Works, Wolverton.

Before September 1901 power in the Wolverton shops came from separate steam or gas engines and two electric power plants. A central power station was then designed by the Works Superintendent, C. A. Park, and Wolverton became the first railway works to adopt electric driving and lighting throughout.

Heating was by a range of Lancashire boilers placed below ground level, some fired entirely with sawdust and refuse from the sawmill. By 1907 Wolverton was the largest building and repair works in Britain, covering 89 acres (35.6 covered). Between 1900 and 1924 the works reached its zenith, in size and production, with a staff of some 4500.

At amalgamation in 1923 the LNWR became part of the LMS, the works becoming the LMS Carriage and Wagon Works, Wolverton. Wagon building was introduced at this time. At nationalisation in 1948 Wolverton continued as a major works, employing 3960 staff (273 professional and technical, workshop supervisory and clerical). By 1954, 875 artisan staff were engaged on new carriages, 375 on new wagons and 2250 on carriage repairs. Other staff worked on road vehicles, office furniture for British Railways and works maintenance.

In 1962, following the rationalisation of all the main works, Wolverton ceased manufacturing new carriages, except saloons for the royal train. Wolverton's record for building specially fitted coaches is unrivalled. The most impressive have been for heads of state, and the greatest variety in coach construction is shown in the royal trains of several generations. The longest continuous story is that of the British Royal Family, whose first saloons were produced in the 1840s. These coaches, from various railway companies, reflected contemporary fashions, and appropriately some are preserved at the National Railway Museum, York. Queen Victoria's 1869 saloon, built at Wolverton, consisted of two six-wheelers connected by a bellows gangway, the first example in Europe of such a feature. The coaches built for King Edward VII's train of 1903 used the best of traditional craftsmanship, but Queen Elizabeth II's 1961 saloon incorporated the fashions of the period of its construction, just as its air-conditioned 100 m.p.h. successor reflected those of the 1970s.

The Queen has visited Wolverton Works on several occasions. One such visit was on 17 December 1976, when she went to inspect the new royal train, comprising eight refurbished inter-city coaches built in 1972 as prototypes for the 125 m.p.h. High Speed Trains, and two new royal saloons, No. 2903 for the Queen and No. 2904 for the Duke of Edinburgh. The modern royal train is spartan compared with the luxury of Queen Victoria's. Lavishly decorated compartments with satin furnishings have given way to carriages which are elegant but plain and functional, with full air-conditioning. The Queen's saloon has a sitting room, bedroom and bathroom, and a bedroom and bathroom for her dresser. The ceiling panels are white melamine, the main wall finishing is a cream patterned PVC and the furnishings are in shades of blue. Prints of Queen Victoria's first train journeys were chosen for the Queen's saloon. Prince Philip's carriage is slightly smaller, with a kitchen, and a shower instead of a bath. Work on the train began in 1974 and the Queen revisited Wolverton to inspect the completed coaches on 16 May 1977.

It is not always appreciated that most special saloons were actually owned by the railway, and the VIP travellers paid to travel in them. The Duke of

TABLE 3.2　*Wolverton Works: output from principal spheres of activity year ended 31 December 1981*

Major modifications and conversions

Refurbishing of Class 307 EMUs	32
Conversion of 2-car EMUs to 4-Car	6
Class 312 trailer bogie transoms	3

Repair work	*C1R*	*C1/C2*	*C3*	*C3T*	*C4*	*Total classified*	*C5*
Catering coaches	—	1	1	—	1	123	17
Sleeping coaches	—	—	7	—	67	74	11
Loco-hauled coaches	—	3	100	14	208	325	52
Loco-hauled coaches (non-passenger-carrying)	—	1	69	—	83 (*C4X*)	153	16
EMUs	32	179	268	—	152	631	19

	GR	*IR/L*	*IR/W*	*IR*	*Total*
Traffic wagons	54	—	—	1	55

	Armature	*Carcase*
Traction motors	979	1012

Sutherland's coach, built at Wolverton after the first world war in bird's-eye maple and owned by the Duke, was a masterpiece of Wolverton craftsmanship.

Apart from its work on the royal train Wolverton became a carriage repair works only after the 1962 rationalisation. This changed role resulted in a reduction of 30 per cent in the size of the works; two carriage building shops of 16 acres (10.5 covered) were sold to the publisher Robert Maxwell, then MP for North Bucks. In 1977 new work was again undertaken: 24 Post Office vehicles and 21 diesel-electric multiple units (DEMUs) for Northern Ireland Railways, followed by 35 newspaper vans for BR. Table 3.2 shows output in 1981.

DERBY LOCOMOTIVE WORKS

The building of Derby Locomotive Works began in 1839 when the North Midland Railway Company commissioned workshops and offices on land adjacent to the newly-built station. Designed by the company architect, Francis Thompson (who also designed the station), the new complex, opened in 1840, had as a central feature two large workshops – the locomotive shop 184'-6" by 70'-6" and the carriage shop 191'-6" by 70'-6" – a polygonal engine house 130 feet in diameter and single-storey offices. Robert Stephenson was in charge of the original stock from 1839 to 1842.

Although not on the scale of the North Midland's buildings, the Birmingham & Derby Junction and the Midland Counties Railways had also built engine sheds and workshops adjoining Derby Station, so that when the three companies amalgamated in 1844 to form the Midland Railway Company there were workshop facilities on a reasonable scale but geographically scattered. One of the tasks facing the newly-appointed Locomotive and Carriage and Wagon Superintendent, Matthew Kirtley, was thus to develop these into comprehensive facilities for stabling and repairing the locomotive fleet brought together by the amalgamation, and for building new locomotives. Over the next 20 years new workshops and a further two roundhouses were built, and by 1866 the works area had increased fourfold. By the end of the century the present form of the works, covering 47 acres with 14 acres of buildings, was almost complete.

The first Locomotive Department Superintendent, at a salary of £200 p.a., was W. P. Marshall, who was the first secretary of the Institution of Mechanical Engineers from 1848 until he retired in 1877. When Matthew Kirtley became (on the recommendation of George and Robert Stephenson) the first Locomotive Superintendent of the new Midland Railway in 1844, a position he held until 1873, his elder brother Thomas, Locomotive and Carriage Superintendent of the North Midland Railway at a salary of £250 p.a., resigned and went to found Thomas Kirtley & Co. of Durham.

By constructing new lines and absorbing others the Midland Railway spread out in every direction, eventually connecting Carlisle, Liverpool and Manchester with London; York with Bristol and Bournemouth; and Swansea with Lynn; while its branches communicated with most important towns. Its headquarters were at Derby, where it built the Midland Railway Institute, a handsome building with a 500-seat lecture hall, library, reading and billiards rooms, committee rooms and restaurant. It remains popular with the staff and was the venue for the Derby Railway Engineering Club for over fifty years, until the Railway Technical Centre was built in 1965.

The works had three large messrooms. Two, one allowing smoking, the other not, each seated 800; the third, where weekly religious services were held during the breakfast interval, seated 400. In 1940 these were combined into a modern canteen, the largest in all the main works, seating 1000, with a stage and dressing rooms for social events. The Midland Railway Company acquired the original Derby Gasworks, next to the locomotive works, from which 119 132 000 cubic feet of gas were supplied to its works, station, offices, sidings and all signals in the Derby area.

Around 1890 the locomotive works had 22 stationary engines, with a total of 2400 horsepower, to drive the workshop machinery; today all machines have their own motors. On average 40 new engines were built each year, 120 were rebuilt with new boilers and 750 to 800 underwent heavy repairs. The introduction of electricity by Sir Henry Fowler, Midland Railway CME, started with the construction of a new power station in 1910 adjacent to the tube shop but outside the original works boundary, on the far side of the canal. The installed capacity was 3000 kilowatts, the turbo operators of disc and drum type running at 3000 rev./min. and each of 1250 kilowatt capacity.

Steam was supplied by three Stirling superheated boilers. It was common to see Fowler, a tall, stout man, who eventually became CME of the LMS, travelling from one shop to another by pedal cycle before the advent of the car.

Derby Works has long occupied a special place in the annals of locomotive repair and construction. As early as 1849 it was reported to be undertaking a large proportion of the locomotive repairs, and in September 1851 the first new locomotive – a six-coupled freight tender engine No. 147 – appeared. Until the building of the new carriage and wagon works it also repaired and built rolling stock, but this was then undertaken wholly by the new works and the locomotive works was able to concentrate on the role which, with the exception of wartime munitions work, has remained its speciality.

From Kirtley to Stanier, Derby was involved in building types of locomotive which have become legendary. From the 2–2–2 passenger tender and 0–6–0 freight tender locomotives of Kirtley's design, it went on to produce the Johnson rebuilding of the Kirtley designs and an 0–6–0 shunting locomotive was fitted with a 350 horsepower English Electric 6-cylinder diesel engine and electric transmission, the drive from the traction motor to the coupled wheels being by a geared jackshaft. In all 40 units were built, until at Fairburn's instigation a new design, embodying axle-mounted traction motors, was introduced in 1944; produced in considerable numbers, it became the model for the BR standard shunting locomotive.

In 1947–8 the first diesel-engined main-line locomotives in Britain were built, a joint initiative by Sir George Nelson of the English Electric Company, which produced the engine and electrical gear, and Ivatt, the works producing the mechanical parts. The first, No. 10 000, driven from the paint shop by Ivatt on 8 December 1947, made its first run to London on 16 December; the second, No. 10 001, went into service on 10 July 1948. The works also built the Fell diesel-engined locomotive which went into service in 1952. Although it proved unsuccessful, this was a further pioneering project, a joint venture by British Railways and Lt. Col. L. F. R. Fell.

The last steam locomotive constructed was No. 73 154, a 4–6–0 mixed traffic tender locomotive of BR standard design fitted with Caprotti valve gear. This brought the total number of locomotives built by the works in the years of steam traction to 2941. Construction of diesel-engined traction units and components continued and from 1953 the principal products were 0–6–0 diesel-electric shunting and Types 2 and 4 main-line diesel-electric locomotives. Following the 1962 main works rationalisation all new construction was concentrated at Crewe, whilst Derby continued to produce assemblies including bogies.

Derby has been to the fore in repair work, introducing new and more efficient techniques in both practices and organisation. As early as 1858, under Kirtley, a system of templates and gauges based on Whitworth's system was introduced as part of a revision of methods of measurement aimed at achieving dimensional consistency in manufacture. An important early application was in establishing the correct degree of interference in the pressing of cranks and wheel centres on to axles; another was the use of surface plates and fixtures in the initial stages of erection of locomotives, such that the location of components in relation to one another could be achieved with consistent accuracy.

Shortly before the first world war Fowler introduced a system of authorisation and inspection to bring under closer control the amount of work performed on locomotives brought in for repair. Craftsmen with specialised knowledge of particular aspects – cylinders, motion and brakework, for example – were promoted to the grades of Initial Examiner and Finished Work Inspector. They were allocated to the erecting and other shops, but were directly under the control of the Assistant to the Superintendent responsible for repairs. In 1982, under BREL management, the two grades were merged into one at all main works.

Prior to 1926 there were normally 200 to 300 locomotives in the works for repair. Any reduction in this figure meant better utilisation of workshop space and equipment and availability of locomotives for traffic. Central to the new system was the establishment of 'repair stages': instead of remaining in one berth in the erecting shop throughout, the locomotive was moved through a series of stages at which specialised staff using specialised equipment carried out a defined section of the repairs. This movement was related to a timetable, to which in turn were related the times by which other shops were to return components to the erecting shop. As a result the number of locomotives in the works at any one time was reduced to 60–65.

In the mid-1930s seven subsidiary locomotive works – Bristol, Carlisle, Grimesthorpe, Highbridge, Kentish Town, Leeds and Saltley – all equipped to undertake light classified repairs and customarily referred to as outstation locomotive shops by the former Midland Railway, were closed and the work-

TABLE 3.3   *Derby Locomotive Works: output from principal spheres of activity year ended 31 December 1981*

Repair work	General	Intermediate	Light	Total classified	Unclassified
HST power cars	—	40	66	106	3
Diesel main-line locomotives	22	—	3	25	66

				Armature	Carcase
Traction motors				977	951
Main generators				223	187

				Torque converters	Final drives
		Engines	Gearboxes		
DMU traction components		1 371	1 391	59	248

load absorbed by Derby. This was made possible by the introduction of improved methods of repair while Ivatt was superintendent.

At nationalisation the staff totalled 4361, engaged on locomotive building and repair, including all LMS diesel locomotives, hot-brass pressings, brass castings for Derby Carriage and Wagon Works, and chair castings for the Chief Civil Engineer's department. The works was responsible for the maintenance of 2576 locomotives. In 1947 the average number of days in the repair pits was 8.5 and the overall number of days on the works was 15.7. There were 768 heavy and 280 light classified repairs. The works also built 49 new locomotives. In 1954 Derby carried out 462 general, 473 intermediate and 330 non-classified repairs, a total of 1265; 3125 staff were engaged on this work. Derby also built 29 new steam locomotives and 35 diesel-electric locomotives, involving 540 staff. In 1962, in common with all main works, control of Derby Locomotive Works was transferred to the newly-formed British Railways Workshops Division. Output of repairs in 1981 is shown in Table 3.3.

BROMSGROVE WAGON WORKS

Bromsgrove Works at Aston Fields, built in 1840 for the Birmingham & Gloucester Railway Company mainly to repair freight wagons, merged into the newly-formed Midland Railway in 1844 and the LMS in 1923. The works was located on the main line from Bristol to Birmingham at the foot of the famous Lickey Incline between Bromsgrove and Blackwell. The gradient of the incline, 1 in 37.7, and its length of two miles make it the stiffest main-line gradient in Britain; Bromsgrove had the only decapod locomotive in the country, No. 2290 (popularly known as 'Big Bertha') built in Derby Works in 1920, to push trains up the Lickey.

Bromsgrove was a famous centre of hand-made nail production for over three centuries, a craft almost certainly introduced to England by Huguenot refugees. It was a sweated industry, the nailers being manipulated by the nail masters who supplied the iron rod from which the nails were made. In 1869 a man working his hardest for twelve hours a day could earn no more than seven shillings (35p) per week. If his wife worked – it was a cottage industry – another three shillings (15p) might be added to the family income. When the railway company opened the wagon works it paid its employees 12s 6d per week, and soon afterwards 15 shillings. With progressive increases and limited hours of work it must have seemed the realisation of a dream, and it was many nailmakers' ambition to transfer their skill to the works. The 'stationers', as they were called, were, with the bricklayers and carpenters, the aristocrats of the local labour market. The development of the works, built more than a mile from the town centre, did not however result in any expansion of Bromsgrove.

Although a relatively small works, Bromsgrove had an exceptionally good economic record. It repaired wagons and containers in the Birmingham and

West Midlands area, obtaining major components from Derby Carriage and Wagon Works, except laminated springs which it manufactured itself. During the second world war the initiative of the Works Manager resulted in the recovery of used wagon timber and ironwork for reuse at the many LMS outstation wagon repair shops, a practice which continued until the works closed.

In 1949, following nationalisation, the wagon repair output was 6941 classified repairs, 4853 heavy and 2088 light, an average of about 140 a week. There were also 973 classified repairs to containers. The average earnings of the artisan staff were the highest of all British Railways carriage and wagon works, a reflection of the high local rate of productivity rather than looseness in the fixing of piecework prices, most of which applied in other works for identical work content. At the time of closure in September 1964 Bromsgrove employed a total staff of 400, and after closure the workload was absorbed by Derby Carriage and Wagon Works.

CREWE LOCOMOTIVE WORKS

The history of Crewe Locomotive Works began in 1840, when the Board of the Grand Junction Railway Company ordered the purchase of a large area of land 'at the junction of Crewe' and asked its Engineer-in-Chief, Joseph Locke, to prepare plans and estimates 'which shall include the shops required for the building and repairs of carriages and wagons as well as engines'. The company's existing workshops were scattered, its main locomotive repair shop, rented from the Liverpool & Manchester Railway, being at Edge Hill, Liverpool. A contract for building the works and some 200 workers' cottages went to a Liverpool firm, and in March 1843 the works began production. Located in the fork between the lines to Liverpool and Chester, it initially occupied an area of 2½ acres, the nucleus of what later came to be known as the 'old works'.

Railway companies were notoriously unmindful of the welfare of the temporary labourers who constructed their lines, but took a different attitude towards the highly-paid skilled artisans and workers in their establishments. At Crewe the absence of an efficient, old-established system of government and urban economic organisation in the hitherto rural township of Monks Coppenhall meant the company had to undertake the task of building up a new community itself. The 1841 Census shows the population of Monks Coppenhall as 203; at the end of 1842 it had about 1000 inhabitants.

In 1842 the directors appointed an architect, John Cunningham, to 'superintend the whole of the buildings'. He held the post until 1850 at the princely salary of £300 p.a. The board had agreed to leave space for a church and school when laying out the town. Christ Church, consecrated on 18 December 1845, cost over £2000 to build and was endowed with £1000 and a guaranteed stipend of £150. The patronage remained vested in four directors, who acted as trustees. The vicar enjoyed half- or quarter-fare travel, with some free passes, as did the nonconformist ministers and day-school teachers, privileges not abolished until 1897. In 1842–3 a barn at the side of the rectory was converted into a small National School, and a separate National School for infants was completed in 1847. The directors' wives formed a Ladies' Committee to help in its management. There were about 300 children, for whom the company made a small charge each per week.

In 1844 Edwin Edwards (who died in 1865) was appointed first company surgeon at Crewe, at a salary of £50 p.a. The company supplied a surgery, and a scheme of health insurance was worked out. As early as 1843 the company had established the gasworks, which generated 20 000 cubic feet per day by 1849 and over 40 000 per day by 1856. The waterworks which supplied the works was adapted to supply domestic water, and there was a brickworks which by 1875 was producing 6 million bricks a year. The enlightened action of the company in providing public baths made a great impression in the 1840s.

Dining rooms were opened in 1866 for the men in the works 'who bring their breakfast and dinner with them'; in 1884 a second dining room was built in Goddard Street to serve the steelworks; and in 1892 a new one in Eaton Street replaced the first, the two accommodating about 800 men. The preparation and sale of dinners by the company began in 1918, when Bowen Cooke established the present canteen.

A centre of railway and town life was the Mechanics' Institution. In the spring of 1844 the newspaper room and a library against the school in Moss Square were organised under two separate committees, but in September 1845 they amalgamated under the title of The Crewe Mechanics' Institution. When the 54-hour working week was introduced in 1872 membership rose steadily to over 2000. In 1880 an extension was financed by the railway: ten more classrooms were added and small machine tools installed. From 1876 it produced Whitworth Scholars and Exhibitioners (53 of them by 1909) and gave sound technical training in theory and practice to large numbers of apprentices and craftsmen for a span of three generations. For many years it was a centre for both social and civic amenities. The building deteriorated steadily from the 1950s and was finally demolished in 1970.

Extensions to the works in 1853 necessitated 100 more cottages in the town, built at a cost of £94 each for the No. 1 and £120 for the No. 2 types. Another 75 were built later for workers at the new rail mill. Before the establishment of the works Crewe was inhabited by a few farmers and cottagers, but it soon developed into a flourishing town of 30 000 inhabitants, consisting almost entirely of the company's staff and their families, and the tradesmen who supplied them. In 1877 Crewe was granted a charter of incorporation, and F. W. Webb, Chief Works Superintendent, was elected Mayor for the Queen's Jubilee year of 1887 (and re-elected for 1888). In commemoration of the Jubilee and the fiftieth anniversary of the opening of the railway through Crewe, the company presented the town with a public park of about 40 acres.

Dedicated by Sir Richard Moon, Bt, chairman of the company, on 4 July 1887, it was formally opened by the Duke of Cambridge on 9 June 1888.

In 1846 the Grand Junction Railway was amalgamated with the Liverpool & Manchester, Manchester & Birmingham and London & Birmingham companies to form the London & North-Western Railway Company (LNWR). Locomotive matters were administered in three divisions: the Northern Division based on Crewe under Francis Trevithick (son of Richard); the North-Eastern based on Longsight (Manchester) under John Ramsbottom; and the Southern based on Wolverton under J. E. McConnell.

It was Trevithick who was responsible for the layout, erection and equipment of the Crewe shops and town. Despite the introduction of some primitive machines in 1848–50 most work was still undertaken by hand. The normal working week was 58½ hours: from 6 a.m. to 5.30 p.m. Monday to Friday and 6 a.m. to 4 p.m. on Saturday, with two breaks totalling 1½ hours a day. Payment was fortnightly, made on Saturday afternoon.

In July 1853 a rolling mill was commissioned and the LNWR became the only British railway company to produce its own rails; in the same year wrought iron was produced for the first time. The main business of the rolling mill for around 20 years was the production of iron rails in 21-foot lengths, along with fishplates. By 1854 the output of these items amounted to 90 tons a week, eventually rising to 150 tons.

At Trevithick's retirement in 1857 the Northern and North-Eastern Divisions were merged, based on Crewe, and John Ramsbottom, inventor of the safety valve and water pick-up scoop, became Locomotive Superintendent there on 1 August 1857. He was responsible for much pioneering work, including new machine tools of relatively advanced type and revising shop procedures with a view to greater accuracy and interchangeability. By the mid-1860s he had introduced templates, fixtures and gauges for the machining of component parts to an extent scarcely practised elsewhere.

In 1862, when McConnell retired, all locomotives were brought under one chief, with Crewe the locomotive centre of the LNWR. Several hundred Wolverton men and their families (some 1700 persons) came to Crewe with the transfer of locomotive work from Wolverton in 1865–6. The Crewe wagon work was transferred to Earlestown and the carriage work to Wolverton. The developing works embraced a substantial range of non-locomotive activities. When Sir Henry Bessemer invented his steel-making process Ramsbottom was so impressed that the new material was tested in the rail mill, and the first Bessemer steel rails were laid down at Crewe Station in November 1861. In 1864 the company opened its own Bessemer steel-making plant. Over the years other activities included manufacturing signals and signal equipment such as locking frames, crossing-gates, carts and barrows, station lamps, gas and water mains and even footwarmers. Nor was much wasted: soap was made from grease recovered in laundering handcloths!

The building of a new erecting shop in 1861 marked the end of development on the original site. Up to 1864 the line to Chester passed through the works site, but increasing traffic made realignment necessary, releasing land for further workshops, between the old line and the deviation, which became known as the 'deviation shops'. The first workshop on this site was commissioned in 1867. From 1867 onwards most new building was in the area around the steel plant, and in 1895 the rail mill was moved to this area. By this time the works area had risen to 116 acres (36 covered) and the number of employees to 7000.

The total number of locomotives constructed at Crewe up to 1890 was 3135, 146 of them in the year ending 30 November 1872. Some 2000 engines annually underwent repairs, and there were usually as many as 330 in the works for repair at any time. In 1926–8 a major development took place, with the building of a new erecting shop laid out with the specific aim of achieving high output of repaired locomotives by a system of progressive movement of locomotives through repair stages: this came to be generally described as the 'belt system'. This high output caused serious concern to private manufacturers – indeed, around 1873 Crewe had supplied to the Lancashire & Yorkshire Railway ten 2–4–0 passenger and 86 0–6–0 DX class freight locomotives, both Ramsbottom designs. In 1876 the private manufacturers obtained an injunction restraining Crewe from manufacturing any locomotives or rolling stock except those required for its own purposes. Apart from relaxations during the two world wars this remained the principle underlying new construction until the formation of BREL in 1970.

From the emergence in 1843 of the first new locomotive, 'Columbine', Crewe was involved with the building of many famous types of steam locomotive and with numerous innovations in design. From the Ramsbottom Problem (Lady of the Lake) class 2–2–2 passenger and DX class 0–6–0 freight locomotives the list embraces such locomotives as the Webb 2–4–0 Jumbo class and various Webb Compound classes, the Whale Experiment and Precursor classes, the Bowen–Cooke Claughton class and the Beames G2 class of freight locomotive. In later times, after the LNWR was absorbed into the LMS in 1923, the famous Princess and Coronation classes of passenger locomotive were built, including the unique Turbomotive No. 6202 and the Jubilee and Black Five classes.

While Sir William Stanier was CME of the LMS (1932–44) he designed some of the most successful and best-known steam locomotives ever built in Britain. Many thousands of railway enthusiasts will remember his handsome and powerful Pacific type locomotives, the first two of which (the Princess Royal class) were built at Crewe in 1933. Ten more were built in 1935, followed in 1937 by the still larger Duchess Pacifics, the first of which (No. 6220 'Coronation') gained a speed record of 114 m.p.h.

At nationalisation Crewe's principal activities were locomotive building and repair, the manufacture of all new boilers for standard LMS locomotives, steel castings, drop stampings and heavy forgings for all LMS works, chair castings and points, crossings for the Chief Civil Engineer's department and the manufacture of signals, locking frames and crossing-gate work for the

TABLE 3.4   *Crewe Locomotive Works: output from principal spheres of activity year ended 31 December 1981*

New construction					
HST power cars for BR					36
				Total	
Repair work	*General*	*Intermediate*	*Light*	*classified*	*Unclassified*
Diesel main-line locomotives	6	60	90	156	107
Electric locomotives	35	6	42	83	46
				Armature	*Carcase*
Traction motors				1884	1884
Main generators				173	206

Signal and Telecommunications Department. The total staff was 7433. In 1947 Crewe was responsible for 2779 maintained locomotives, the average number in the works was 109, the average number of working days in a repair pit was 8.1 and the average number of calendar days in the works was 19.2. There were 779 heavy and 714 light classified repairs. The works also built 36 new locomotives. In 1954 there were 514 general, 713 intermediate and 404 non-classified repairs, totalling 1631, a workload involving 5375 staff. Crewe also built 43 steam locomotives, with 1040 staff.

When, following nationalisation, the BR standard designs emerged under R. A. Riddles, Crewe built the Britannia and Clan passenger locomotives as well as the successful Class 9 and the 2–10–0 freight locomotives. By the end of the steam era Crewe had built over 7000 locomotives for the LNWR, LMS and BR, the last steam locomotive being the BR standard 2–10–0 freight locomotive No. 92250. Construction of diesel locomotives began in 1957 with a series of diesel-electric shunting locomotives and has continued with a variety of types of diesel-electric, diesel-hydraulic and electric locomotives.

The main effect on Crewe of the major rationalisation and re-equipment in 1964 was the abandonment of the old works and deviation areas and the concentration of activities into the steelworks area, reducing the occupied area from the former 137 acres to 89. Output in 1981 is shown in Table 3.4. Crewe is BREL's largest main works – and one can scarcely imagine British Railways as a locomotive builder without it.

BARROW-IN-FURNESS LOCOMOTIVE AND CARRIAGE AND WAGON WORKS

The Furness Railway, generally considered to be among the most efficient of the smaller railway companies at the 1923 amalgamation, was granted Royal

Assent in 1844. The earliest cottages built by the company, which created the town, are at 1–22 Salthouse Road, solidly built in red sandstone. The company also owned the Barrow Town Hall, gasworks and waterworks. From its inception in 1846 the Furness Railway built its works on land next to its headquarters off St George's Square. The erecting shop had three bays, each 480 by 50 feet.

The first Locomotive Superintendent was James Ramsden, who in 1850 became General Manager. He was followed by R. Mason (retired 1896) who was succeeded by W. F. Pettigrew, who completely changed the locomotive policy. Until then all the locomotives were standard productions of the contractors from whom they were obtained. Pettigrew immediately began his own new locomotive designs, all of which were built by outside firms. (No locomotives were built by the Furness Railway. The first locomotive was supplied in 1844 and the last in 1921, involving fifteen contractors.) There were no 'standard' designs at the time and Pettigrew introduced his own ideas of standardisation. In 1918 D. L. Rutherford took over the duties of Locomotive Superintendent as well as being Civil Engineer. On the mechanical engineering side he was assisted by E. Sharples and they held their positions up to the works' closure in 1923.

There were substantial carriage and wagon shops. The carriage shop was 210 by 120 feet and the wagon shop 300 by 160 feet. The paint shop had capacity for 20 carriages and there was a wagon repair shop and a large timber-drying shed. Many wagons and coaches were built in the works and all heavy overhauls and general repairs successfully undertaken. Barrow Works also carried out engineering and maintenance for the Barrow Docks equipment.

As the works was run down, many of the shopmen were transferred to Horwich Locomotive Works and other staff went to Derby or Crewe. At amalgamation the works was taken over by the Horwich Works Manager, who was responsible for the closure in 1923–4.

BOW LOCOMOTIVE WORKS

Bow Locomotive Works in the east end of London was opened by the North London Railway (NLR) in 1850. The line ran from Broad Street in the City to Poplar Docks and Richmond. The NLR Carriage and Wagon Works was also at Bow, with the steam sheds at Devons Road.

In December 1908 the NLR directors made an agreement with the LNWR that the NLR would continue as a separate concern but its officers would be those of the LNWR, who would operate the NLR and be responsible to the NLR Board. The NLR remained a distinct entity after 1908; just before grouping its 99 locomotives operated over 1½ million engine miles, there were some 400 passenger vehicles and in all it handled about 14 million passengers. The Broad Street–Richmond/Kew services were electrified in 1916 and after the war the NLR services to Chalk Farm were extended to

Watford and electrified. The LNWR owned half of Broad Street Station and all electrical workings were its responsibility, not that of the LNR.

The first Locomotive Superintendent in 1853 was William Adams, one of the most forward-looking of the Victorian locomotive engineers. He left in 1873, becoming the Great Eastern Locomotive Superintendent at Stratford. His successor J. C. Park reorganised, almost completely rebuilt and enlarged Bow Works; a number of the machine tools were built at the works. A class of outside-cylinder 0–6–0 tanks was introduced. Park can be said to have made Bow one of the foremost railway works of the smaller British companies.

The first NLR engines were supplied by various contractors. After five 0–4–2 saddle tanks in 1860, all other NLR motive power was constructed at Bow, and none of these early locomotives was fitted with a cab. All locomotive work had a fixed price. Erecting an NLR standard passenger tank was set at £48. Turning the treads of a pair of driving or coupled wheels, or a driving or coupled axle from the forging, was charged at 12 shillings (60p) and reckoned as a day's work. This applied to one axle-end only: the complete axle was 24 shillings, two days' work, a bogie axle being half this price.

Bow Works was the smallest of the fifteen LMS main works. It carried out all major repairs to the NLR locomotives and classified repairs to locomotives operating on the LMS London Tilbury & Southend (LT&S) section after the outstation at Plaistow was closed in 1927. Bow included a sizeable wagon repair shop and a chain and lifting gear repair shop which were invaluable in dealing with the heavy workload in the LMS London area. Both suffered heavy damage during the second world war. A notable Bow activity was the development and manufacture in the 1930s of the Hudd automatic train control system for locomotives working on the LT&S section, administered by BR Eastern Region after nationalisation. Subsequently a small team from BR HQ was set up in the works to develop a new BR standard of automatic warning system (AWS).

In LMS days, before the introduction of diesel-electric locomotives, the weekly output of classified repairs at Bow had risen to 2 heavy and 1 light, as well as casual repairs. In 1956 Devons Road became the first all-diesel motive power depot (MPD) with Bow Works conveniently placed to deal with maintenance needed between regular shopping. The freight locomotives were found to require modifications to the bogies, involving lifting and cleaning. After a while it became practicable to accept a locomotive into the works at 8.00 a.m. and return it the same day. At first this put the MPD's statistical returns in doubt, the same locomotive being shown in Bow Works and back in service on the same day!

The last Works Manager when the works closed in December 1960 was Bruce Carmichael, trained at Crewe, a descendant of the Carmichaels of Ward Foundry, Dundee, who built the first locomotives with four-wheeled bogies for the Dundee & Newtyle Railway in 1834. At its peak Bow Works employed 750, but there were only 150 men when the workload was transferred to Derby.

EARLESTOWN CARRIAGE AND WAGON WORKS

Earlestown Works was established by Jones Turner & Evans, who built colliery pumping machinery and locomotives for many emerging railways, some overseas. They included six broad-gauge locomotives of the famous North Star type to Gooch's design – Firefly, Spitfire, Fireball, Fireking and Fire-brand – for the GWR in 1840. By 1853 the owners were Jones & Potts, who built over 300 locomotives. At the end of 1852 Crewe Works was inadequate for the number of wagon repairs needed and alternative accommodation for wagon building and repairs was sought for the LNWR's Northern Division. Jones & Potts were prepared to lease the factory for two years at £650 p.a. or seven at £600 p.a., stating that there was accommodation for building 1000 wagons and 50 locomotives each year, and that the premises included:

> one 24-horse engine, one 18-horse engine, 40 smith's fires, one large hooping furnace, one foundry, three cupolas, one brass foundry, gas apparatus, one office and drawing-room, warehouse, dining-room for 22 men, and stable for eight horses.

At the end of the LNWR's lease of the property, dating from 1 March 1853, the company bought it for £15 000. The director under whose guidance the works was bought and developed was Hardmann Earle, whose name is perpetuated in the township built to house the employees. The lane leading to the works, originally Pepper Alley Lane, was also later named Earle Street. The works was referred to locally as the Viaduct Foundry, from Stephenson's famous Sankey Viaduct nearby, carrying the Liverpool & Manchester Railway over the St Helen's Canal. The Rainhill trials took place only a few miles away in 1829.

By 1873 the 60 cottages (each housing two families) were insufficient and another 50 were authorised. Plans were approved for a two-storey building with a staff dining room at ground level and a library and reading room above, which opened late in 1877, when the Viaduct Institute came into being. Works personnel made a weekly contribution from their wages: 1d for men rated over 10s per week and ½d for those under, entitling them to enjoy its amenities. The LNWR provided 5000 library books and six acres of sports grounds. The building was also used as a technical school for apprentices until a modern school was built at Newton-le-Willows.

By 1901 the staff totalled some 2000. Annual production capacity was 4000 new wagons, 13 000 heavy classified wagon repairs and 200 new horse-drawn vehicles of various types for the cartage department. A new shop was built – called the 'white shop' because it was in concrete, not brick – in 1913 and was equipped with two 20-ton and two 6-ton overhead travelling cranes to enable the concentration of goods brake vans, bogie wagons and special vehicles there.

Earlestown continued as a self-contained works for freight wagon stock and for manufacturing and maintaining LNWR Northern Area road vehicles until

1931. Two years after the 1923 amalgamation Ernest Lemon became Super-intendent of Earlestown and of the former Lancashire & Yorkshire Railway (L&YR) Carriage and Wagon Works at Newton Heath. He introduced mass production methods of wagon construction. This necessitated the purchase of new equipment and structural alterations to speed up the flow of timber. During the first seven years of mass production Earlestown built 19 540 standard type wood-framed wagons. The system was not applied to repairs until 1931, when William Anthony became Superintendent, and on him fell the task of reorganisation to absorb the wagon, lorry and wood motor body repair work transferred from Newton Heath. By this time many new types of pneumatic and electrical power-operated hand tools had been introduced, reducing the overall time of a repair.

Progressive methods were also applied in the spring shop, where an oil-fired rotary furnace accommodating eight sets of spring plates heated the plates already punched, sheared and nibbled in the 'Pels' machine, which were then shaped hot under a hydraulic press, hardened and tempered in

TABLE 3.5 *General information and output for Earlestown Carriage and Wagon Works, 1955*

General information		
Area of works (acres)		36
Covered area occupied by workshops and offices (acres)		15
Total staff employed		1 900
Total number of machines		530
Fuel, power and water used per annum:		
Coal (tons)		4 000
Coke (tons)		550
Gas (cu. ft.)		13 000 000
Electricity (units)		3 000 000
Fuel oil (gallons)		244 000
Petrol (gallons)		16 000
Domestic water (gallons)		2 750 000
Well water (gallons)		44 000 000

Repair output	Heavy	Light
Open goods wagons	6 200	325
Covered goods wagons	3 400	100
16-ton all-steel wagons	2	—
Mineral non-hoppered wagons	700	15
Mineral hoppered wagons	25	10
Special vehicles	60	90
Cattle wagons	125	2
Rail and timber wagons	400	30
Goods brake vans	750	10
Service vehicles	250	5

another oil-fired furnace, the operation being facilitated by gravity-operated rollers. Finally the buckling operation was carried out under a hydraulic press. The manufacture of one 5-plate standard wagon spring took five minutes after heating, and the output of the shop was enough to meet all the LMS system's wagon spring requirements.

In October 1943 the old method of manufacturing 3-link wagon couplings by hand forging was discontinued and an electric flash-butt welding process brought into use. Wagon coupling requirements for the LMR, for new wagons as well as those in service, were manufactured on this plant, the average weekly output being 1000 complete couplings. For the remainder of the LMS period, 1923–47, mass production of new wagons was undertaken and the manufacture of wagon laminated springs and 3-link couplings for the entire LMS system was concentrated at Earlestown. In 1946 a progressive layout for the repair of standard steel-framed open goods wagons was introduced, raising the weekly output from 5 to 25. This was followed by the weaving of standard lubricating pads by women, producing 2000 weekly. In June 1946 a factory was erected to convert waste timber into firelighters, totalling 650 gross weekly, for use at motive power depots.

Output and general statistics for 1955, the year the training school opened, are shown in Table 3.5. In 1963, ten years after its centenary. Earlestown Works closed as part of the BR rationalisation plan and the workload was transferred to Horwich. A large proportion of the 1900 staff agreed to move to Horwich, most of the remainder finding work with the firms which bought individual workshops from BR and turned the works into an industrial estate.

ST ROLLOX LOCOMOTIVE WORKS

St Rollox Works was built by the Caledonian Railway on the site of the original terminus of Glasgow's earliest railway, the Garnkirk & Glasgow, at whose opening ceremony in autumn 1831 the 'George Stephenson' (one of two locomotives supplied by Stephenson's Newcastle works), weighing a mere 6½ tons and loaded to slightly over 100 tons, is said to have 'advanced under this prodigious load not only with perfect freedom, but at the speed of a stage coach'.

By the mid-1840s Glasgow's Springburn district to the north-east of the city was fast becoming Scotland's main centre of locomotive and carriage building. Consequently the Caledonian Railway, which had absorbed the Garnkirk & Glasgow, decided to move its works from Greenock nearer to the heart of Scotland's railway centre; the site chosen was in Springburn Road close to Buchanan Street and Queen Street stations, in an angle between the original Garnkirk & Glasgow line and the new main line to Buchanan Street. The new works, christened St Rollox after the nearby church of St Roche, was one of the few railway works which, from its beginning in 1856, was designed to build and repair locomotives, carriages and wagons; for this reason the various shops were closely integrated.

By the end of the nineteenth century the fame of the works had spread, as such well-known locomotives as the 'Cardean' and the Dunalastair ranges emerged from its shops. The latter, designed by J. F. McIntosh, had a considerable effect on Belgian and Dutch locomotive designs for many years. In 1901 members of the International Engineering Congress visited St Rollox. Prior to their extensive tour they were supplied with the following information:

The capital expended by the company amounted to £53 000 000. The length of track was about 1000 miles of railway, and 52 miles of canal. There were 21 000 employees. The company owned:

902	Locomotives	
287	First-class carriages	
1 205	Third-class carriages	
304	Composite and saloon carriages	
5	Post Office vans	Total coaching vehicles
116	Horse boxes	2 262
41	Carriage trucks	
93	Fish and milk trucks	
3	Stores vans	
207	Luggage vans	
1	Prison van	
14 644	Open goods wagons	
1 459	Covered wagons	
875	Cattle and sheep trucks	
523	Brake vans	Total merchandise in mineral
1 853	Swivel wagons	wagons
43 542	Mineral wagons	63 183
11	Gunpowder vans	
13	Tank wagons	
9	Crane wagons	
254	Ballast wagons	

The total train miles run by the company's trains during the year 1900 was 16 857 547, and the passengers conveyed, exclusive of season ticket holders, numbered 2 219 215 first class, and 42 084 022 third class. In the same period the gross receipts amounted to £4 210 858, and the expenditure to £2 368 053.

The canteen was used daily by some 400 employees; a substantial breakfast cost 8d (3½p) and a dinner 5d (2½p).

Within a few years of amalgamation new construction was discontinued, but all classified repairs of LMS locomotives in Scotland were concentrated at St Rollox. The staff employed in 1954 was 2348. Output of repairs in 1947 and 1954 is shown in Table 3.6. In 1962 St Rollox was renamed Glasgow Works and reorganised. The estimated annual financial effect of the reorganisation

TABLE 3.6 *Output at St Rollox, Glasgow, Locomotive Works, 1947 and 1954*

	Locomotive repairs			
Year	Heavy	Intermediate	Light	Non-classified
1947	354	—	239	—
1954	181	234	—	413

TABLE 3.7 *Glasgow Works: output from principal spheres of activity year ended 31 December 1981*

Major modifications & conversions

Refurbishing DMUs	29
Refurbishing MR1 catering vehicles	5
Replacement of 150HP AEC engines – DMUs	21

Repair work	General	Intermediate	Light	Total classified	Unclassified
Diesel main-line locomotives	23	24	—	47	72
Diesel shunting locomotives	2	—	—	2	14

	Armature	Carcase
Traction motors	785	725
Main generators	90	90

	C1R	C1/C2	C3	C3T	C4	Total classified	C5
Loco-hauled coaches	—	40	207	62	515	824	83
Loco-hauled coaches (non-passenger-carrying)	—	—	16	—	20	36	8
DMUs	29	5	48	—	33	115	14
EMUs	—	24	33	—	85	142	5

	Engines	Gearboxes	Torque converters	Final drives
DMU traction components	300	488	—	180

was a reduction in costs from £3 387 020 to £2 809 230. With the closure of Cowlairs (1968), Inverurie (1970) and Barassie Works (1972) the reorganised Glasgow Works has covered all classified repairs to locomotives, electric and diesel multiple units, carriages and wagons for Scottish Region as well as special mobile equipment such as cranes and track weeding machines. In 1979 the works employed some 2300 staff. Overhauls and repairs included 222 main-line locomotives, 36 diesel shunters, 1055 locomotive-hauled coaches including sleeping and catering cars, 193 diesel multiple units (including 48 which were fully refurbished) and 176 electric multiple units. Output in 1981 is shown in Table 3.7.

By 1986 the works was in the throes of a rundown as part of BREL's corporate strategy. BREL launched a £1 million alternative employment scheme to assist redundant staff and formed an industrial development enterprise consisting of a three-year package of grants and incentives with the aim of creating jobs by stimulating local industry. In retrospect the span of time favoured the former St Rollox Works because, unlike its counterparts, it survived to become the only main works in Scotland.

ST ROLLOX CARRIAGE AND WAGON WORKS

St Rollox Carriage and Wagon Works was built integrally with the locomotive works in 1856, and both were extended and reorganised during 1882–4. In 1900, when the two works employed 3130 staff, the Caledonian Railway owned 2262 coaching vehicles and 63 183 merchandise and mineral wagons. The company's trains ran a total of 16 857 547 train miles and 2 219 215 first- and 42 084 022 third-class passengers were conveyed, excluding season ticket holders. In the same year gross receipts were £4 210 858 and the expenditure £2 368 053 – at 1900 prices.

At amalgamation St Rollox became the major works of the LMS Northern Division. New manufacture ceased, and in 1929 the management decided that all wagon repair work should be done at Barassie, which made more space available at St Rollox for repairs to the stock of 5000 carriages. Each came in for a general repair every six years and on average every 18 months for lifting and varnishing. The average weekly output of classified repairs in the 1930s was 25 carriages and 14 milk trucks and motor vans.

In 1949 the works carried out 1171 heavy and 1091 light classified repairs, involving a total of 876 staff. In 1954 it undertook 398 heavy and 1537 light classified repairs.

Since 1962 the works has been in amalgamation with St Rollox Locomotive Works under the name of Glasgow Works.

KILMARNOCK LOCOMOTIVE AND CARRIAGE AND WAGON WORKS

Kilmarnock Works, Ayrshire (adjacent to the main line at Kilmarnock Station), the headquarters of the Locomotive, Carriage and Wagon Department of the Glasgow & South-Western Railway, was absorbed by the LMS in 1923. Established in 1856, it had built no fewer than 392 locomotives by 1921. In 1920 it employed 1100 men, some 400 on the night shift. Following amalgamation heavy locomotive and carriage repairs were transferred to St Rollox, light locomotive and wagon repairs remaining. Part of the works was demolished in 1929.

After nationalisation the main change was the establishment by the Carriage & Wagon Engineer of an outdoor district at Kilmarnock; and as locomotive repairs ceased in 1952 the shops were reorganised to repair Scottish Region's steam, electric and manually operated cranes. The region's scrapping of locomotives and boilers was also concentrated here. At this time the salaried and wages staff totalled 284 (62 on outdoor C&W work). The average weekly output was 1.7 general and intermediate and 1.0 casual locomotive repairs, and 343 light wagon repairs. The works closed in 1959.

STOKE LOCOMOTIVE AND CARRIAGE AND WAGON WORKS

The North Staffordshire Railway (familiarly known as the 'Old Knotty Railway' from its emblem, the Staffordshire knot) came into being in April 1845, with George and Robert Stephenson very much involved from its earliest conception. It proved an efficient, compact and successful railway. The earliest locomotives were built by outside contractors: in 1848, 41 were delivered from eight companies. Sharpe Bros & Co. supplied six, the first being No. 1 'Dragon', with which the line was opened. They were of Sharpe's standard design for the 1844–8 period, known as the Little Sharpes. Other contractors included Robert Stephenson & Co., Vulcan Foundry, Hudswell Clarke, Kitson's and Neilson & Co., and by the early 1860s the railway possessed 64 locomotives.

Stoke Works opened in 1864. All repairs and heavy rebuilding took place there, but facilities for new building were not completed until 1868, when the first three locomotives were built: Nos 5, 13 and 24. They were 0–6–0 tanks, very similar to a Hudswell Clarke product supplied in 1866, small and weighed just under 21 tons in working order, with inside cylinders 13″ by 18″ and 3-foot diameter wheels. The locomotive stock gradually rose over the years: by 1882 there were 128; by 1901 – when the locomotive works employed 450 men – there were 166, a mixture of contractor and works built. In 1901 there were 422 carriages and 5942 wagons, the carriage and wagon works then employing 400. In the early years the Locomotive and Carriage and Wagon Superintendent was J. H. Adams, the Locomotive Works Manager J. A. Hookham and the Carriage and Wagon Works Manager R. Dent.

The 0–6–0 tanks were built between 1879 and 1901, 30 locomotives in all. The initial design was carried out by J. C. Park, who had succeeded William Adams. They were sturdy locomotives with cylinders low slung and horizontal and the crossheads running on single slide bars. It speaks well for their construction that 14 passed into BR ownership in 1948, the last disappearing in 1958 at the age of 70. Up to 1883 all NLR locomotives were painted green with black bands edged with red and white, with all brass and copper work polished. The livery was then changed to black with yellow, red and pale blue lining. No new locomotives were built after 1923. Four inside-cylinder 4–4–0 tanks were taken into LMS stock, the last being scrapped in 1925; 74 outside-cylinder 4–4–0 tanks also absorbed had all disappeared by 1929, replaced by new standard LMS 0–6–0 tanks.

The Engineer of the line from 1865 to 1870 was James Johnson, father of Samuel Waite Johnson, Locomotive Superintendent of the Midland Railway at Derby and designer of the renowned 4–4–0 compound locomotives. The last Works Manager, 1919–27, was H. G. Ivatt, subsequently CM&EE of the LMS. Stoke Works was closed by the LMS in 1927 and the work transferred to Crewe Locomotive Works. Most of the Stoke men went to Crewe, and a special train from Stoke-on-Trent has continued to run daily into Crewe Works, near to the works training school.

DERBY CARRIAGE AND WAGON WORKS

In 1873 the Midland Railway Company decided to create a separate Carriage and Wagon Works Department at Derby. Thomas Gething Clayton, who had been in charge of the design and construction of the Great Western works at Swindon, was appointed Carriage and Wagon Superintendent and given a brief to reorganise and modernise the Midland Railway's stock of vehicles as well as to design and construct the new Derby Carriage and Wagon Works. His method of planning the works was unique as it incorporated workshop layouts which made possible sequenced production from input of raw materials to completed vehicles. It also created a true 'flow line method' of production which established patterns of excellence in production techniques which remain to the present day.

A 50-acre site was purchased a mile south of the Midland Railway Station and the first workshops were in operation in 1876. By 1878, at a cost of £300 000, some 13½ acres of workshops, stores and offices had been constructed. Twelve months later a new wagon shop, carriage shop and carriage painting shops were erected. While these were being built a new paint shop at Etches Park, Derby, was opened. By July 1887 the works was producing the first new carriages, Clayton retaining the Etches Park shop to store freshly-painted carriages while the paint and varnish hardened.

In 1873 carriage vehicle length was of the order of 40 to 47 feet, whereas Clayton's planning had allowed the workshops to be spaced 70 feet apart, enabling lateral movement of vehicles from shop to shop first by steam traverser and later by electric powered traversers. One hundred years later these electric traversers were still hauling vehicles nearly 70 feet in length, a tribute to Clayton's foresight. The assembly shops were separated from the component manufacturing shops by five feed lines running north–south. The sawmill measured 320 by 200 feet.

Production commenced in 1876, the first carriages to be built consisting of 40-foot 6-wheeled passenger vehicles, 26-foot third-class carriages, passenger brake vans and 30-foot Post Office vehicles. The first 54-foot bogie vehicles were built in 1883 for the Midland–Scottish joint stock services which operated between London (St Pancras), Edinburgh and Glasgow. Ten of these were completed by June 1879 at a cost of £956 each. Further schemes were introduced in 1883 for the extension of the works.

A 6-wheeled Derby-built carriage of 1885 is preserved in the National Railway Museum at York. At this period 26 coats of primer, filling, paint and varnish were applied to each carriage. The painting process, including lining and varnishing, lasted over three weeks. The modern coach has only one priming coat, one filling coat, one undercoat and one top coat of Uro-Alkyd, this process taking only 5 days.

By the end of the nineteenth century the works averaged 8 new passenger vehicles and 180 new wagons per week, in addition to a heavy repair programme. In 1901 Clayton was succeeded as Carriage and Wagon Superintendent by David Bain of the North-Eastern Railway. His initial contributions were sleeping cars and dining carriages, the first of which was built in 1903. In 1904 the carriage portions of the two steam rail motor carriages, numbered 2233 and 2234, for the Morecambe–Heysham services were completed in the works. They left under their own steam and are credited with having attained to 50 m.p.h. in service.

By 1912 the works facilities were fully extended. The growth of the works included iron and brass foundries, heavy forges, drop stamps, nut and bolt manufacturing capacity, wheel machining and assembly, spring manufacture, smithy and machine shops, internal finishing and carriage finishing. A major asset was the lifting and erecting shop built in 1908, measuring 579 by 200 feet. Most of the works machinery was converted from steam to electric power, provided from the new power station built by the Midland Railway at the nearby locomotive works.

The production of 10-ton and 12-ton wagons had developed to the stage where, starting with a set of components at 9 a.m., the main framework would be finished by midday and the wagon completely assembled ready for painting by 4 p.m. Stocks of first-class timber included oak, pine, elm, hickory, walnut, mahogany, farrah maple, teak, deal, larch and lignum vitae. Altogether 59 different varieties of timbers were recorded. Stock orders dealt with 57 miles of oak, 2000 miles of sawn timber lengths undergoing natural seasoning in the timber drying sheds, and a further 1000 miles of fir timbers undergoing outdoor seasoning.

E. J. H. Lemon, who subsequently became a member of the wartime Railway Executive and was knighted, was appointed Works Superintendent under Reid in 1917. Reid succeeded Bain as Carriage and Wagon Superintendent in 1919. A survey of American flow line methods was undertaken by Reid and Lemon, who implemented similar methods at Derby. Wagon building was reorganised on a progressive line basis using a mechanical continuously-moving layout for the construction of wagons at the rate of 200 a week, equivalent to one 13-ton wagon every 16 minutes. Additionally, carriages 57 feet in length were built at the rate of 10 a week.

The sawmill, modernised in the 1920s, contained separate bays, one of which was equipped for converting timber logs to scantlings, whilst others specialised in the manufacture of carriage and wagon components. Some 200 logs per week were a normal output and these provided the timber for a mechanised bay of 12 machines capable of milling 200 sets of open wagon components. Bandsawing and morticing machines were in extensive use for the production of morticed joints and light apertures for carriage stock, whilst another bay known as the 'toy shop' was equipped for manufacturing interior finishing timbers. At this stage of development the sawmill was recognised as the largest and most modern in Europe.

Following the 1923 amalgamation Derby Carriage and Wagon Works had to compete with Wolverton and Earlestown on the LNWR and Newton Heath on the Lancashire & Yorkshire system. Metallic arc welding began to be developed in the early 1930s when Ernest Pugson, Works Superintendent, realised the importance of this technology and initiated the building of the first all-welded underframe and composite welded steel/timbered bodies to operate on BR. He also introduced the manufacture of welded fabricated alternatives to cast, forged, stamped and smithed components. From this beginning the use of electric arc welding techniques involved the gradual displacement of 92 smiths' hearths. By the end of the 1930s complete all-welded steel vehicles were being produced for the Liverpool & Southport electric service of the LMS. The average output was 300 new carriages and 5000 wagons per annum, including heavy bogie bolster wagons of up to 120 tons capacity for carrying steel bars, transformers and other special loads. The late 1930s also saw the production of an all-steel welded experimental streamlined 3-car diesel set and a complete Coronation Scot train built to tour the American railroads as part of a publicity campaign. Work was also concentrated on the replacement of LMS stock with all-steel welded vehicles.

In 1948 the works became the principal carriage and wagon works of the newly-constituted London Midland Region, the largest of the six new regions. A. E. Bates was Works Manager and produced the first all-steel carriages built for locomotive-hauled trains. Collaboration between design and production staffs and the introduction of a flexible jigging system, adaptable for any type of carriage, facilitated unit construction and progressive assembly.

TABLE 3.8   *Output at Derby Carriage and Wagon Works in 1949 and 1954*

Year	New construction		Classified repairs			
			Carriages		Wagons	
	Carriages	Wagons	Heavy	Light	Heavy	Light
1949	261	3 674	2 971	460	8 050	4 978
1954	220	3 659	716	2 720	10 218	2 407

In 1950 a new standard all-steel carriage embodying all the best features of design from the six regions of British Railways was produced and was known as the Standard Mark I carriage, and by 1955 some 1000 various permutations of this vehicle had been produced.

In 1949 the total number of staff employed in the Derby Carriage and Wagon Works was 5127, of whom 379 were professional and technical, workshop supervisory and clerical staff. Five years later, in 1954, the allocation of artisan staff was as follows.

Carriage construction	1300
Classified carriage repairs	1700
Wagon construction	500
Classified wagon repairs	1300

Table 3.8 shows the output in the significant years 1949 and 1954.

The modernisation and re-equipment plan called for the introduction of diesel-powered multiple units, and Derby was chosen in 1953 to build all aluminium railcars of an integrated design with aluminium extrusion riveted underframe body structure. The body panelling was welded before being riveted to the body structure. The manufacture of diesel multiple units saw the introduction of reinforced glass fibre products for the making of the roof-end canopies. Within 10 months of receipt of the order eight 2-car units entered service as the first of a fleet of 414 light alloy railcars built at Derby and recognised at that time as the largest fleet of aluminium railway vehicles in service in the world. The year 1956 saw the introduction of all-steel railcars manufactured in the works, and by the end of the decade over 1000 diesel rail-cars had been built.

Repair activities were maintained during this period with 70 classified carriage repairs and 250 wagon repairs being achieved weekly. Simultaneously 120 new wagons were being produced and a new 16-ton all-steel mineral wagon was being developed. These were subsequently produced at the rate of 80 per week on progressive production lines largely based on the techniques applied to carriage building. The 1950s also witnessed a massive programme applied to the fitting of vacuum brakes to wagons. 'S' shop, built in 1883 primarily for refurbishing privately owned wagons, was adapted to accommodate these conversions at the rate of 100 per week. Another achievement during this period was the successful tender for the building of 169 trailer cars for the London Transport Executive, the first time a BR works had built electric rolling stock for London Transport. The LTE required 676 vehicles to act as replacements on the Piccadilly Line. The works won a contract for building 169 of the vehicles, which were made of aluminium alloy; the exteriors of the cars were not painted.

In 1962 Derby Carriage and Wagon Works was renamed Derby Litchurch Lane Works. The building of wagons was discontinued and wagon repairs curtailed. A total of £1.4 million was expended in reorganising the works and space vacated by wagon building was adapted to improve the carriage building and repairing production flow lines. By the end of 1981, 180 carriages and 11 000 containers had been built for overseas and shipping administrations (see Table 3.9 for 1981 output). Container building ended in 1979 and the space was used to provide a centralised sheet-metal manufacturing and machining shop and a new central store with mechanical order picking and computerised stock control.

Over the years the 'black' trades have virtually disappeared and electronically-controlled machines and automatic processes have replaced much of the heavy manual work and the steam- and hydraulically-powered equipment. Wood and iron used in vehicle construction has largely been superseded by steel, aluminium and plastics, and the vehicles produced have developed from the simple 4-wheeled locomotive-hauled carriages to computer-designed vehicles with air conditioning, electro-pneumatic brakes, hydro-kinetic brakes, disc brakes, body tilting mechanisms and an ever-increasing volume of electronically-automated controls. The operating speed of vehicles has increased from 50 to 125 m.p.h. and mileage between shopping for overhaul has been extended from 50 000 to 250 000 miles.

TABLE 3.9   *Derby Litchurch Lane Works: output from principal spheres of activity year ended 31 December 1981*

New construction
For British Rail

HST coaches	32
Mark III sleeping coaches	27
EMUs	17
Diesel-electric multiple unit – prototype	3
BREL/Leyland Railbus	1

For Tanzania

First-class couchette coaches	14
Buffet coaches	10

Major modifications & conversions

Re-furbishing of DMUs	14
Screw-out battery module – Mark IIIa	55
Improvement of battery chargers – HST trailer coaches	43

Repair work	C1R	C1/2	C3	C3T	C4	Total classified	C5
HST trailer coaches			151		294	445	24
Loco-hauled coaches		16	173	21	279	489	65
Loco-hauled coaches (non-passenger-carrying)		9	86		40	135	15
DMUs and EMUs	14	18	88		8	128	5

	GR	IR/L	IR/W	IR	Total
Traffic wagons	40		20	2	62

Derby Litchurch Lane Works has had its share of interesting characters, probably the most noteworthy being Newton Hibbert, whose work as a fitter for no less than 72 years is commemorated on a plaque in the fitting and machine shop.

NEWTON HEATH CARRIAGE AND WAGON WORKS

Following a fire in the small engine sheds and shops at Miles Platting steps were taken to relieve pressure there by building a carriage and wagon works beside Thorp Bridge Junction to the south-west of Thorp Road at Newton Heath, about two miles out of Manchester Victoria. Charles Fay, the Carriage and Wagon Superintendent, was responsible for the general layout and equipment. Born in 1812 and apprenticed to Thomas Clarke Worsdell (one of the first to supply passenger coaches to the Liverpool & Manchester Railway, then under construction), he was appointed C&W Superintendent on the Manchester & Leeds in 1846 and later achieved distinction as the inventor of the mechanical continuous brake which bore his name.

In 1874 Robert Neill & Son's tender for £98 330 for the buildings was accepted. Details of machinery were prepared in 1875 and Fay submitted an estimate of £3394 for woodworking machinery, which Thomas Robinson & Son of Rochdale undertook to supply in three months. The Lancashire & Yorkshire appointed John Hopkinson consulting engineer, and he proceeded to plan a much larger works. Costs of heating the works were compared in 1876: hot water would cost £8300, steam £3300, so the latter was chosen. A tender from Thomas Robinson & Son for £475 for a 10-ton steam crane was accepted in 1877. Production of new carriages began in the summer of 1877, and Miles Platting then undertook locomotive work. Fay retired in 1877 and his place was taken by F. Attock, who came from the Great Eastern Railway where he had served under his father George in the carriage and wagon department.

In 1882 Smith's automatic vacuum brake was specified for 100 new carriages being built at Newton Heath and for all carriage renewals. Miles Platting wagon work was transferred to Newton Heath in 1889. A 12-wheeled dining car was completed at Newton Heath in 1904 while Gresley was Works Manager, for George Hughes, later the first CME of the LMS. The last goods vehicle order was in 1930 for three 40-ton LMS goods brake vans. The works was closed in 1932 during the depression and some 2500 staff were discharged or else transferred to Derby Carriage and Wagon, Horwich Locomotive or Wolverton Carriage and Wagon Works.

Since 1932 the Chief Civil Engineer's department has converted some workshops for manufacturing concrete units, steel fabrications, and points and crossings. They also maintain the track-laying machines. Some of the original shops have been demolished, and Lightbowne sidings is now a local council housing estate.

HORWICH LOCOMOTIVE WORKS

When the first Lancashire & Yorkshire (L&YR) works was built at Miles Platting the district was very open, but by the 1870s it was heavily built up and expansion of the small works was impossible. John Ramsbottom was chiefly responsible for the decision to build new works elsewhere. The main criteria for choosing a new site were the price of labour, a good water supply, cheap coal and a central situation. The site at Horwich was secured in 1884 for £36 000.

The works, begun in 1886, was to build and repair locomotives and carry out mechanical, electrical and hydraulic engineering work throughout the L&YR. It originally had a steel foundry and forge with tyre and rolling mills as well as the manufacturing shops.

In 1889 the first engine, a 2–4–2 radial tank locomotive, was constructed and put into service under the superintendence of John Aspinall, one of the all-time great British locomotive engineers. By his retirement in 1899, 677 engines had been built. A further 220 were added under H. A. Hoy, who was later succeeded by George Hughes; these three were successively appointed CME of the L&YR and also held office at Horwich. Hughes became CME of the new LMS in 1923, continuing to work from Horwich. By 1901 the Atlantic type express locomotive, designed by Aspinall, had been built – claimed to be the most powerful inside-cylinder passenger locomotive so far produced for British railways. Horwich built its thousandth locomotive, a four-cylinder balanced compound eight-wheeled coupled engine, in 1907.

As early as 1908 the L&YR had equipped an instruction car as a portable lecture room to be sent to the locomotive depots on its line, where mutual improvement classes were held. An exceptionally well-equipped dynamo-meter car was also built, for testing locomotives on the track, and was widely used by the LMS after amalgamation. Sir Nigel Gresley, after serving as a premium pupil at Crewe Locomotive Works, went to Horwich in 1898 to study locomotive design under Aspinall. There he met Sir Henry Fowler and R. E. L. Maunsell, later CMEs of the LMS and Southern Railways, both pupils at Horwich. Thus three of the four CMEs of 1925–30 were former Horwich men. Another of Aspinall's pupils, Sir Alliot Verdon Roe, became a world-famous air pioneer, creating the earlier 'Aero' aeroplanes.

As a locomotive works the production shops comprised a general iron foundry, brass foundry, smithy, boiler, machine, wheel, tin and copper, erecting and paint shops. Other shops included the millwrights', pattern and joiners', electric machine and electric car shops and mechanised iron foundry. The total staff in 1949 was 3083, including 237 professional and technical, supervisory and clerical staff. The accountant's and supplies sections accounted for another 250.

In 1947 Horwich maintained 1122 locomotives. The average number on the works was 48, the average number of days on the pits was 10.7 and on the works, including the days of arrival and departure, 15.2. In the same year the

TABLE 3.10 *Horwich Works: output from principal spheres of activity year ended 31 December 1981*

Major modifications & conversions

Refurbishing of Class 415/6 EMUs	40
Passenger heating – Class 313 vehicles	96
Refurbishing van wide vehicles, phase 2	60
Overhead line maintenance vehicles	24

Repair work	*C1R*	*C1/2*	*C3*	*C3T*	*C4*	Total classified	*C5*
Loco-hauled coaches	—	23	1	44	—	68	—
Loco-hauled coaches (non-passenger-carrying)	—	1	10	—	13	24	7
					C6		
EMUs	40	42	102	—	4	188	4

	GR	*IR/L*	*IR/W*	*IR*	*Total*
Traffic wagons	216	—	115	491	822

	Armature	*Carcase*
Traction motors	339	339

Manufacture/repair of wagon sheets	*Manufactured*	*Repaired*
Wagon sheets	1063	5219

output was 440 heavy and 228 light repairs, the total mileage of the maintained stock was 31 484 382, and 28 new locomotives were built. Horwich built new locomotives after nationalisation, and 20 new BR standard 2–6–0 tender engines, Class 4, were completed in 1953. Output in 1981 is shown in Table 3.10.

BARASSIE WAGON WORKS

Barassie Works (near the town of Troon on the Ayrshire coast, 81 miles from Edinburgh, 33 from Glasgow and about 8 from Kilmarnock) was built in 1901 as the principal carriage and wagon works of the Glasgow and South-Western Railway and was one of the few main works built in the twentieth century. This area conjures up sandy beaches and holidays, not work, but in a suburb of Troon from 1901 to 1968 was Barassie Wagon Works, the principal works for steel wagon repairs in Scotland. The total staff was 650, more than half living in Troon, about 250 in Kilmarnock and the remainder in Glasgow. The works, with good rail and road access, had an area of 22 acres (6 covered) and another 40 acres of undeveloped land, some of which was used during the second world war for repairing Spitfires, for which a runway was built. At one time Barassie did carriage repairs, but these were transferred to St Rollox in 1929, after which the output was confined to wagon and container repairs.

4 The Main Works of the Former LNER

The London & North-Eastern Railway (LNER) and some of its predecessors enjoyed the great distinction of having started the railways of Britain. The Stockton & Darlington Railway, built mainly for carrying coal, was opened in 1825. By the early nineteenth century there were already more than 1500 miles of primitive railways, largely concentrated in the industrial north, especially in Durham and Northumberland, conveying coal from local collieries for shipment. The north-east of England had pre-eminence in the development of the steam locomotive, and many thousands of its products have been supplied to countries all over the world.

The LNER was the second largest of the four group companies created in 1923, with the largest number of main works (sixteen), the most northerly being Inverurie in the north of Scotland and the most southerly Temple Mills Wagon Works at Stratford, in London's east end. Unlike the other three companies, which each had several subsidiary works, the LNER had only one, at Gateshead, Northumberland.

The world's first workshops specialising in constructing railway locomotives were established by Robert Stephenson & Co. at Newcastle-upon-Tyne in 1823, and it is not surprising that the Newcastle & Darlington Junction Railway, later part of the NER, chose a site in nearby Gateshead in 1845 to repair and (until 1910) build a small number of locomotives. Gateshead Works closed in 1932 but, under the pressure of war, reopened for light classified locomotive repairs in 1944, finally closing in 1959 when the work was transferred to Darlington.

SHILDON WAGON WORKS

Shildon Works in south-west Durham, adjacent to the Teesside industrial belt and nine miles north-west of Darlington, began as a pioneering locomotive works but soon became a wagon works, and so had the double distinction of being the oldest main works and the largest and most important BR wagon works. The original shops, built in 1833 by the Stockton & Darlington Railway, were extended and progressively modernised over the years, growing to an area of 40 acres (11 acres roofed) with a staff of 2750.

The first Railway Institute, built at Shildon in 1833 and inspired by a handful of employees, appointed Timothy Hackworth as its first President. In 1827 he had built the 'Royal George' locomotive at the nearby Soho Works (bought by the Shildon and Darlington Works in 1855 and closed in 1883). Amongst many other inventions he introduced the blast pipe – the life-breath

TABLE 4.1 *The main works of the former LNER at amalgamation in 1923*

Works	Date built	Railway Co. for which built	Total acreage	Covered acreage	Principal activities following amalgamation
Shildon Wagon	1833	Stockton & Darlington	40	11	Building all-steel wagons and steel underframes; repairing wagons; fabricating wagon axle-boxes; repairing wagon wheel sets; forging drop stampings and pressings for locomotives, carriages & wagons.
Cowlairs Locomotive and Carriage & Wagon	1842	Edinburgh & Glasgow	167	7	Locomotive repairing; new boiler building; mechanised foundry for brake blocks; area outdoor machinery maintenance.
Stratford Locomotive	1847	Eastern Counties	31	12	Locomotive repairing; new boiler building; area outdoor machinery maintenance.
Stratford Carriage	1847	Eastern Counties	27	8	Carriage repairing.
Gorton Locomotive	1849	Manchester, Sheffield & Lincolnshire	30	15	Locomotive repairing; new boiler building; cylinder castings for all LNER works; chair castings and points & crossings manufacture for Chief Civil Engineer's Dept; area outdoor machinery maintenance.
Doncaster Locomotive	1853	Great Northern	61	13	Locomotive building and repairing; new boiler building; area outdoor machinery maintenance (Crimpsall repair shops separate from new building and manufacturing works).
Doncaster Carriage	1853	Great Northern	25	8	Building and repairing carriages; chromium plating plant for all LNER works.
Darlington Locomotive	1863	North-Eastern	27	11	Locomotive building and repairing; new boiler building; outdoor machinery maintenance.
York Wagon	1865	North-Eastern	17	5	Repairing wagons & containers; repairing road vehicle bodies.
Gorton Carriage & Wagon	1881	North-Eastern	6	3	Repairing carriages (light repairs only, without lifting); repairing wagons, containers & horse-drawn vehicles.
York Carriage	1884	North-Eastern	45	15	Building and repairing carriages; timber conversion; area outdoor machinery maintenance.
Doncaster Wagon	1889	Great Northern	32	5	Repairing wagons & containers; repairing road vehicle bodies; manufacturing grease.

TABLE 4.1   *Continued*

Works	Date built	Railway Co. for which built	Total acreage	Covered acreage	Principal activities following amalgamation
Temple Mills Wagon	1896	Great Eastern	24	5	Repairing wagons & containers; repairing road vehicle bodies.
Walkergate Carriage & Wagon	1902	North-Eastern	14	5	Repairing carriages and all Tyneside electrical stock; repairing wagons.
Inverurie Locomotive	1903	Great North of Scotland	15	3	Locomotive repairing; area outdoor machinery maintenance; limited carriage & wagon repairing.
Faverdale Wagon	1923	North-Eastern	60	10	Building timber wagons & containers; building timber bodies for steel underframe wagons; repairing wagons and containers; timber conversion.

of the steam locomotive – and later the 'Glove', the first engine with a crank axle. Hackworth was the first of the works' 22 managers in its 151-year history, holding the post from 1833 to 1840.

At nationalisation in 1948 BR operated a fleet of over a million wagons; most new mineral and merchandise wagons were constructed with timber bodies, and there were many thousands in service with wooden underframes. Since then BR policy has been to standardise with all-steel construction as far as possible, because of the reduced annual maintenance costs and the advantage of increased availability. Timber is only used for the bodies of covered stock and floors of merchandise and some other open wagons. The use of corrosion-resisting steels and a scheduled programme of scraping and painting produces a useful life equivalent to that of the wooden wagons.

In 1951 the turnround of wagons in service was investigated, giving an average of 8 days. Assuming some 10 per cent under or awaiting repair, this left 47 weeks for revenue earning, during which a wagon averaged 41 journeys assumed to average 50 miles – a total of 2000 miles, not high by today's standards. Some high spots were also revealed: it was quite normal for wagons taking china clay from Cornwall to Scotland to run over 100 000 miles a year. Steel-carrying wagons had a turnround of just under 10 days. With the more modern 'merry-go-round' trains using 40-tons capacity hopper wagons on a shuttle service between coalmines and power stations, the turnround was greatly reduced. By 1964 BR's wagon fleet had been reduced to 700 000, and since then declining traffic has caused further substantial reductions.

Under the main works modernisation scheme which followed the creation of the BR Workshops Division in 1962, Shildon was modernised at a cost of £800 000 and equipped to construct and repair wagons for BR and, from

1970, for overseas. Shildon Works, always synonymous with progress and development, earned a justifiably proud record, constructing new mineral and freight wagons of riveted and welded design, and repairing and converting existing wagons and bogie vehicles. Many new designs were proved and manufactured, notably the 'Presflo' air-discharge cement wagon, high capacity coal and Freightliner wagons. A large proportion of drop stampings for other works were also manufactured in the Shildon forge. The repair shops had capacity for overhauling and repairing up to 800 wagons a week.

Between 1965 and 1982 Shildon built 11 083 'Merry-go-round' 32.5-tonnes capacity coal hoppers with a tare weight of 13 tonnes. Table 4.2 shows the output in 1981. The standard wagon frame could be produced as a welded or riveted unit, but the former was preferred for its lower cost and weight. The average steel wagon has between 250 and 900 component parts making up its tare weight, each requiring an average of six distinct manufacturing operations. Handling and transfer between these is highly important, needing the most efficient use of overhead gantry and mobile cranes, fork-lift trucks, tractors, capstans, electric hoists and roller conveyors. Wagon building stands out as the railway workshop product offering unique opportunities for mass production techniques, and Shildon responded fully to this challenge.

Despite Shildon's exemplary record, achieved by the skill of its craftsmen and the use of modern machines and equipment, the volume of freight traffic transferring from rail to road became so great that by the early 1980s the need for new BR freight stock – Shildon's lifeblood – had largely disappeared, and so this historic works closed in 1984 after 151 years. A total of 1200 people

TABLE 4.2   *Shildon Works: output from principal spheres of activity year ended 31 December 1981*

New construction					
For British Rail					
'Seacow' service wagons					145
Steel-carrying wagon conversions					266
MGR wagons					655
Bogie hopper ballast wagons					6
40-ft container carrying vehicle					1
44-ton 2-axle van					1
OCA wagons					265
For private parties					
'Warflat' wagons for Ministry of Defence					26
Tank conversions for BP Oil					220
Major modifications & conversions					
50-ton Flatrol vehicles – bogies & air brakes					15
Repair work	*GR*	*IR/L*	*IR/W*	*IR*	*Total*
Traffic wagons	1 588	96	1 974	5 760	9 418

were employed when the works closed, and 730 new jobs had been created at Shildon by 1986. A forge, a sawmill and two steel fabrication companies were among the new businesses which started at Shildon.

COWLAIRS LOCOMOTIVE, CARRIAGE AND WAGON WORKS

Railway communication was first established between Glasgow and Edinburgh on 18 February 1842, when both cities were decorated in honour of the event. This important inter-city line, 47½ miles long, enters Glasgow on the north side, with Queen Street as its terminal station. Just before this trains pass through a small suburban station: Cowlairs. The Cowlairs Works at Spring-burn, Glasgow, named after the mansion at Cowlairs, was built by the Edinburgh & Glasgow Railway (later part of the North British) in 1842, and from the outset it was a combined works, dealing with locomotives, carriages and wagons. Employees' cottages were built on both sides of the track to Springvale Farm, and this and the works site were soon known as Cowlairs Road.

The basic layout was very compact; rail and road access were difficult, with no room for expansion. This was the first railway-owned works in Scotland, although there were already two famous private locomotive works, and subsequently the Caledonian Railway's St Rollox Works, within the Springburn area. Together they formed the largest concentration of railway works in the British Isles, employing many thousands and producing a cavalcade of famous engineers whose locomotives travelled the world.

William Paton, the first Locomotive Superintendent, supervised the building of Cowlairs. The first locomotives were bought from the trade in 1842, but the works was in full operation in 1843, and in January 1844 Paton produced his first locomotive, 'Hercules', a powerful six-wheel coupled track engine, with 4'-3½" diameter wheels and weighing 26½ tons. Eighteen months later a Bury-built locomotive, 'Napier', which had been giving steaming trouble, was put on a train at short notice, and because it failed and was not carrying a tail lamp a passenger was killed. Paton and Richard McNab, the driver, stood trial in the High Court on a charge of culpable homicide, and despite Paton's high credentials he was sentenced to 12 months' imprisonment, during which the railway had to manage without its much-respected Locomotive Superintendent.

After the 1923 amalgamation Cowlairs ceased new production, except for boilers. In 1947 the output was 393 heavy and 189 light classified locomotive repairs, and there were 2475 staff, including those of a well-designed mechanised foundry responsible for brake blocks and other repetitive castings for all LNER works. After nationalisation this work went to Horwich Locomotive Works, which had a more extensive mechanised foundry plant. The output of classified repairs in the carriage and wagon works in 1949 was 443 heavy and 2367 light carriage repairs and 5005 heavy and 3812 light wagon repairs. The staff totalled 1260. For a short period after nationalisation some LNER steel wagon repair work was done at Townhill Works, near Dunfermline, in rented premises adapted for LNER use.

Cowlairs was one of many main works closed after the formation of the Workshops Division in 1962. The closure took place in 1963 and the workload was transferred to St Rollox, which then became known as Glasgow Works.

STRATFORD LOCOMOTIVE WORKS

The Eastern Counties Railway, forerunner of the Great Eastern, was incorporated on 4 July 1836 and built the Stratford Works in 1847, during 'King' Hudson's reign, at a cost of £100 000 – at a time when it was not considered the richest of companies. The original works, the hub of this busy works centre, was hemmed in on one arc by Stratford New Town (formerly 'Hudson's Town') and on the other by a network of main lines and sidings. Great ingenuity in covering in here or adding a storey there made the most of the available space, but traffic growth and periodical modernising of plant and rolling stock necessarily demanded many extensions, so modern buildings were erected on the other side of the main line, away from the marshes. Stratford was notorious for its sprawling layout, the shops being interspersed with the Great Eastern running lines.

The first Stratford-built engines, designed by the Locomotive Superintendent J. V. Gooch (brother of the GWR chairman) in 1850, were passenger tank engines with single driving wheels of 6'-6" diameter and outside cylinders of 12" diameter and 22" stroke; they weighed 23 tons in working order. They were used for express trains, and as water capacity was limited, there were instances of supplementary tanks being fitted under brake vans. The first recorded compound locomotive was originated and tried on the Eastern Counties line. Although this two-cylinder goods engine – compounded about 1848 from the ideas of John Nicholson, a Stratford fitter – was in service for some years, and experiments were made with others, little is known of their performance.

For some years after 1847 all locomotive, carriage and wagon shops and the 'round house' engine running shed stood on a roughly triangular area bounded by the Leyton High Road and the two main lines forming the Stratford Junction. According to an old record no additions were made to shops or machinery until a small amount of machinery was bought in 1870. During the half-year ended June 1875, 66 engines were repaired, whereas in the first half-year of 1920, 267 modern locomotives were turned out: 216 heavy repairs, 40 rebuilds and 11 new engines.

In 1947 the works maintained 1062 locomotives, averaging 60 in the works (5.6%), occupying 20 working days on the pits including stripping and a total of 34 days on the works. The output was 390 heavy and 354 light classified repairs, plus a weekly output of 8 boiler repairs. A total staff of 2032 was employed. The works closed in 1963 as part of the rationalistion of the main works.

STRATFORD CARRIAGE WORKS

In common with Stratford Locomotive Works, the carriage works was built in 1847 by the Eastern Counties Railway. The works, intersected by running lines and sidings which created complications in shunting from shop to shop, depended on the locomotive works for all smithing work.

The carriage repair output in 1949 was 1090 heavy and 4608 light repairs, and in 1954, 743 heavy and 3849 light repairs. The allocation of carriages and other rolling stock, including fish vans, was made from the Coaching Stock Control Office at Doncaster. There was a very satisfactory progressive system for carriage underframe and bogie repairs at Stratford.

The works would have been difficult to extend and adapt to meet the needs of modern stock such as diesel-electric railcars. There was some land near the paint shop, but this was operationally and physically remote from the parent shops. At the time of closure in 1963 the total staff employed was 1498. The work was transferred to Doncaster.

GORTON LOCOMOTIVE WORKS

This works, known locally as 'Gorton Tank', was built in 1849 for the Manchester, Sheffield & Lincolnshire Railway, later the Great Central. In its heyday – probably between 1947 and 1957 – it was an excellent and comprehensive establishment, despite the difficulty of the principal shops being on two different levels. Its original value in 1849 was £193, but in 1954 its replacement value was recorded as £1 359 407.

Gorton carried out locomotive repairs and new boiler building and produced all LNER cylinder castings and chair castings, points and crossings for the Chief Civil Engineer; there was also a brass foundry. Another activity was outdoor machinery maintenance, mechanical and electrical, for all railway departments in the area, except low voltage equipment for the Regional Chief Signal and Telecommunications Engineer.

At nationalisation the works maintained 1061 steam and 65 electric locomotives. The average number of days in the works for steam locomotives undergoing general or intermediate classified repairs was 33, identical to Stratford Works, but higher than the 27 days of Darlington and Doncaster. In 1954 Gorton, the first BR works to build and repair electric locomotives, built 6 electric Co-Co locomotives and did 23 heavy and 10 light casual repairs and 17 non-classified repairs to electric locomotives. The total staff in 1954 was 2724. Storage of parts for this great variety of work needed careful planning, and in this respect the works had a very commendable modern installation.

After the BR Workshops Division was formed in 1962 Gorton Works closed and the workload was transferred to Doncaster. Since the works ceased production in 1965, the shops have been demolished and a supermarket built on the site.

DONCASTER LOCOMOTIVE WORKS

Doncaster Locomotive Works, situated on the west side of Doncaster passenger station on the main line from London to Edinburgh, Leeds, Bradford and Hull, and also on the cross-country route between Liverpool and the east coast, was built for the Great Northern Railway in 1853 and became one of the principal locomotive main works of the LNER in 1923. Originally temporary accommodation was used for locomotive repair work in Boston, Lincolnshire, but Doncaster was preferred because of its proximity to large coalfields and centres of iron-founding, together with good water communications.

No wonder that the townspeople rang the Church bells – in the words of a contemporary account – 'till the wild ear ran giddy with their joy' upon receipt of the news that the 'Plant' was to be established in Doncaster.

In March 1852 tenders were invited and a contract made with the firm of G. & A. Holme for the construction of the new works. The same firm also built the bridge over the lines providing ready access to the south side of the works; the bridge was originally 300 feet long and 30 feet wide, but in 1865 it was extended by two additional arches over four new lines. By July 1853 approximately 500 men had been transferred from Boston to form the nucleus of the extensive plant in Doncaster, and by the end of the year the number of employees had risen to 950. In New England, a suburb of the City of Peterborough, the Great Northern Railway established a locomotive repair centre together with a motive power running shed, which accommodated 106 locomotives, around the mid-nineteenth century. The railway company owned 227 cottages and built two schools. Eventually the locomotive repair work was transferred to Doncaster, but the motive power shed continued to operate. Sir Henry Royce (1863–1933), designer of the Rolls-Royce cars and aero engines, served his apprenticeship to engineering, starting in 1876, in the Peterborough locomotive workshops, thanks to his aunt who paid the railway company an annual premium of £20. He was described as a dedicated apprentice.

With the coming of the railways the increase in Doncaster's population gave rise to many problems and an extensive housing programme commenced. In addition the Chairman of the Great Northern Railway expressed 'great concern at the bringing of some 3000 souls into this small town without some provision being made for their spiritual welfare' and made an attempt to obtain from the railway company the cost of building a new church. He was not completely successful, but many of the directors and shareholders contributed substantially to the sum necessary for the building of St James's

Church, and the railway company for many years contributed towards its maintenance. The Plant Church, as it became known, has continued to maintain a close relationship with the works. St James's Schools, for the education of the children of railway employees, were built by the company at a cost of £1290 and by 1836 there was accommodation for 120 boys, 120 girls and 240 infants.

Originally the works comprised 11 acres, including 5 acres of covered shops. There was, however, an almost continuous process of extension throughout the next 130 years. In 1854 the original smithy was found to be inadequate and was enlarged. In 1866 the existing erecting shops were extended to provide for the construction of new locomotives, which until then had been purchased from private builders, and about the same time a gas plant was built to supply the works' needs. This was extended in 1881 and in the same year an iron foundry was built. No new construction took place at Doncaster until after the appointment of Patrick Stirling as Locomotive Superintendent in 1866.

The year 1882 saw the erection of a new boiler shop and 1890–1 the building of a new erecting shop and the provision of an additional machine shop. The erecting shop was divided into three parts, the two outside being used for erecting, while the middle was for many years reserved for equipment used in locomotive erection. The first of the No. 875 class of locomotive was built in 1886. Around 3500 men were employed in the Doncaster Locomotive and Wagon Works in 1891; in that year 300 locomotives, 3735 carriages and 15 226 wagons passed through for repair and, in addition, 99 new locomotives, 181 new carriages and 1493 new wagons were built. In 1907 drop stamps were installed and the boiler shop extended, and in 1910 and 1913 the electric generating equipment at the wagon works was modernised. A new engine weigh-house was provided in 1935 and a central air compressor station in 1936.

Some of the most successful locomotives ever built have been turned out at Doncaster by its artisan staff: the Stirling singles, Ivatt Atlantics and Gresley Pacifics, which in their time have had the task of hauling famous trains such as the *Flying Scotsman*, *Silver Jubilee*, *Coronation* and more recently the *Elizabethan*, the carriages for which were built at Doncaster. These famous trains and many others have been able to achieve justifiable fame only through the efforts of successive generations of men trained at Doncaster. Sir Nigel Gresley's streamlined Pacific-type locomotive, 'Mallard', has held since 1938 the world speed record for steam traction of 126 miles per hour. By the time the last steam locomotive built at Doncaster left the works in October 1957, over 2200 steam locomotives had been constructed at Doncaster and the works was preparing to switch over to the building of diesel-electric locomotives.

The works has been an important factor in the development of Doncaster and the staff has a long record of public service in local affairs. By 1953, Centenary Year, no fewer than seven members of the works staff had been elected Mayor of the Borough. The first surgeon of the Great Northern

'The Rocket', built by Robert Stephenson & Co., winner of the 1829 Rainhill Trials. Weighing 4 tons 5 cwts, it hauled a 13-ton train at an average of 12 m.p.h.

Prototype Advanced Passenger Train undergoing tests on the West Coast main line.

1c.   BR Standard Class 7 Type 4–6–2 passenger tender locomotive No. 70 000, 'Britannia', built at Crewe in 195
seen hauling a 9-coach train.

1d.   LMS locomotive No. 10 000, built at Derby in 1947, the first main-line diesel-electric locomotive to rur
Britain.

Diesel locomotives under repair in bay of No. 5 erecting shop, Swindon, 1968.

Inaugural run of 2200 HP diesel-hydraulic Maybach/Mekhydro locomotive hauling the Cornish Riviera Express, passing over the River Exe at Dawlish, July 1958. Locomotive and carriages were built at Swindon.

2c. Diesel locomotives undergoing repairs, Swindon, 1968.

2d. Diesel multiple units undergoing repairs, Swindon C. & W. Works, 1965.

(above) BR Standard steam locomotives Class 4 Type 4–6–0 under construction, Swindon, 1951.

(below) Building of BR Standard Class 4 Type 4–6–0 locomotive No. 75 000, Swindon, 1951.

THE FIRST AND EACH THOUSANDTH LOCOMOTIVE
BUILT AT CREWE WORKS.
REPRODUCED TO THE SAME SCALE.

2000TH.   BUILT MAY 1876.

L.&N.W.R. NO 2233.
2-4-0 4'-6" PASSENGER TANK.

5000TH.   BUILT MAY 1911

L.&N.W.R. NO 1800 "CORONATION"
"GEORGE THE FIFTH" CLASS 4-4-0 PASSENGER TENDER.

1000TH.   BUILT DEC.1866

L.&N.W.R. NO 613.
DX. CLASS 0-6-0 GOODS TENDER.
PHOTOGRAPH SHOWS NO 29 OF SAME CLASS.

7000TH.   BUILT SEP.1950

B.R. NO 41272
CLASS 2 2-6-2 MIXED TRAFFIC TANK.

1ST.   BUILT FEB.1845

GRAND JUNCTION RLY. NO 49 "COLUMBINE."
"CREWE" TYPE 2-2-2 PASSENGER TENDER.

3000TH.   BUILT JULY 1887

L.&N.W.R. NO 600.
3 CYL. COMPOUND 2-2-2-2 PASS. TANK.

4000TH.   BUILT MARCH 1900

L.&N.W.R. NO 1926 "LA FRANCE"
"JUBILEE" CLASS 4 CYL. COMPOUND 4-4-0 PASS. TENDER.

6000TH.   BUILT JUNE 1930

LM&SR. NO 13178   (NOW B.R. NO 42878)
CLASS 5 2-6-0 MIXED TRAFFIC TENDER.

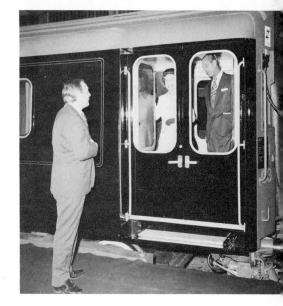

(top) Queen Victoria's 1869 saloon, built at Wolverton.
(above left) Interior of Queen Elizabeth II's saloon, built 1974–7 at Wolverton.
(above right) Sir Peter Parker, then Chairman of BR, having just handed the keys of the new royal train to the Queen and the Duke of Edinburgh.

Shildon Wagon Works machine shop in 1910, showing overhead countershafting and belting.

Conversion from steam to diesel-electric working, locomotive repair shop, Stratford, 1956.

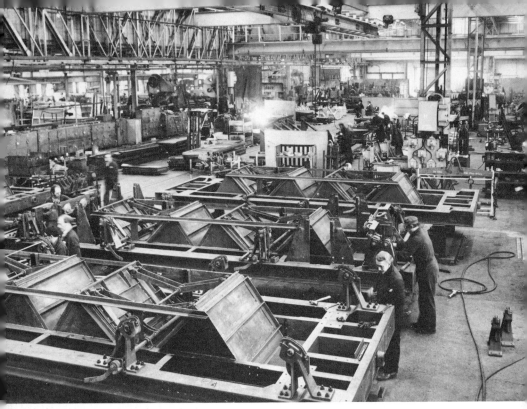

4d. HBA hopper wagons under construction, Shildon, 1968.

4e. Bogies being fitted to new AC6 Type electric locomotives, erecting shop, Doncaster, for the West Co main line.

Diesel locomotive repairs concentrated in a group of shops in the west portion of Doncaster Loco. Works, known as the 'Crimpsall' shops.

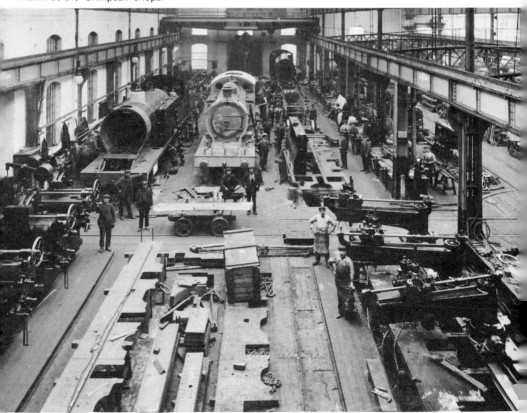

New locomotive building bay, erecting shop, Darlington, 1910.

4h. Class 313 electric multiple units under construction, York Carriage Works, 1960.

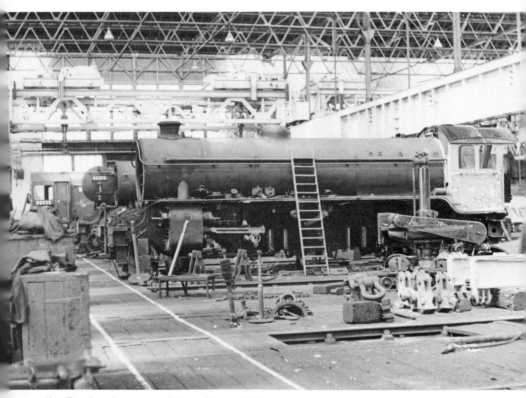

4j. Erecting shop, Inverurie Loco. Works, 1963.

(right) Exterior view of Walkergate Wagon Works, Newcastle, with Walkergate Station close by.

5a. *(left)* Eastleigh C. & W. Works, 1968: trimming shop, providing cutting and sewing sections and floor coverings.

(right) Manufacture of wagons for Kenya State Railways, Ashford, 1978.

6a. Locomotives under repair in the erecting shop, under overhead craneways running on a pair of longitud
tracks, Derby, 1910.

6b. Lifting a modern Mark III carriage body, Derby, 1981.

Removing an air-conditioning module from a Mark III carriage, Derby, 1982.

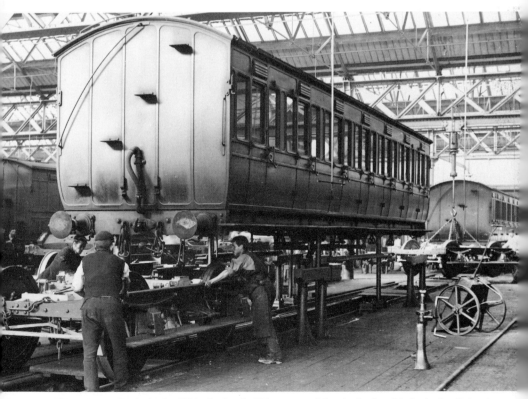

A carriage lifting shop at Derby in the 1890s: hydraulic lifting rams raising the body, with the hydraulic bogie lift on the transverse girder runner.

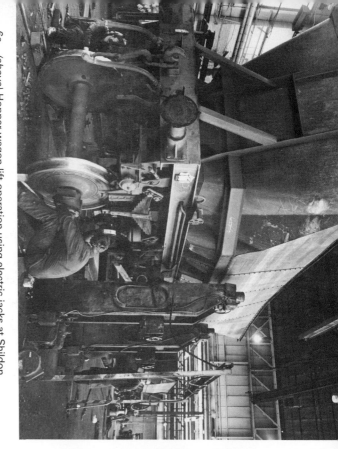

6e. *(above)* Hopper wagon lift operation using electric jacks at Shildon.

6f. *(top right)* Repair of electric traction motors, Crewe, 1975.

6g. *(bottom right)* Diesel locomotives and electric locomotive *(left foreground)* undergoing repair in Crewe erecting shop, 1960.

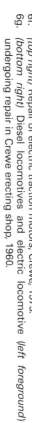

Railway, Dr Dunn, was largely responsible for the scheme which resulted in the provision of the town's first hospital while the works was still under construction.

The output in 1947 was 7 new locomotives, 582 heavy repairs and 156 light repairs. Days on the works are shown in Table 4.3. The total number of staff was 3185. The works was modernised in 1962 as part of the main works rationalisation plan following the formation of the British Railways Workshops Division. The diesel locomotive repair shop is the largest shop in the works, with a floor area of 140 000 square feet. Until recently it was devoted entirely to the overhaul and repair of diesel main-line and shunting locomotives. There are separate sections for the repair of power units, train heating boilers, traction motors, generators and ancillary equipment.

In more recent years, under the BREL organisation, new building has included diesel shunting locomotives, 25 kV electric locomotives, battery-driven locomotives for London Transport's underground trains and, since 1976, the Class 56 diesel-electric freight locomotives for British Rail. The works now manufactures diesel locomotives and repairs and overhauls diesel main-line locomotives, diesel multiple units and wagons. It also manufactures container lifting frames; repairs, overhauls and tests rail cranes, lifting tackle, bridge sections and signal gantries; and carries out a wide variety of fabrication and machining work for outside customers. The 1981 output is shown in Table 4.4. In 1986 the works was designated to become BR's new national stores for locomotive and rolling stock spare parts.

DONCASTER CARRIAGE WORKS

Doncaster Carriage Works – which with the locomotive works together became known locally as the 'Plant Works' – was built in 1853 as the carriage repair shop for the former Great Northern Railway Company, but subsequently developed to include both the construction and repair of carriages. In 1950 annual figures of classified repairs and new vehicles constructed were around 2000 and 140 respectively.

As with locomotives, it was the practice of railway companies a century ago to obtain new coaches from private builders and the earliest Doncaster-built

TABLE 4.3   *Locomotive statistics, Doncaster Locomotive Works, 1947*

No. of steam locomotives maintained	Average no. on works	% on works	Average no. of days		No. of boilers under repair	Average weekly output of boilers
			on works under repair	including arrival and departure		
1 241	56	4.5	16	27	87	13

TABLE 4.4   *Doncaster Works: output from principal spheres of activity year ended 31 December 1981*

New construction	
Class 56 diesel main-line locomotives	14

Major modifications & conversions

Refurbishing of DMUs	86
Replacement of 150 HP AEC engines – DMUs	17
High impact cab windows – DMUs	2

Repair work	General	Intermediate	Light	Total classified	Unclassified
Diesel main-line locomotives	30	61	5	96	99
Diesel shunting locomotives	3	—	—	3	2

	Armature	Carcase
Traction motors	702	703
Main generators	156	151

	C1R	C1/C2	C3	C3T	C4	Total classified	C5
Loco-hauled coaches	—	4	4	48	12	68	8
Loco-hauled coaches (non-passenger-carrying)	—	10	109	—	172	291	37
DMUs and EMUs	86	8	262	—	—	356	47

	GR	IR/L	IR/W	I/R	Total
Traffic wagons	224	26	93	236	579

	Engines	Gearboxes	Torque converters	Final drives
DMU traction components	—	—	—	478

passenger coaches on record were built in 1866. They were 25 feet long, with five compartments, three of which were open to each other. The seats were of greater width and spacing than had hitherto been provided and the degree of comfort was such that 'a person of ordinary stature could stand upright and there was abundant natural lighting'. Later in the same year a complete new train built for the London to Scotland service consisted of ten firsts, five seconds, two third-class and two brakes. The first-class carriages were 20'-1" long, the second 22' and the third 23'. These last were in striking contrast to the ill-constructed thirds in use on many lines during the 1860s. In the centre they were 6'-11" in height, and the seats were broad, with ample spacing between. Each carriage had two compartments, one containing two and the other three divisions with a door 2 feet wide in each. The second-class had four compartments and the first-class three.

The first sleeping car to be built at Doncaster was in 1873 for the East Coast route. The first dining car in the United Kingdom was constructed at Doncaster in 1879. In 1875 the company built a Prince of Wales Saloon with a length of body of 38'-6", a width over body of 8' and a weight of 22 tons. In the mid-1870s the underframes for bogie carriages were fabricated, this possibly being a link between the all-timber and all-steel underframe. The sole bars or longitudinal members were built up to form an I section, using 4 by 3 inch and 2½ by 2½ inch angle iron together with ⅜ inch steel plate. The channel on each side was built in with timber to give added strength. In 1882 the first British side-corridor coach was designed and built at Doncaster for the East Coast Joint Stock. All-steel underframes were introduced in about 1902. The lengths of 12-wheeled coaches ranged from 62 to 65 feet, with tare weights from 32 to 37 tons, whilst similar vehicles on eight wheels weighed about 28 tons.

Over the years all the various types of coaching stock have been built at Doncaster, including restaurant and kitchen cars, sleeping cars and main-line corridor stock. Before 1948 the bodies of the carriages were of composite construction, with timber framing and steel panels. The BR standard carriages subsequently became all-steel, the body and roof being built up from a pressed steel framework covered with a steel skin. Construction on the all-steel cars commenced at Doncaster in 1951, but since 1962 new coaching stock has been concentrated at Derby and York as part of the main works rationalisation plan. A considerable amount of work is still undertaken for other railway departments.

The original carriage building shop was destroyed by fire in December 1940, and new buildings built in 1949 were specially designed and equipped for the progressive construction of modern types of coaching stock. These consist of the trimming shop, carriage construction shop including machine and jig section, sawmill and joiners' shop. The west carriage shop, built in 1897, is segregated into three departments, comprising the machine shop, lifting shop and woodmen's repair roads. The works has a well-equipped canteen consisting of two dining halls for 450 staff.

A Royal Saloon, No. 2408, built in 1907 with a length of 63'-10" and a weight of 29 tons 18 cwt, was carried on two bogie carriages of six wheels each, fitted throughout by electric light and heated by hot water pipes. The saloon was fitted with both automatic vacuum and Westinghouse continuous brakes, and contained six compartments and a corridor. The first compartment was the sleeping apartment for the Princess. The saloon and dining apartment contained two tables and six easy-chairs. The Prince's sleeping apartment was fitted with a coach and bed exquisitely upholstered. There was a sleeping apartment for the lady-in-waiting, similar to that of the Princess. Adjoining was the sergeant footman's apartment, trimmed in royal blue; and lastly the attendant's room. The introduction of carriage steam heating about 1900 had displaced the early method of heating by footwarmers, which were portable cans filled with hot water at local stations.

During 1924 two new trains for the *Flying Scotsman* were built at Doncaster to run on the East Coast route from King's Cross to Edinburgh, and the first articulated triple restaurant car set using electric cooking was on this route. Articulated twin sleeping cars built in 1926 weighed 63¼ tons compared with 74¾ tons for two single cars carrying the same number of passengers. The first shower bath to be installed on a British train was fitted to one of these articulated cars in 1930. In 1928 the LNER decided to run the *Flying Scotsman* non-stop from London to Edinburgh during the summer months. The width of the carriages was increased to 9 feet and new triple restaurant car sets were built. Refrigeration plants were installed for the first time and a hairdressing saloon and ladies' retiring room were other amenities of the train. Four years later, in 1932, a cocktail bar was introduced on the train.

The desire to improve the amenities available to the travelling public was further demonstrated during 1935 with the introduction of the first cinema car to run on a British railway, converted from a 60-foot passenger brake. The year 1935 also saw the building of the Silver Jubilee train, which was the first high-speed train in Britain. Over the 268 miles from Newcastle to London it took four hours, average speeds of 71 miles per hour being attained between Darlington and London. Because of the high speeds – 90 miles per hour over long stretches – improved vacuum brakes were fitted. In 1937 two trains to commemorate the Coronation of George VI were built at Doncaster. They ran between London and Edinburgh in six hours and facilities for having meals in one's own seat were introduced. A streamlined car was added to the rear and this accommodated a mail compartment together with an observation saloon featuring fitted armchairs from which an excellent view of the track was obtained through perspex windows.

In 1949 the number of staff employed was 1585, whilst output of classified carriage repairs was 1002 heavy and 1941 light, and in addition 19 new carriages were built. Coach construction ceased at Doncaster in 1960, since when the works has specialised in vehicle maintenance. The diesel multiple-unit repair shop was originally used for carriage repairs, but was reorganised to repair diesel multiple units. When the wagon works at nearby 'Carr' was closed in 1965, provision was made for the work to be undertaken in the carriage works. For 1981 output see Table 4.4 above.

DARLINGTON LOCOMOTIVE WORKS

Darlington is a name pre-eminent in the locomotive world, not only for the opening of the world's first steam-operated public railway between Stockton and Darlington on 27 September 1825, but also because of its long-standing fame as a locomotive building and repair centre. The town was already large before the works was built and its growth in the 1860s resulted from a major change in industrial emphasis in which the hegemony of iron replaced the primacy of textiles. As the 1871 Census observed, the increased population in the district was not due to an increase in the cotton and woollen mills, but to the introduction of the iron industry – the erection of blast furnaces, rolling mills, forges and engine-building works.

The locomotive works, built by the Stockton & Darlington Railway to undertake work from Shildon and Gateshead, opened in January 1863. Within a few months the company amalgamated with the North-Eastern Railway, but it was not until 1877 that S&DR designs ceased to be built and NER locomotives were introduced. The works was in North Road, part of the former Edinburgh–London stagecoach route, within easy reach of North Road and Bank Top Stations, the former the old Stockton & Darlington Station. The first Locomotive Superintendent, William Bouch (who had succeeded Timothy Hackworth at Shildon), took charge of the North Road works at a salary of £450 p.a. and held the post until 1875, a longer period than any who followed him. In 1918 A. C. Stamer, Acting CME, published the following account of the works' development:

These Works were opened on the 1st January, 1863, and covered an area of about 6 acres, although the land, purchased for extensions, etc., was 27 acres. Prior to this all repairs to Stockton and Darlington Engines were done at Shildon.

The Works have been added to from time to time:
In 1867 a New Storehouse was built.
In 1873 a New Blacksmiths' Shop, Brass Foundry, Coppersmiths' Shop, and Joiners' Shop were erected.
In 1876 a New Boiler Shop was built.
In 1884 a New Forge and two New Erecting Shops.
In 1898 New Stores Offices, Mess Rooms, Extensions of Brass Finishing Shop, etc.
In 1903 a New Erecting Shop.
In 1911 a New Paint Shop, and Boiler and Tender Shop, were erected at Stooperdale, to relieve the congestion at North Road.

In October, 1910, the Chief Mechanical Engineer and his staff removed from Gateshead, when Darlington was made headquarters, the New Offices of the Department being occupied in April, 1912. About that time all New Engine Building and Boiler Construction was concentrated in these Works, much Machinery being transferred from Gateshead Works.

The number of men and boys employed when the Works were first opened in 1863 was about 150, and the wages about £143 per week. In July, 1914, the staff was 2,396, the wages being £4,480 per week, an average of 37/6 per week in 1914, as against 19/- per week in 1863. During this period the Shop Hours have been reduced from 59 to 53 per week.

Official photographs of NER locomotives can be traced from about 1884. The camera was so large and heavy that it was carried on a handcart, and it was easier to turn the locomotive on the Stooperdale triangle to photograph its other side than to dismantle the camera and set it up again. Around 1890 a new tank locomotive needed two books of gold leaf at 1s 0½d each to complete the livery, and the cost of labour to apply three coats of paint and four of varnish by hand amounted to £6 15s 0d! Typical building costs are shown in Table 4.5.

In 1863 the works employed 150 men. By 1927, sixteen years after the Stooperdale Shops were built, the staff had increased to 2760, making the works one of the town's largest employers. At nationalisation it had risen to 3548 and by 1954 to 3815. From 1864 new steam locomotives were regularly built at Darlington every year, making an impressive total culminating in the year 1952, when 48 steam locomotives and 36 diesel-electric locomotives were built.

Some of the principal shops in Darlington Works were:

Erecting shop	114 300 sq. ft
Main machine shop	33 300 " "
Diesel railcar engine shop	10 350 " "
Wheel and axle shop	19 800 " "
Brass foundry and brass finishing shop	17 150 " "
Spring shop and smiths' shop	27 370 " "
Axle-box shop	5 000 " "
Fabrication shop	11 275 " "

The erecting shop had three main bays. The centre bay, laid out for the repair of main-line diesel locomotives, featured the use of locomotive stands, eliminating the need for pits except for the removal and fitting of bogies. The two side bays were used for diesel-engine unit repairs, diesel shunting locomotive general repairs and the repair and construction of bogies for main-line diesel locomotives.

TABLE 4.5   *Typical costs of new*
locomotives built at Darlington at
ten-year intervals

Class	Type	Year built	Cost
1001	0–6–0	1873	£2 300
59	0–6–0	1883	£2 346
N	0–6–2T	1893	£2 162
U	0–6–2T	1903	£2 114
T2	0–8–0	1913	£2 971
S3	4–6–0	1923	£6 789
J39	0–6–0	1933	£4 458
V2	2–6–2	1943	£9 756
2MT	2–6–0	1953	£14 377

TABLE 4.6 *Highlights of the story of Darlington Locomotive Works*

1854	Stockton & Darlington Railway amalgamates with the NER. Committee appointed of 2 NER directors, 3 S&D directors, 7 S&D shareholders to run the line for 10 years.
1854–75	William Bouch in charge of Shildon Locomotive Department, Stockton & Darlington Railway.
1857	Bouch undertakes survey, decision to transfer locomotive work to Darlington.
1863	Darlington Locomotive Works opens on 1 January for repairs only. Hours of work 59 per week, reduced to 54 in 1871. Men supplied with a pint of tea a day at 2d per week or coffee at 2½d. Wages 21s per week for labourers, 36s for craftsmen, apprentices at fourteen 4s per week rising to 16s per week at twenty.
1864	First locomotive built (to S&DR design).
1878	West Hartlepool Harbour & Railway Works at Stockton closed. 250 men (weekly wage bill £322) transferred to Darlington with responsibility for maintaining 92 engines.
1879	28 Leeds & Northern engines, previously repaired at York and Hull, transferred to Darlington. 41 engines, previously repaired at Hartlepool, transferred to Darlington.
1881	20 Whitby engines, previously repaired at York, transferred to Darlington.
1883	Soho Works at Shildon closed.
1907	New erecting shop comes into use with 72 pits in 3 bays in a building 500 × 200 ft; remains in use until the works close.
1914	Darlington builds first electric locomotive for electrified line from coal-collecting yard at Shildon to marshalling yard at Newport.
1923	Amalgamation: Darlington continues to play important part in development of LNER locomotives.
1924	First design by Gresley, K3 2–6–0, built.
1926	52 locomotives built at rate of one a week.
1927	Water-tube boiler locomotive built. Boiler subsequently used in Stooperdale boiler shop to provide steam for boiler testing.
1939–45	War work; many American locomotives put into running order.
1948	After nationalisation, both steam and diesel locomotives built at Darlington. Locomotive stock maintained at Darlington: 1476. Average number of locomotives undergoing repairs 83, representing 5.6%. Number of working days on works 19, total calendar days on works 32.
1954	BR Modernisation and Re-equipment Plan: staff increased from 3548 in 1948 to 3815. Output 49 new locomotives (one a week), of which 16 diesel-electric shunting locomotives; 481 general and 48 intermediate classified and 230 non-classified repairs.
1962	BR Workshops Division created, with centralised control, and main works rationalised; many, including Darlington, to be closed due to considerable reduction in overall workload.
1966	Darlington Works, with a reduced staff of 2759, closes, ending more than a century of locomotive building and repairing.

The diesel railcar engine repair shop was laid out to repair and test diesel railcar engines, gearboxes and transmissions. After reassembly they were tested on a Heenan and Froude Dynamometer, painted and stored ready for interchange at other works and motive power depots on request.

Recreational facilities provided by the Darlington Railway Athletic Club catered for a membership of over 2000 involved in a variety of sports. The Railway Institute had a membership of 400 and provided a reading room, library, lecture hall, billiards room and table tennis.

Many LNER high-capacity steam locomotives, including the Class V2 and Class A1, were built at Darlington. After nationalisation BR Standard Type 2 locomotives were built, and the last steam locomotive built at the works was a Class 2 BR (T) completed in June 1957 and numbered 84029. The Class E1 0–6–0 tank locomotives built in 1898 cost £1412 each, whilst identical locomotives built fifty years later each cost £5314 – the price today, allowing for inflation, would be over £40 000!

YORK WAGON WORKS

York Wagon Works, built in 1865 by the North-Eastern Railway, was equipped to repair wagons and horseboxes and, in later years, containers and road-vehicle bodies. It was separated from the carriage works (built in 1884) by traffic roads and sidings spanned by a long pedestrian bridge, but one Works Manager usually controlled both carriage and wagon shops.

In 1949 the wagon works (total staff 801) repaired 12 963 freight vehicles, consisting of 5891 heavy and 7072 light classified repairs; there were also 246 heavy and 849 light classified container repairs. Progressive repair layouts were introduced in 1955, at which time the Eastern and North-Eastern Regions jointly maintained 250 000 freight vehicles of all types. The works was closed under the 1962 main works rationalisation plan, because of the heavy loss of freight traffic to the road haulage industry. Many staff were transferred to York Carriage Works.

GORTON CARRIAGE AND WAGON WORKS

In 1881, some thirty-two years after the Gorton Locomotive Works, the Manchester, Sheffield & Lincolnshire Railway built a relatively small carriage and wagon works, with workshops covering 3.2 acres, on a nearby 5.8 acre site. The works did only light repairs to carriages – there were no lifting facilities for removing the bogies – and repairs to wagons and horse-drawn vehicles. They relied on the locomotive works for springs, smithing work, axleboxes and bearings, and in more recent years upon Faverdale Wagon Works for some machined timber. At nationalisation a total of 544 staff were employed in the works. The works closed in 1965.

YORK CARRIAGE WORKS

It was not until 1884, almost twenty years after York Wagon Works was built, that the North-Eastern Railway decided to build its carriage works there. The works is divided into two sections, one for the building of new coaches and the other for the complete reconditioning and overhaul of coaches, both locomotive-hauled and diesel multiple-unit stock. The staff in 1982 was 2600.

In the works' early days timber logs arrived at one end and went out at the other as coaches. Since then there have been several transitional stages: first composite timber and steel underframes with timber bodies were introduced; followed by steel underframes with timber bodies; replaced in turn by steel underframes with composite steel and timber bodies; and finally all-steel coaches became the norm.

In 1958 the works undertook the construction of multiple-unit electric stock operating at a line voltage of 25 kV AC for the overhead electrification system; since then various types of multiple-unit electric stock have been built at a rate of about 4 vehicles a week. In 1982 the repair shops had a combined capacity for renovating (heavy and light classified repairs) approximately 80 carriages a week, mainly locomotive-hauled, including Pullman cars, sleeping cars, catering vehicles, passenger and non-passenger stock, Post Office and service vehicles.

Since the formation of the Workshops Division (1962) and BREL (1970) York Carriage Works has been one of the only two main works manufacturing new coaching stock to cover the whole of BR's requirements. Table 4.7 shows output in 1981. Modernisation, begun in 1965 and completed in 1967 at a cost of £976 000, included new buildings, plant and equipment, staff amenities, centralised stores facilities and reception sidings. Redundant shops were demolished.

A fire destroyed the original carriage building shop, and a new shop was designed and equipped for the progressive flow line construction of carriages.

TABLE 4.7 *York Carriage Works: output from principal spheres of activity year ended 31 December 1981*

New construction							
Class 315 EMUs							95
Class 317 EMUs							54
						Total	
Repair work	*C1R*	*C1/C2*	*C3*	*C3T*	*C4*	*classified*	*C5*
Catering coaches	—	—	11	—	27	38	3
Sleeping coaches	—	—	7	—	76	83	20
Loco-hauled coaches	—	94	247	135	828	1 304	65
Loco-hauled coaches (non-passenger-carrying)	—	35	79	—	123	237	22

These are mainly built from steel, the bodies and roofs built up from pressed steel sections electrically welded and skinned with steel sheet. Main assembly jigs are used for the framework of body sides, roofs and body ends, which is progressed through stages where doors, window frames, partitions and interior details are fitted, after which the vehicle is traversed into the paint shop before final test and inspection.

The sawmill, equipped and laid out as a high capacity wood machine shop, produces parts for constructing and repairing carriages. Next to the sawmill is the log yard, served by a 95-foot span Goliath crane reputed to be the largest in Europe when it was built in 1884. The fully-equipped works training school, built in 1962, takes 80 apprentice trainees, who spend a year there before further training in the works or regional running depots.

DONCASTER WAGON WORKS

Doncaster Wagon Works was built by the Great Northern Railway in 1889 – some 36 years after the Locomotive and Carriage Works – at the 'Carr', about 2 miles from the 'Plant Works'. It built all types of wagons, including open and covered vehicles for carrying goods such as fruit, milk and fish, gunpowder vans, and refrigerator vans for meat. Others for special purposes were machinery wagons, timber trucks, travelling gasholders, oiltanks, horseboxes, cattle wagons and 50-ton brick wagons. After 1923 wagon building ceased at Doncaster, work subsequently being confined to repairs.

The original wagon shops were sited as shown on an 1855 plan of the Plant Works, their position no doubt influenced by the convenience of having repair shops close to the marshalling yards whilst keeping wagon stock clear of the main line. The main repair shop was a single-storey brick and slate building, 740 by 225 feet, with five bays. At the south end were the stores, supplying material to the works and some 40 wagon stations. The Works Manager controlled both carriage and wagon works. Owing to declining rail traffic the 'Carr' works was closed in 1965 and the workload transferred to the carriage works.

TEMPLE MILLS WAGON WORKS

The Great Eastern Railway built Temple Mills Wagon Works in 1896, almost 50 years after its forerunner, the Eastern Counties Railway, had built the nearby Stratford Carriage Works. The wagon works, the last main works to survive in the London area, was equipped to repair wagons and, later, containers and LNER London area road-vehicle bodies. For many years wagons were made in wood, and so the equipment included machinery for timber conversion.

In 1949, when the total staff employed was 400, the output was 2025 heavy and 18 023 light classified repairs, and 1408 classified light repairs to containers. Five years later, in 1954, the output was higher.

Although Stratford Locomotive and Carriage Works closed in 1963, Temple Mills continued despite an overall decrease in freight traffic until shortage of work led to closure in 1984. Over the years the works developed prototype vehicles such as Cartics, Road-railers and Channel Tunnel wagons, and was among the first to repair Freightliner vehicles and containers in 1964; Cartics were repaired from 1967.

TABLE 4.8   *Temple Mills Wagon Works: output for year ended 31 December 1981*

Repair work	GR	IR/L	IR/W	IR	Total
Traffic wagons	622	113	607	1968	3310

In 1974 the need for refurbishment facilities at the works became apparent, and two shot blast areas were developed. The facilities and high quality of work attracted private customers, and transport costs were minimised by the close proximity to Stratford and other London Freightliner terminals. Layouts and facilities were regularly reviewed to enable efficient repairs to new forms of freight traffic. In the early 1980s the total staff was 400, and approximately 200 wagons and 30 containers were repaired each week. Output of repairs in 1981 is shown in Table 4.8.

WALKERGATE CARRIAGE AND WAGON WORKS

This works, established in 1902 by the North-Eastern Railway, was within the city of Newcastle-upon-Tyne, next to Walkergate Station on the North Tyneside electrified line. Equipped for carriage and wagon repairs, it replaced repair shops of the Newcastle & Carlisle and Blyth & Tyne Railways, absorbed by the NER. In 1899 these had been extended to 14 acres (5 covered) to maintain carriages and wagons in the area bounded by Berwick-upon-Tweed, Durham and Carlisle – in effect all Tyneside stock. Much stock was destroyed when the building was gutted by fire in August 1918.

The well-equipped works had many shops: lifting, brake cylinder repair, wagon repair, smiths', machine, diesel railcar heater repair, carriage repair and a wood machine shop. In 1949 the works employed 508 staff. The main works rationalisation plan brought Walkergate Works' sixty-year existence to an end, with some of the work transferred to Shildon and the rest to York Wagon Works. The Northern Gas Board subsequently acquired the site.

INVERURIE LOCOMOTIVE AND CARRIAGE AND WAGON WORKS

The Royal Burgh of Inverurie lies in the fork of the two rivers, the Don and the Urie, sixteen miles north-west of Aberdeen. A quaint village of 500 inhabitants in the mid-nineteenth century, it is now a thriving community of 5000, the centre of a large agricultural district and home of several well-known industries. Important among its varied industries until the 1960s was the railway works, the most northerly of all main works, 147 miles from Edinburgh and 169 miles from Glasgow. Started in 1898 and completed in 1903 for the Great North of Scotland Railway, it was an impressive, compact works with good rail and road access.

The locomotive shops were engaged on repairs and outdoor maintenance. In 1947 413 staff were engaged on this work, and the output of classified locomotive repairs was 118 heavy and 76 light. The carriage and wagon shops employed 240 staff. Their output in 1949 was 259 heavy and 753 light carriage repairs, and 853 heavy and 6160 light wagon repairs.

The total staff in the locomotive and carriage and wagon works in 1958 was 750, compared to some 110 when production started in 1901. The works survived the 1962 main works rationalisation scheme but, owing to falling traffic, closed on 31 December 1969.

FAVERDALE WAGON WORKS

Faverdale Wagon Works opened in 1923 on a 60-acre site two miles from the centre of Darlington, near the junction of the lines from Darlington to Barnard Castle and Bishop Auckland and the main Bishop Auckland road. There was single-track rail and good road access, and land for expansion. The NER authorised the building, but by the time the works opened it belonged to the LNER.

The layout was originally designed for constructing 10 000 timber-framed wagons a year, using timber details produced internally and ironwork details from Shildon Works, nine miles away. The buildings were heated by the Plenum Hot Air System, and the large sawmill and wood machine shop were protected from fire by automatic sprinklers. In 1949 the total staff was 572, working to a well-organised progressive system. Wells Hood, Works Manager for fifteen years from the opening to 1938, set a high standard. Output in 1949 and 1954 is shown in Table 4.9.

After the building of wood-frame wagons ceased in 1960 Faverdale began building 200 high goods wagons a week. The new steel underframes were manufactured complete at Shildon and sent forward on their own wheels. This programme ran for a long time. Faverdale built the first railway grain wagons used in Britain, and many other special wood-body wagons, at one time building 60 covered goods vans – of standard types, pallet or banana vans –

TABLE 4.9   *Carriage, wagon and container repairs undertaken at Faverdale Wagon Works in 1949 and 1954*

	Carriage repairs			Wagon repairs			Container repairs			New	
Year	Heavy	Light	Total	Heavy	Light	Total	Heavy	Light	Total	Wagons	Containers
1949	17	2	19	1 793	2 048	3 841	976	372	1 348	1 588	295
1954	132	7	139	1 317	3 180	4 497	998	872	1 870	2 262[*]	—

* Underframes from Shildon

and 30 goods brake vans each week. Shildon supplied underframes and ironwork. All standard BR goods brake vans were built at Faverdale, and also rail/road containers, but from the beginning of 1961 there was a change-over from new building to wagon and rail/road container repairs.

In the works' early days some 9000 logs a year were converted in the saw-mill. After accidents caused by foreign materials in the logs breaking saw teeth, electrical scanners were provided to check logs for such items as nails, wires, bolts and even cast iron pipes, to eliminate hazards to staff. The mill and wood machine shop were considered showpieces for the progressive manufacture of timber details for wagon and container building.

Because of a fundamental change in wagon-building policy coupled with loss of traffic, Faverdale, youngest of all main works, closed under the 1962 main works rationalisation plan and so was also the shortest-lived, with a life-span of only 39 years. When the LNER took over both Shildon and Faverdale in 1923 it had become owner of the oldest and youngest British railway works.

5 The Main Works of the Former SR

The history of the Southern Railway (SR) began with the opening in 1803 of the Surrey Iron Railway, the first public rail transport undertaking in the world. The earliest workshop accommodation in south-east London was provided for the London to Greenwich Railway, opened in 1836, by which time the railways were proliferating, with the opening of the London to Southampton line (1840), the London to Brighton line (1841) and the London to Folkestone line (1843). These routes developed into the London & South-Western Railway, the London, Brighton & South Coast Railway (LB&SC) and the South-Eastern & Chatham Railway until the amalgamation of 1923. The first locomotive for the South-Western Railway was built by contractors in 1835, and by 1844 locomotives were being built at Nine Elms by Daniel Gooch, who was responsible for the construction at Nine Elms in 1849 of the express locomotive 'Etna'. In 1890 carriage and wagon work was transferred from Nine Elms to Eastleigh, and locomotive work was similarly transferred in 1909. The first of the Drummond 463 class locomotives were built at Eastleigh in 1912.

In 1923 the newly-formed Southern Railway had 2178 route miles of track, 2281 locomotives, 7500 passenger-carrying vehicles, 36 749 wagons and 41 steam boats. The number of passengers carried on the system was 197 379 698 in 1923, and 235 964 599 in 1937. Unlike the other three group companies, which had 70 per cent of receipts from freight traffic, the SR drew 70 per cent of its receipts from passenger traffic. In no area were circumstances more favourable for rapid expansion than in electrification of the suburban services. The western, central and eastern sections of the new organisation all had some electrified services in the London area prior to amalgamation. In 1926 the decision was taken to abandon the overhead power supply equipment of the former LB&SC and adopt as standard the third-rail system favoured by the other sections. It was then not long before virtually all lines in the London area ran electric services.

BRIGHTON LOCOMOTIVE WORKS

Relatively few people would associate the south coast resort of Brighton in Sussex with a main locomotive works. Yet one was built on piles in 1840, next to Brighton Station, by the London & Brighton Railway. It was a compact works of 9 acres, with 7 acres covered, the highest proportion of covered accommodation of all the 42 main works of British Railways. There was no room for further expansion and the provision of road access was economically

TABLE 5.1   *The main works of the former SR at amalgamation in 1923*

Works	Date built	Railway Co. for which built	Total acreage	Covered acreage	Principal activities following amalgamation
Brighton Locomotive	1840	London & Brighton	9	7	Mainly new locomotive and boiler construction; remainder locomotive repairs.
Ashford Locomotive	1847	South-Eastern	26	9	Mainly locomotive repairs; some new manufacture.
Ashford Wagon	1850	South-Eastern	37	7	Repairing wagons.
Lancing Carriage	1888	London Brighton & South Coast	42	7	Repairing carriages; building carriage underframes; special carriages & wagons; building containers; drop stampings for SR carriages & wagons; breaking up carriages & wagons and recovery of non-ferrous scrap.
Eastleigh Carriage & Wagon	1891	London & South-Western	54	14	Building and repairing carriages; repairing wagons; building and repairing containers; timber conversion.
Eastleigh Locomotive	1909	London & South-Western	41	11	Mainly locomotive repairs; some new manufacture.

impracticable. After twelve years Brighton built its first steam locomotive in 1852.

A notable activity at Brighton during the second world war was the construction of LMS type 4–6–0 freight locomotives for the War Office. These were produced at the rate of one every four and a half days, with manufacturing assistance from Ashford and Eastleigh and Lancing Carriage Works. Although, like Brighton, the Southern Region locomotive works at Ashford in Kent and Eastleigh in Hampshire were equipped for and capable of building new engines and boilers, the manufacturing capacity of all three works was pooled and Brighton undertook the larger part of the new engine and boiler assembly. This arrangement had no counterpart in any other works and operated extremely smoothly. Brighton Works also undertook a limited number of classified locomotive repairs.

In 1947 Brighton turned out 18 new steam locomotives, but no classified repairs. The number of staff employed of all grades was 679. In 1954 Brighton Works erected 22 new steam locomotives and also carried out a total of 134 repairs, consisting of 24 heavy classified repairs, 33 intermediate repairs and 77 non-classified repairs. The staff employed worked approximately equal time on new construction and repair work.

With the modernisation and re-equipment plan of BR in 1954 it was clear that the work of assembly so successfully undertaken at Brighton could not continue for much longer, though the works survived until the BR Workshops Division was formed in 1962. With the proximity of the works to Brighton Station and an intensive electric train service making access difficult, steam locomotive work was divided between Ashford and Eastleigh, and the rationalisation plan provided for Brighton to close in 1964. Brighton Works has since been demolished and the area converted into a large car park.

ASHFORD LOCOMOTIVE WORKS

Ashford in Kent is a small, thriving town of 37 000 population. It has been a market centre for the cattle and sheep farmers of the Weald of Kent and Romney Marsh since the Middle Ages, and its industry developed after railway works were established there in the mid-nineteenth century. The Directors of the South-Eastern Railway decided in 1846 to purchase 185 acres of Kentish countryside on which to lay the foundations of a 'Locomotive Establishment'. In the summer of 1847 a cluster of 72 labourers' cottages were the first signs of the new railway project. In the same year the inaugural meeting of the Ashford Works Mechanics' Institute took place, at which the chairman of the board stressed that the construction work constituted not merely a fine and well-equipped locomotive works, but a complete village. It was soon announced that work from the railway's locomotive depot at New Cross would be transferred to the new works at Ashford.

The locomotive works was long, with somewhat narrow bays, giving an excess run of wall. The shops were soundly constructed and the impressive erecting shop, combining long roads with short transverse pits and served by a traverser, was the only composite example on BR. James I. Cudworth was Locomotive Superintendent of the South-Eastern Railway Company in 1845. In 1853 the first locomotive he designed and built at Ashford Works was one of 10 'Hastings' locomotives with 2–4–0 wheel arrangement, 5'-6" diameter driving wheels and 15" by 20" cylinders. They had double frames – inside and outside frames – and compensating beams. Two years later Cudworth built two freight engines with 4'-9" wheels and 16" by 24" cylinders at Ashford. A new feature he introduced was a double firebox, divided longitudinally, each side of which was fired alternately. He also introduced a sloping grate which greatly improved combustion.

Between 1855 and 1876 Cudworth built 53 freight locomotives at Ashford and between 1856 and 1875 some 80 larger locomotives with 6'-0" driving wheels. In 1861 came the first of his 16 express passenger locomotives with 7'-0" driving wheels, known as 'Mails', 8 of which were built at Ashford. He also produced four classes of 0–6–0 tank engines, totalling 28, 11 of which were built at Ashford and 17 by outside firms. Cudworth resigned in 1876 and was succeeded by A. M. Watkin, son of Sir Edward Watkin, Director of the Manchester, Sheffield & Lincolnshire Railway and the Metropolitan.

In 1878 James Stirling was appointed Locomotive Superintendent. He came from the Glasgow & South-Western Railway and was the brother of Patrick Stirling of the Great Northern. Stirling held the post for 20 years and, although he produced only 6 classes of locomotive, he introduced a high degree of standardisation. He believed in the use of the bogie truck and produced a design in which the side movement was controlled by rubber pads; he also invented a successful form of steam reversing gear. The first locomotive he introduced was of 4–4–0 wheel arrangement with 6'-0" driving wheels and 18" by 26" cylinders. Twelve of these were built at Ashford between 1879 and 1881. His standard goods engine (0 class) with 5'-1" wheels followed. There were 122 of these, of which 57 were built at Ashford, many surviving to be taken into the Southern Railway stock at amalgamation in 1923. He was responsible for 118 tank engines of 0–4–4 wheel arrangement, 48 of these being built at Ashford, and between 1883 and 1898 he produced 88 F Class locomotives with 7'-0" wheels and 18" cylinders at Ashford. Many of Stirling's locomotives eventually became part of the Southern Railway fleet and No. 240, built in 1889, was shown at the Paris Exhibition of that year.

In 1888 the South-Eastern Railway amalgamated with the South-Eastern & Chatham Railway, and the works was extended and modernised. In the following decade Stirling produced his 0–6–0 tanks, 25 in number, all built at Ashford. In 1898 his B Class express appeared, having the same size driving wheels and cylinders as the F Class but larger boiler and tender and an improved cab; 14 of the total of 34 were built at Ashford. In the same year, on formation of the South-Eastern and Chatham Joint Committee, Stirling resigned.

Stirling was succeeded by H. S. Wainwright, who had been Carriage and Wagon Superintendent since 1895. His first product, a 6-coupled freight locomotive, was first put into service in 1900; 109 of these were built, all at Ashford. Wainwright was also responsible for other classes of locomotive built at Ashford.

Wainwright retired before the first world war and R. E. L. Maunsell became CME. During the war Maunsell introduced his N Class 2–6–0 mixed-traffic locomotive, 12 of which were built at Ashford. Before the amalgamation of 1923 he produced a 2–6–4 tank locomotive (K Class) similar to the N class but with 6'-0" driving wheels.

Ashford Locomotive Works was extended before 1923 and included a new locomotive erecting shop and a new wagon shop, enabling the works to provide classified repairs to locomotives allocated to the eastern section, and a proportion of the central section locomotives of the Southern Railway. Following amalgamation a further 17 N Class locomotives were built at Ashford, and in 1925 Ashford produced parts for 9 K Class engines which were assembled by Armstrong, Whitworth and Company of Newcastle-upon-Tyne. After 1923 Ashford became one of the main centres of the newly-formed Southern Railway and dealt with the construction and repair of locomotives, carriages and wagons.

In 1941–2 Ashford built 1600 12-ton open wagons for shipment to Persia within a period of 12 weeks. By 1944, when it ceased to build, Ashford had built a total of 639 steam locomotives. The works also built main-line diesel-electric locomotive No. 10202 which was completed in 1951. In 1947 Ashford was responsible for the maintenance of 839 locomotives. The staff employed in the works was 1572.

In 1962 all locomotive repair work at Ashford was transferred to Eastleigh, thus terminating the locomotive era at Ashford. The works obtained its first major order for 250 continental ferry vans in 1962 and during the same year more specialised rolling stock designs including fly ash wagons and the Cartic 4 articulated car transporter were produced. Later the building of the first Freightliner vehicle was followed by the production of the high-capacity coal wagons for introduction to 'merry-go-round' traffic. Some of the former locomotive shops were retained for wagon work. An extensive reorganisation took place in the locomotive, carriage and wagon works at Ashford between 1964 and 1966 for progressive working, and to accommodate the construction and repair of modern wagon stock.

In the 1970s, besides fulfilling the requirements of British Rail, the works built large-capacity steel wagons for overseas. As one of BREL's two main wagon works Ashford undertook its first major export order – the construction of 800 covered vans for the Yugoslavian Railways – in the early 1970s. Subsequently Ashford's varied output included steel-carrying wagons and covered vans for BR, bogie hopper wagons for the Middle East and bulk tank wagons for various private firms. Other later export projects included the construction of 1200 wagons for Kenya Railways, 510 wagons for the Tanzania Railway Corporation and 825 wagons for the Bangladesh Railway.

On the home front Ashford built 500 45-tonne open wagons and refurbished and modernised 200 bogie steel-carrying wagons and 50 covered wagons. It also manufactured sub-assemblies for the Class 56 freight locomotives built at BREL's Doncaster Works. In addition it undertook the repair of revenue-earning and civil engineering service wagons and provided a heavy maintenance service for wheels. Output for BR and other customers in 1981 is shown in Table 5.2.

ASHFORD CARRIAGE AND WAGON WORKS

The creation of the carriage and wagon works by the South-Eastern Railway began at Ashford in 1850. Some three years after the commencement of the nearby locomotive works, the adjoining railway village – known at first as Alfred Town – was expanded by 60 houses, and the gasworks made its appearance on the site. The staff employed in 1923 totalled 827, all of whom were engaged on carriage and wagon building and maintenance. In 1949 the works built 2756 new wagons of various designs and carried out 2889 heavy and 3703 light, a total of 6592 classified wagon repairs.

TABLE 5.2   *Ashford Works: output from principal spheres of activity year ended 31 December 1981*

New construction					
For British Rail					
102-ton steel-carrying bogie wagons					12
'Seacow' service wagons					41
Skip storage wagons					22
For private parties					
Broad-gauge wagons for Bangladesh					128
Bogie covered goods wagons for Tanzania					112
Crew vans for Tanzania					8
Cement tank wagons for Blue Circle					60
Repair work	*GR*	*IR/L*	*IR/W*	*IR*	*Total*
Traffic wagons	6	—	1	28	35

In 1954 the works built 3063 wagons and 352 carriage underframes with a staff of 525, and carried out 3731 heavy and 4952 light classified wagon repairs with a staff of 440. It was estimated that in 1954 approximately 70 000 of the 1 124 710 freight vehicles owned by British Railways (around 6 per cent) were normally on the Southern Region, the smallest region for freight traffic.

The construction of new carriage underframes and new wagons was developed in an extremely efficient manner. The use of inexpensive lifting tackle at appropriate points to speed up the movement between stages of the construction eliminated standing time. The stacking of material, including wheel and axle sets, by the use of fork-lift trucks was widely developed and storage space was used to the maximum. The use of jigs and fixtures at Ashford was commendable. The progressive wagon repair system at Ashford included equipment at one stage of the repair for the straightening of distorted steel underframes and side and end stanchions, and the rapid way these appliances enabled the staff to handle the vehicles was very impressive. Wood waste from the sawmill provided steam for an axle-box bosh tank, the canteen and a certain amount of workshop heating, most of which was by unit heaters.

There were three new construction shops, and the availability of more than one shop for new construction facilitated the layout of self-contained flow lines for more than one new construction project. New freight wagons were manufactured in the new construction shops on a flow line basis. Special jibs and turn-over manipulators were used to enable consistent high quality output. Overhead cranes moved the partially-completed wagons through the various assembly stages until they were finally lowered on to their wheels or bodies. Facilities existed for manual metal arc CO_2 (including fully automatic), submerged arc, stainless steel and aluminium welding.

The organisation at Ashford was always regarded as highly efficient. The works survived the widespread closures of 1962, merging with the locomotive works, but decreasing traffic requirements and insufficient overseas contracts culminated in closure in 1982.

LANCING CARRIAGE WORKS

The carriage works at Lancing in Sussex was built in 1888 under the direction of the CME of the London, Brighton & South Coast Railway, William Stroudley, whose Locomotive and Carriage Superintendent, R. Billington, supervised the activities of the new works. The first Works Manager at Lancing was A. H. Planter (1888–1912), the son of the Carriage Superintendent of the London & South-Western Railway. In 1923 the London & South-Western Railway was merged with the newly formed Southern Railway during the period of office of the second Works Manager at Lancing, G. H. Gardener (1912–40), whose successors were O. G. Hackett (1940–8), F. B. Illston (1948–51), C. Collins (1951–60), L. Cheeseman (1960–3) and W. E. Levett (1963–5).

Environmentally Lancing was a well-chosen area, as a small seaside resort with the sea front and bathing huts opposite the works entrance, and it was common for the works' staff to relax in the sea during their meal break in the summer months! Nearby was Lancing College, the long-established public school, with its majestic chapel soaring above the predominantly rural landscape.

Initially wooden railway carriages on wooden underframes were constructed at Lancing. In addition, wagon stock work which was previously carried out at Brighton was transferred to Lancing. The principal functions of Lancing Works were to repair carriages, build carriage underframes, build special carriages and wagons, undertake conversions, build containers, fit sheeting to new wagons, manufacture drop stampings for both carriages and wagons, and manufacture carriage wheel sets and certain wagon wheel sets for maintenance requirements. The works also undertook the breaking-up of carriages and wagons on the Southern Railway as well as the recovery of non-ferrous scrap.

On the formation of the Southern Railway in 1923 Lancing introduced a progressive system of carriage repairs on the lines of a pioneering works scheme established at Derby Carriage and Wagon Works several years previously. The progressive repair layout catered for the Southern Railway's entire passenger stock. Lancing also constructed steel carriage underframes for the Southern Region stock. Pioneering work in the building of a prototype double-decker carriage for an electric multi-unit commuter train initially showed promise, but the prototype eventually had to be abandoned because passenger disembarkation time from the train proved to be longer than with the orthodox single-decker design. A sleeping car with longitudinal berths and a body formed of plywood with a suitable framework was also built at

Lancing, as well as experimental bodies without the customary centre plate and swing links, but these projects did not materialise.

The systematic repair of carriages continued to be carried out at Lancing under a well-developed progressive repair scheme. The works possessed two progressive carriage repair lines, for heavy and light classified repairs respectively. The shops were well equipped and it is interesting that four steam locomotive type boilers, situated in a central boilerhouse and burning briquettes of scrap timber, were able to provide adequate space heating for the entire works.

The normal output of heavy repairs was 20 per week and of light repairs 25 per week. The output in 1949 was 538 heavy and 2088 light classified carriage repairs, 18 new carriages, 140 new wagons (using wagon underframes built at Ashford) and 60 new containers, produced by a total staff of 1277. In 1954 Lancing completed 352 heavy and 1748 light classified carriage repairs, and also built 2 carriage underframes and carried out 183 carriage conversions. In the same year, when the 15-year modernisation and re-equipment plan of British Railways was launched, a well-considered proposal was put forward for Lancing Works to undertake all repairs to locomotive-hauled coaching stock vehicles of the Southern Region, together with a proportion of electric multi-unit stock large enough to cater for the needs of the Portsmouth and south coast local services. The proposal was abandoned when the rationalisation and re-equipment plan for the main works was implemented in 1962, and Lancing Works was closed. The works site now forms an industrial estate.

EASTLEIGH CARRIAGE AND WAGON WORKS

Eastleigh is a town of some 50 000 people situated five and a half miles from Southampton, Britain's foremost port, and the town has for many years provided a busy airport for the Southampton catchment area. The carriage and wagon works was built in 1891 by the London & South-Western Railway. The area where the works was built was originally called Bishopstoke and the growth of Eastleigh around the railway works was stimulated by good road and rail access.

William Panter, who in 1886 was appointed superintendent of the railway works at Nine Elms, London, directed the transfer of the carriage and wagon department to Eastleigh in 1891 and became the first superintendent of the Eastleigh Carriage and Wagon Works. Panter was succeeded by Surrey Warner, Arthur Shepherd, Fred Munns, Fred B. Illston, Charles Shepherd (son of Arthur) and Lance Sanders, the last transferring the carriage activities to the locomotive works when the original carriage works closed in 1962.

The main activities of the works were the building of new carriages and containers and the repair of carriages, wagons and containers. In 1945 the works commenced the construction of all-steel suburban electric carriages and all-steel carriages for main-line steam routes. In 1948 Eastleigh Carriage

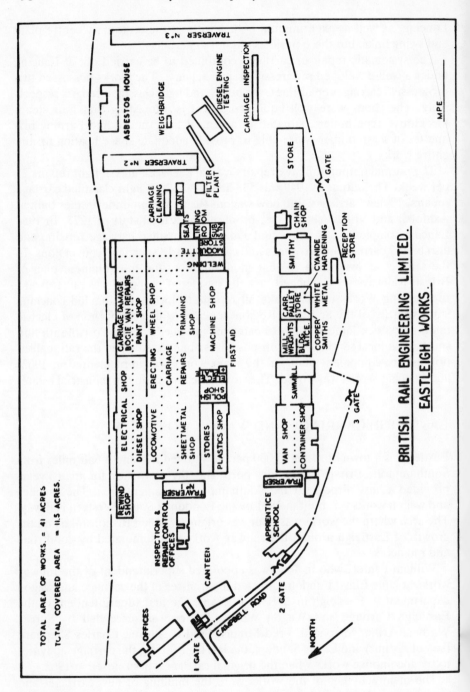

Source   BREL

Figure 5.1   *Plan of Eastleigh Works*

TABLE 5.3   *Output of classified repairs and new rolling stock at Eastleigh Carriage and Wagon Works, 1949 and 1954*

| | Classified repairs | | | | | | New rolling stock | |
| | Carriages | | Wagons | | Containers | | | |
Year	Heavy	Light	Heavy	Light	Heavy	Light	Carriages	Containers
1949	15	1 130	2 362	2 451	281	280	370*	242
1954	58	852	2 198	5 151	260	210	385*	240

* Underframes supplied by Lancing

and Wagon Works employed a total staff of 1822, of whom 1260 were employed on new coaching stock and the remainder almost equally divided between carriage repairs and wagon repairs. Output in 1949 and 1954 is shown in Table 5.3.

In 1962 it was decided that Eastleigh Works should not undertake any new manufacture of locomotives or rolling stock and, furthermore, that the carriage and wagon repair workload should be located within Eastleigh Locomotive Works (see Fig. 5.1). The decision to close Eastleigh Carriage Works and concentrate the large future workload in the locomotive works on a smaller site was not an easy one to reach. The deciding factor was the nature of the buildings: the locomotive works had far higher buildings with a profusion of overhead travelling cranes. Furthermore, road access to the locomotive works was difficult and would have detracted from the saleable value of the site, whereas the carriage works, with easy access to Eastleigh, was eminently suitable for sale for conversion into an industrial estate.

In the reorganised works at Eastleigh carriage repairs became the major function and a comprehensive progressive repair scheme was introduced. This and other features of the reorganised works enabled the whole of the workload required by the Southern Region to be met and also enabled the days on works to be reduced. When the carriage and wagon works closed in 1968 the new manufacture of carriage work was transferred to Derby and York, and locomotive building to Crewe Locomotive Works.

EASTLEIGH LOCOMOTIVE WORKS

Some eighteen years after Eastleigh Carriage and Wagon Works opened, Eastleigh Locomotive Works was built in 1909 by the London & South-Western Railway, sited adjacent to the carriage and wagon works. The Eastleigh Locomotive Works was considered to be the most up-to-date and advanced in the country. The works became the principal locomotive works of the Southern Railway and, by the end of 1947, had built a total of 304 steam locomotives since opening. Subsequently a further 16 locomotives were built in addition to rebuilds and classified repairs.

In 1947 the staff employed in the works totalled 1854, and they were responsible in that year for the maintenance of 988 locomotives and for 327 heavy and 124 light classified repairs. The average number of locomotives in the works at any one time was 44, representing 4.4 per cent of the maintained stock; the average number of working days for a locomotive in the works was 16 and the overall number of days out of service 23. The manufacture of finished locomotive parts for new locomotives being erected at Brighton occupied an average of 75 men at Eastleigh.

With the electrification of the Kent coast lines in 1959 and the withdrawal of steam locomotives, the works gradually changed over to electric and diesel repairs and the construction of electric locomotives. The erecting shop had three 2-road bays with a central service road in each bay and each line of pits was 765 feet long. The workshops rationalisation plan in 1962 led to a major change at Eastleigh. All new manufacture ceased, and it was arranged for the carriage and wagon works to be closed and sold and for the locomotive works to undertake locomotive, carriage and container repairs. This involved fundamental changes in layout to accommodate both major activities. The changes became effective in 1968, and in the combined works there were 430 salaried staff and 2094 wages staff, giving a total of 2524.

The layout of the combined locomotive and carriage works provided for locomotive and carriage repair work to be undertaken. Locomotive repairs were carried out to a schedule planned with the aid of network analysis which almost invariably improved both productivity and production. Introduced in 1966, this effected a spectacular reduction in the days spent by locomotives under repair in the works, with an average repair time for Class 33 DM locomotives of 18.8 days. For carriage repairs the progressive repair layout was double-shifted, and this enabled days under repair to be reduced to less than half the former figure. The time applying to a C1 repair in 1982 was 14.2 days. Table 5.4 shows works output in 1981.

The plastics shop, established primarily for the manufacture of carriage doors in fibre-glass reinforced polyester resin, produced many other items in this medium, including carriage seat-shells, locomotive roof sections and a variety of equipment cases, and similar articles for the signal and telecommunications department. Press-moulding was extensively employed, seat-shells and other items being produced on a Daniels press of 150 tons capacity. The introduction of hot pressing resulted in reduced production times and financial saving. The repair work undertaken at Eastleigh in 1973 was as follows:

Diesel main-line locomotives:	Classified	41
	Unclassified	5
Diesel shunting locomotives:	Classified	4
	Unclassified	11
Electric locomotives:	Classified	3
	Unclassified	2

Electro-diesel locomotives:	Classified	15
	Unclassified	5
		86

Electric multiple-unit coaches	1 660
Diesel-electric multiple-unit coaches	95
Locomotive-hauled passenger coaches	94
Locomotive-hauled non-passenger coaches	319
	1 152

Containers (BR and private party)	655

Some of the most successful classes of locomotive built at Eastleigh were the King Arthur, Lord Nelson, Schools, Merchant Navy, Battle of Britain, West Country and LMS 2–8–0. Repair and rebuilding of steam locomotives were the main activities from 1945 to 1958, repair facilities for diesels being added later, and in 1962 the works took over the whole of the Southern Region's repair work on steam, diesel and electric locomotives, as well as on motors from multiple-unit stock. Extensive modernisation and reorganisation was

TABLE 5.4   *Eastleigh Works: output from principal spheres of activity year ended 31 December 1981*

Major modifications and conversions

Refurbishing of Class 415/6 EMUs	48
Impact-resistant glass cab windows	6

Repair work	General	Intermediate	Light	Total classified	Unclassified
Diesel main-line locomotives	17	14	—	31	12
Diesel shunting locomotives	1	5	—	6	3
Electric locomotives	10	—	—	10	—

	Armature	Carcase
Traction motors	1 563	1 154
Main generators	96	99
DMU engines	36	

	C1R	C1/C2	C3	C3T	C4	Total classified	C5
Loco-hauled coaches	—	13	20	—	—	33	—
Loco-hauled coaches (non-passenger-carrying)	—	1	4	—	13	18	1
DMUs	—	17	77	—	—	94	—
EMUs	48	414	535	—	—	997	7

completed in 1968, which included closing down the carriage works and providing new buildings, plant, equipment and staff amenities within the former locomotive works.

6 Repair of Locomotives, Carriages and Wagons

The history of the repair of railway rolling stock is a sparsely-documented field. Understandably the design and construction of railway vehicles, especially locomotives, has a far greater general appeal than the important task of maintaining the locomotives, carriages and wagons in a serviceable state to enable them to perform their function in a safe and economical way. Yet the cost of a railway vehicle's main workshop repairs over its total life will amount to some four times the original cost of production.

The repair of railway vehicles, both in the day-to-day maintenance in the running depots and for the heavier types of repair and general overhaul, demands the same workshop facilities which were required when the vehicle was built. The main workshop repair activity, as distinct from other types of repair activity, accounts for a high proportion of the overall cost of operating the rolling stock. This high cost makes it essential that the repairs be carried out in the most economical way, which includes doing the work in the shortest possible time. This last factor emphasises the capital cost element of the operation, for the total size of the vehicle fleet will have to take into account the number of vehicles in and awaiting repairs in the works and it will be clear that the quicker the turnround, the fewer vehicles in total will be required and the less capital involved.

In the early days of the railways, with so many different designs of locomotives being produced by a variety of manufacturers, the organisation for dealing with repairs must have presented railway engineers with a major problem. In most instances locomotives would have to be returned to the original contractor's works, often on a road wagon, by canal or even by sea. Generally the repair of carriages and wagons was dealt with locally, as the type of work involved was not unlike that required for the maintenance of road coaches and wagons. However, the size of the various railway undertakings grew, with an increasing number of locomotives and stock, and the railway companies were obliged to establish their own workshops, not only for the lighter repairs but also for major repairs. The main problems to be overcome were the lifting of the locomotive to remove the wheels and lifting the boiler off the frames.

In many of the earlier locomotive erecting workshops locomotives were accommodated on short tracks holding usually only one vehicle each, the tracks being arranged radially around a turntable (on the roundhouse principle) or on parallel tracks fed by a traverser or from a track outside the workshop. With the introduction of overhead travelling cranes most erecting shops were built on the basis of a number of tracks running the length of the workshop, with craneways over the tracks, the locomotives being lifted and moved to any position in the workshop by two cranes. The working tracks were normally provided with a pit running the full length of the workshop to enable work to be performed on the inside connecting rods and valve gear. In some works – particularly Swindon and Darlington – short transverse tracks, accommodating one or two locomotives, were preferred. In the former the locomotive was brought to the end of the repair track by a traverser running centrally down the length of the shop. This arrangement has continued in use today, the lifting being done by a single crane fitted with twin crabs, each lifting one end of the locomotive.

The carriage and wagon repair shops were usually laid out on a longitudinal basis and the repair was carried out in two distinct operations: firstly the lift, to remove wheels, bogies and running gear and to repair and replace these components, and secondly the body repair, for which the vehicle could be moved on its own wheels from stage to stage in the body repair shop, often with vehicles coupled together and hauled forward by a winch.

The concept of a flow line repair layout for locomotives came only later and there are many photographs of locomotives in various stages of repair at fixed positions in the erecting shops. Certainly well into the twentieth century locomotives were being stripped, often to the bare frames, and then reassembled at one position in the shop by a small team of men, in some cases one craftsman and his apprentice, with only the specialist operations, such as the repair of wheels, springs, boiler and valve gear, being carried out in adjacent shops. The concept of a conveyor-belt flow line for the assembly of vehicles, which had revolutionised early car manufacture in the USA, had its attractions, the object being to progress the vehicle chassis to groups of workers at set positions on the production line, to enable the component parts to be assembled in the correct sequence. The mere fact that the conveyor moved, either continuously or in staged steps, required that management have every stage of the production line appropriately manned, equipped and provisioned with components for assembly.

This concept could be applied to the production of new railway vehicles, where a production run was of the same type, although the size and weight of the vehicle presented a movement problem. The difficulties to be overcome were much greater for a vehicle repair line, which had to deal with a number of classes of vehicle and where the full extent of the work to be carried out would not be known until the vehicle had been stripped in the first stage of the repair.

The earliest development in providing a truly progressive repair for a railway vehicle was in the lift shop at Newton Heath Carriage Works of the L&YR, which was in operation in 1910 and was an early model for the LB&SC Railway carriage works system at Lancing. In the lift operation the body of the carriage was lifted from its bogies, mounted on special high-framed 'slave' bogies and attached to a line of bodies which were moved at a continuous slow speed down the shop, during which time work was carried out on the various parts of the running gear attached to the body underframe.

At the same time the bogie, after it was dewheeled, was moved down a bogie repair line. When it had been repaired and the reprofiled wheels fitted it met up with its repaired body, the entire operation being carried out in one day.

When the vehicle was moved to the body repair shop the operation became much more protracted because of the considerable number of body types – such as corridor, non-corridor, compartment, vestibule, brake van and composite – and in those days there were first-, second- and third-class carriages. There was also a wide range of repair classifications to be covered, from a light body repair to a heavy repair, including a complete retrim of all the seats. A number of different trades were involved and, particularly in compartment stock, it was not possible to have body builders, plumbers, electricians, coach finishers and trimmers all working together in confined spaces. Where one line might suffice for the lift operation, some fifteen or more lines might be required for the body repair; vehicles were fed to these lines, segregated by the type of repair and giving the best balance of loading. Even then there was a need for considerable movement of staff from one line to another.

With the financial problems facing the railways after the first world war, following five years of under-investment and increasing competition from road transport, the need for economies in operating performance in all its aspects became of prime importance. One of the major items of expenditure was the cost of rolling stock maintenance and, not surprisingly, the engineers of the four main-line railways which had emerged from the 1923 amalgamation were pressed by their boards to improve the availability of the vehicle fleet and at the same time to reduce the cost of the repairs.

In the early 1920s most works, particularly the locomotive works, had a queue of vehicles waiting to go in for repair and once they had entered the works they remained there far too long. The first steps were to clear the backlog awaiting repairs and then to move forward to some form of planned maintenance in which the locomotives would be called to the works for repair on a period or mileage basis. Carriages and wagons continued to be shopped on a condition basis largely determined by the condition of the wheel tyres and the state of the body.

At amalgamation the 'big four' were faced with the problem of dealing with a multiplicity of vehicle types, and initially the introduction of their own standard classes increased the number of classes to be handled and therefore exacerbated the problem. Each of the four railway companies classified its locomotive repairs in its own particular way, but basically there were two types of planned repair, a heavy or general repair at which the boiler would be changed, and a service or intermediate repair of the running gear and minor boiler work which could be undertaken without the boiler being removed from the locomotive frames.

For carriages there were several grades of body repair, each associated with a lift, the heaviest requiring general body repairs, full retrim and complete repaint. There was also a non-lift light repair. The next step was to reorganise within the works not only the repair facilities but also the repair procedure. The most dramatic way in which this was achieved for repairing locomotives was in Crewe Locomotive Works between 1925 and 1927. In 1921 the LNWR had started on the clearance of a site for a new erecting shop to replace most of the nine existing shops, but the scheme had been put in abeyance. This site was available for the scheme drawn up by the LMS, and at the time was the most notable advance in progressive repairs to locomotives, with the time in the shops reduced from 60 days to 12. The new erecting shop, 670 feet in length, had five repair lines and one new construction line. Each repair line operated as a 'belt' timed to move at different intervals of time to suit the various types of locomotive and type of classified repair. The 'belt' dealing with the largest types of locomotive for a general repair was divided into two stripping stages and ten repair and assembly stages, each stage taking 7 hours 50 minutes. As a boiler took considerably longer to repair than the rest of the locomotive, it was necessary to have a stock of spare boilers, and the number of boilers in excess of the number of locomotives was calculated using a formula based on the total locomotive stock in each class, the average boiler life between major repairs and the average number of days for a boiler repair compared to the days for a locomotive repair. It was known as the 'economic stock of spare boilers', and in due course was introduced in all the main locomotive works.

At Swindon in 1934, following the introduction of a special axle-box guide grinding machine and the provision of Zeiss optical frame alignment equipment, a progressive locomotive repair system was introduced. However, instead of longitudinal repair lines as at Crewe and the majority of other locomotive erecting shops, Swindon A erecting shop, which dealt with the larger GWR locomotives, was arranged with transverse repair pits on each side of a traverser, each of the pits accommodating two locomotives. The pit roads were divided into four sections, A, B, C and D, dealing with stripping, frame repairing and boiler, wheel and motion fitting, before being moved to D on the far side of the traverser for finishing and painting. Locomotives were moved between sections by double crab overhead cranes running longitudinally over the transverse roads.

In the same year H. G. Ivatt introduced a well-devised progressive repair layout, combined with the use of Wageor electrically-operated equipment, in the boiler and boiler mounting shops in Derby Locomotive Works. The turnround of boilers under repair increased dramatically and the scheme was highlighted in the technical press.

Significant improvements were made in the control of repair standards introduced in the early 1930s at locomotive, carriage and wagon works. Up to this stage the decision as to the details requiring repairs or to those which could be allowed to run again had mainly been left to the individual repair sections, with the risk that the decision might be influenced by the current load on the section. The LMS was in the lead in laying down clearly-defined limits of wear and scrapping limits. Initial Examiners were appointed to examine the various components after stripping and cleaning and to make the decisions as to the repair work required. Their guidelines were the 'limits of wear' (for example, if a cylinder bore was more than 0.030″ oval or taper it must be rebored) and 'scrapping limits' (for example, wheel tyres had to be scrapped when the thickness of the tread was reduced to 1¾″). These salaried Initial Examiners were independent of the shop supervisory staff and were directly responsible to the management.

Towards the end of the 1930s the railway workshops had reached a high state of efficiency in vehicle repairs. Most of the rolling stock of the pre-amalgamation companies had been withdrawn, leaving a fleet of more standard vehicles to be maintained and enabling the repair layouts to be improved. It should be appreciated that standardisation is only a comparative term. There has always been a demand by the railway operating and commercial departments for a multiplicity of vehicle types, and as their average life might run to thirty or more years, there was always a problem in catering for all the variations. All in all, the repair activity in railway works is more complex than the production of new vehicles.

The second world war greatly disrupted the railway workshops, particularly in respect of vehicle repairs. By 1945 the vehicle fleets were well below the desirable standard of maintenance, very few new vehicles having been added to the fleets. Any new equipment introduced into the works over the war years was for war work, only a small amount of it being of value for railway work. A number of Austerity 2–8–0 and 2–10–0 locomotives, built for war service, were transferred to the four railway companies, and it is noteworthy that when a steady stream of the former were given a service repair at Crewe in 1946–7 the entire repair was completed in 5 days, owing to the fact that one repair line was devoted to one class of locomotive in which each required an identical type of repair.

When British Railways came into existence on 1 January 1948 there was still a vast backlog of repairs as a result of the war. In 1939 the proportion of locomotives undergoing or awaiting works repairs had been as low as 4.5% of the fleet, whilst in 1948 at some works the proportion was as high as 25% of the total, making it necessary for some classes to be transferred for repair to works which had previously belonged to a different railway company. Under the Railway Executive a committee with representatives from each of the four former companies was set up to co-ordinate repair procedures and establish the future repair standards for all BR works. This was an exceptionally challenging period for the railway workshop engineers, who had to cope with the introduction of a complete new range of standard BR steam locomotives, carriages and wagons, as well as ensuring that both the old and new types of stock were maintained to the high standards required.

The decision embodied in the 1954 railway modernisation plan to replace all steam motive power by electric and diesel traction made yet another fundamental change for the locomotive works – and to a lesser extent for the carriage works – with the advent of a large number of diesel railcars produced

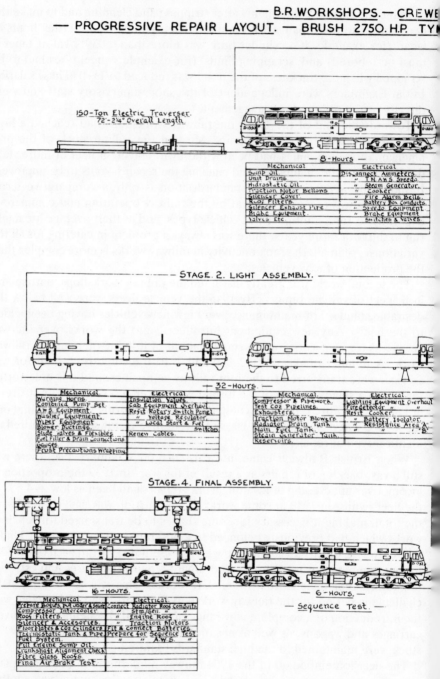

SOURCE BREL

FIGURE 6.1 *The progressive repair of a diesel locomotive at Crewe in the 1970s*

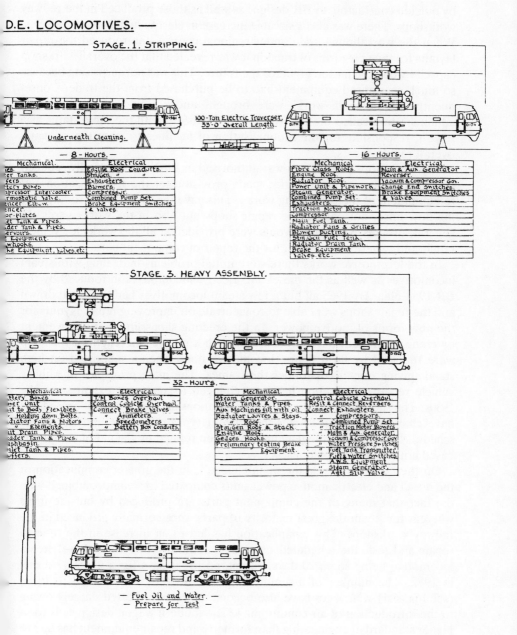

Jig & Tool Drg. Office.
Crewe Works.

by outside contractors to BR design, as well as those produced in the railway workshops. There was also a sizeable increase in electric multiple-unit vehicles. When the workshops – then under regional control – introduced the repair layouts for the new forms of traction it was revealed that the overall workshop capacity would be far too great for the future. This was not surprising because so much specialised equipment had to be purchased from the trade. Consequently all the main works were brought under a newly-formed central administration called the BR Workshops Division, with the same status as a region, responsible for the rationalisation of facilities to meet the railway's overall requirements.

The workshops plan, which was authorised in 1962 and drastically reduced the total number of main works, made provision for the reorganisation and re-equipment of the continuing works. This gave the opportunity to improve the flow lines, not only in the repair shops but also in the works yards. In general, progressive repair layouts were provided at all the works for vehicle repair and, wherever possible, for the repair of component parts.

In the locomotive works there were initial problems in dealing with steam locomotives as well as the diesel and electric locomotives introduced by the BR 1954 plan. By 1965 all but a few steam locomotives had been withdrawn and the repair shops were able to concentrate on improving repair layouts for the new forms of motive power. In the erecting shops lifting and movement by crane continued, but the old tracks with a pit the full length of the shop were replaced by flush floors, locomotive bodies being supported on high stands giving easy access under the frames. The main principles of railway vehicle repair organisation have not changed to any great extent since the 1930s. The shopping periods, repair specifications and stock control procedures have changed in detail to suit the current types of vehicle and the repair schedules. Manning arrangements have been refined by the aid of computer-based critical path techniques.

On the locomotive side the main change is in the greater complication of the diesel and electric motive power units compared to steam, combined with the fact that many of the component parts are produced by outside firms whereas for steam the great majority of parts were normally produced in the railway workshops. This complication has led to an increase in the time to repair and test, the scheduled time for a general repair for a 4–6–2 steam locomotive being some 20 days, compared to 42 days for a Class 47 diesel in 1982. The number of assembly stages, however, was reduced to three (see Fig. 6.1). Carriages have also become more complicated, largely owing to the introduction of air-conditioning. The modern wagon design calls for a higher standard of engineering than formerly and repair equipment has had to be provided for a number of newly-introduced features.

Apart from changes in procedure brought about by the changes in design, the basic repair organisation is likely to continue, making use of progressive repair lines wherever there is a sufficiency of similar vehicles or components to justify this method of operation.

7 Building a Locomotive of the 'Princess Royal' Type in 1935

Bigger trains, higher speeds, longer non-stop runs, more economical working – these have been the oft-repeated cries of the Railway Operating Department since railways were first created. Test runs carried out in 1934 demonstrated the capabilities of the largest type of LMS express passenger engines and gave a convincing answer to the latest demands for big loads (500 tons) to be hauled at average speeds of 60 to 70 m.p.h. The engine in this instance was the 4–6–2 Pacific type locomotive No. 6200, 'Princess Royal', built in 1933 (see Plate 7a), and 1935 saw the introduction of a further ten locomotives of this very successful class, all of which were built in Crewe Locomotive Works.

PRELIMINARY CONSIDERATIONS

The efficient manufacture of any steam locomotive necessitated a large amount of co-operation in the works and was dependent not only on the skill and craftsmanship of the men in the workshops, but also on the organisation and vision of the supervisory staff who had to carry out much preliminary work before actual production commenced. At this stage the most important consideration was the date when the engine was required to be ready for traffic, because on this hinged all calculations for the dates when various material would be required from contractors and also when work needed to be put in hand in the different shops, taking into account the length of time certain items took for their completion. A keen appreciation of the requirements in this respect might result in a very considerable economy in the interest on capital expended on material which might otherwise be lying idle for many months (see Table 7.1).

TABLE 7.1 *Material required to build one engine, with period allowed between ordering and date of completion of engine*

Part	Material	Quantity (tons)	Period (months)
Boiler plates	steel	14·5	6–7
(including smokebox)	copper	4·5	6–7
Frame plates	steel	13	5–6
Cab and ashpan plates	steel	1·5	4
Steel castings (rough)	steel	18	3–4
Cylinders (rough)	steel	6	3–4

Special materials included monel metal, which was used for the stays in the firebox, manganese molybdenum high-tensile steel for tyres and coupling and connecting rods, silico manganese steel for springs, stainless steel for valves and fittings and copper-bearing steel for smokebox and ashpans. A scheduled programme for every component delivered to the erecting shop was the major concern of everyone connected with production work. The erecting shop was the focal centre for all finished material but this had to arrive in sequence if the complete assembly of the engine was to be carried out in the three weeks allotted immediately before the engine was due to be put into traffic.

THE BOILER

One of the earliest items was the boiler, which was the largest individual unit to be supplied to the erecting shop. The boilers for the 'Princess Royal' class were in 1935 the largest to have been constructed at Crewe and without tubes or mountings weighed approximately 18 tons. Special provision was made for handling and transporting them, and certain new features in design introduced fresh problems in carrying out the work: for example, the bottom half of the throat plate or saddle plate was flanged and pressed in one operation from a single flat plate, a considerable achievement for so large and complicated a shape.

When completed in the boiler shop, the boiler was merely a steel shell containing a copper firebox but no tubes or boiler mountings. The latter were fitted in the boiler mounting shop over a period of approximately 6 days. The tubes for this class of boiler were nearly 20 feet long and approximately 3 000 feet of tubing were used. Steel and copper pipes for steam connections and boiler fittings accounted for a further 1 500 feet of tubing, making a total of almost one mile. The bedding-on of the boiler fittings took place simultaneously with tubing – the regulator was connected up as well as the water gauges, injector steam valves and whistle.

Finally the boiler had to undergo a thorough testing composed of a hydraulic test considerably above the normal working pressure and also two steam tests. The last stage in the boiler's progress to the erecting shop was completed when the lagging was fitted to prevent loss of heat from the boiler by radiation.

CYLINDERS AND FRAMES

Shortly after early operations had been started on the boiler, there was considerable activity in the foundries to produce the next largest components – cylinders – which were made of cast iron and resulted from the most skilful and delicate work by patternmaker, moulders and core makers alike. More than 120 intricate cores went into the making of a set of inside and outside cylinders which in the rough state weighed around 6 tons.

Frames were the foundation upon which the engine was built. Plates 1⅛″ thick were cut out to shape by burning with oxy-coal-gas blow pipes and were then machined on a massive slotting machine weighing almost 100 tons. All the necessary holes were then drilled, ready for riveting and bolting on the various horn cheeks, stretchers, motion plates, gussets and so on. The cylinders were bolted in position after first undergoing much patient boring to within fine limits, planing of the flat surfaces, drilling and tapping of the holes for studding on cylinder covers and testing with water to 250 pounds per square inch.

A special feature was the newly-developed application of welding which had partly superseded riveting and was used for fabricating frame stretchers and other parts and for reinforcing joints and splicings. Finally buffer planks and footplating were riveted on and the frame was placed on temporary wheels to be sent to the erecting shop for the major stages of assembling.

WHEELS AND AXLE-BOXES

Work in the steel foundry had meanwhile produced wheel centres from molten steel at a temperature of 1500° C. These castings were machined in the wheel shop and after the axles had been turned, including the crank axle which was built up from steel slabs and bars, the wheels were forced on to the axles hydraulically in a press capable of exerting more than 100 tons pressure. During these operations other machines were engaged on boring out the tyres. These were shrunk on by heating the tyre until it had expanded sufficiently to allow the wheel centre, which was kept cold, to slip in. For wheels of 6′-6″ diameter a difference of approximately $\frac{1}{16}$″ in diameter at normal temperature was allowed for shrinking on the tyre.

The final operation on the wheels was to turn the outside of the tyres and to fit the crank pins to carry the coupling rods. The machine shop had meanwhile been busy planing, shaping, drilling, metalling, turning and fitting up the axle-boxes so that they would be ready for bedding on to the axles as soon as the wheels were finished. Some of the experimental engines, including the Turbomotive, made use of roller bearing axle-boxes.

RODS AND MOTION

Many of these parts were forged under steam or drop hammers from various grades of steel according to the work which the component had to perform in service. The connecting rods which transmitted the power from cylinders to wheels were made considerably lighter by the use of special steel of high-tensile strength. As the four-cylinder arrangement required four sets of components per engine, the machine shop was working 24 hours a day on all the parts for pistons, valves, valve gear and rods. Most of these had to be machined all over, which involved the removal of a large amount of material by milling and planing operations.

Apart from the major components which were delivered to the erecting shop, there was also a very substantial amount of smaller work, equally important and proceeding simultaneously to a prepared timetable. The smithy was busy forging rivets, of which over 3 000 were used in the frames and 3 500 in the boiler for one engine. Thousands of bolts and nuts were forged and these, together with boiler stays, motion pins and washers, were constantly feeding automatic lathes. The brass foundry cast boiler fittings which in turn had to be machined, and valves fitted and tested for correct working. Hundreds of items were transported daily by motor scooters all over Crewe Works, which covered 137 acres.

ERECTION

Eventually the scheduled time arrived for the frames to be put down in the erecting shop. The foundation was tried over for alignment and adjusted as required; gradually items were fitted in position as they arrived – horn stays, slidebars, mechanical lubricators, pistons, valves and pipework of various kinds for steam and oil. The boiler, weighing 26 tons, was lowered into position with the smokebox, and further pipes and components were connected. The cab and chimney were positioned while the motion and valve gear was being fitted and tested.

On each of the later engines there were 56 points in the motion where needle roller bearings were utilised and were arranged for grease-gun lubrication. The final stage in erection was wheeling the engine, after which connecting rods were fitted, the valves were set and the coupling rods put on. The engine was then painted, lined, lettered and varnished.

TENDER

The engine was by this time almost ready for the road, and in similar manner to the erecting shop process the organisation was such as to ensure that a tender was completed at the right time to couple to the engine. The tender shop was also the focal centre for all the tender material and components produced in many other shops during the immediately preceding months.

WEIGHING AND TESTING

After assembling the engine and tender complete, it was important to check over the weight on each wheel by means of a specially constructed weighbridge to ensure that the weight was distributed correctly. The total weight of these engines in working order was 105 tons and the tender 50 tons, with 9 tons of coal and 4 000 gallons of water.

The engine was then fired up and a very thorough examination made to test the working of valves and gauges, the soundness of joints, the operation of the brake gear, sanding, lubrication and injectors; also the whistle, regulator, reversing gear, water pick-up gear and many other items. Finally the engine was taken for trial runs at various speeds. As soon as any necessary adjustments had been made the Motive Power Department took over for running-in on local trains and eventually put the engine into service on the traffic for which it was designed.

So another of the largest engines was completed by the united efforts of a large force of men spread over many months. As diesel and electric locomotives came to displace the steam locomotive throughout British Railways, No. 6200 'Princess Royal', built in 1933, was broken up in 1962 with 1 568 808 miles to its credit.

8 Works Organisation and Management

In the days of George Stephenson the railway workshops were no different from most if not all other engineering workshops. Apart from the designers no specialist engineers were employed. Machines and equipment were mostly of a very simple character and a high proportion of hand work was involved. The key man was the foreman, or workshop supervisor, on the shop floor, essentially a practical man whose main function was to hand out work in the order he thought fit, to say how it should be done and to see that his staff produced what was required.

Prior to the 1923 amalgamation of the railways, there were 120 independent railway companies – some of which were already amalgamated companies – each of which had gone its own way in every sense of the term. The major railway companies built their own works, initially for the maintenance of their stock but subsequently for new building also. Not unnaturally, those railway engineers who decided to build a main works planned it in conformity with their own ideas, and one can assume that in those pioneering days each works organisation followed a different path influenced mainly by the Locomotive Superintendent, the predecessor of the Chief Mechanical Engineer, who was in charge of design and all the new construction and repair work involved.

Broadly the workshop organisations remained relatively simple in character and the workshop supervisors in each of their respective departments remained the key men and reported directly to the Works Manager or Locomotive Superintendent. There is evidence that by the turn of the century some of the Works Managers were beginning to develop their organisation by introducing various simple documents in order to exercise a measure of control over the materials required and, in some instances, of the wages to be paid, especially important if an incentive scheme was being introduced.

After 1923 each of the CMEs of the four great companies had several main works to control, and they made changes in the works organisation to the extent which they considered desirable in the interests of their own company. Three of the four companies had one basic feature in common right up to nationalisation in 1948. They relied mainly on their workshop supervisors to carry out all the planning required, with a number of relatively junior technical staff in the Works Manager's office to assist them; in the case of the LNER these were mostly wages staff. In contrast the LMS had introduced before the second world war a standard functional type of works organisation in each of its locomotive and carriage and wagon works. All the planning for new manufacture was undertaken in the production planning office which operated at each LMS works. This relieved the workshop supervisory staff of

116

time-consuming office work and gave them the opportunity to spend much-needed time with their productive staff on the shop floor.

Different practices were in operation for the employment of Initial Examiners and Finished Work Inspectors in the four group companies. On the LNER and SR those two grades were responsible to the foremen, as were the Shop Inspectors on the GWR. Initial Examiners on the GWR and Initial Examiners and Finished Work Inspectors on the LMS did not come under the jurisdiction of the foremen. The piecework checkers on the LNER were selected craftsmen who remained wages grade staff.

Within the first weeks of nationalisation the Railway Executive appointed two policy committees and they were followed by several others totalling nearly twenty over a period of a few years. These committees consisted of senior railway officers drawn from the Mechanical and Electrical Engineering and Carriage and Wagon Departments. Some members came from Regional HQ whilst others were Works Managers and specialist engineers, according to the nature of the survey to be undertaken. All the committees were differently constituted but, exceptionally, seven served under the same chairman (E. J. Larkin). The Productive Efficiency Committee was full-time except for the chairman. Its wide-ranging investigations, covering all the main works, extended over a year but pointed the way to many substantial cost-saving improvements, including transfers between works in the manufacture of components.

These all-region committees had an impact on various facets of policy and organisation, an overall development which was not possible in the former privately-owned railway companies. At that period there were 18 main locomotive works employing a total staff of 39 787 and 21 main carriage & wagon works employing 33 604 staff, a total of 73 391 railway shopmen in the 39 main works. There were also 17 460 staff employed in the outdoor C&W depots, which formed an integral part of the C&W Department but were not under the jurisdiction of the Works Managers. Figures 8.1 and 8.2 show staffing levels at the time of nationalisation.

In 1962, 14 years after nationalisation, the BR Board decided to transfer control of all the main works from the six regions (later reformed into five regions) to a central authority known as the British Railways Workshops Division (see Fig. 8.3). Sir Steuart Mitchell, a member of the Railways Board who later became Vice-Chairman under Dr Beeching, carried out a comprehensive survey of all the works and recommended that only sixteen should be retained, following rationalisation on an unrestricted scale. The first General Manager of the newly-formed Workshops Division was brought in from outside the railway service.

A significant feature of this new organisation was the inclusion of the Works Accountant and the Supplies Officer located at each works under the jurisdiction of the Works Manager. Each senior member of the management staff at the Derby HQ of the Workshops Division was given clearly-defined areas of responsibility to ensure that the professional and technical staff, as

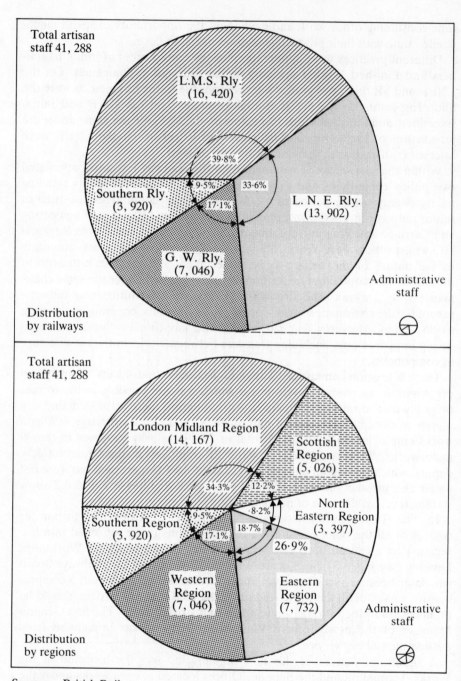

SOURCE   British Rail

FIGURE 8.1   *Distribution of main works artisan staff by former main-line companies and by regions, 1948*

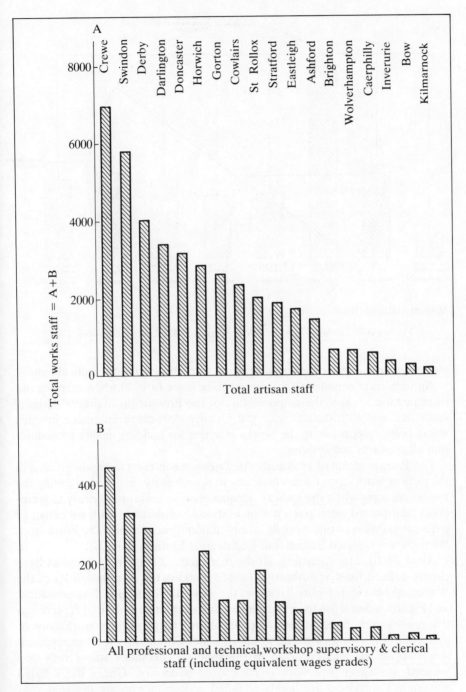

Source   British Rail

Figure 8.2   *Staff of the main locomotive works, in order of total artisan staff, 1948*

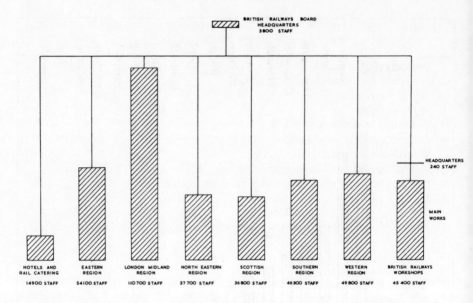

Source   British Rail

Figure 8.3   *Relative sizes of BR regions and Workshops Division, 1965*

well as those who were dealing with them, were directed to the right channels.

An important organisational change took place in 1980 when carrying out of inspection became the responsibility of the Production Manager. Quality assurance was introduced, with the Quality Assurance Engineer in each works being responsible to the Works Manager for building quality procedures into all products and systems.

The Transport Act of 1968 authorised outside contracts to be undertaken in the railway workshops for the first time in their history, apart from during the two world wars when the railway companies were under temporary Government control and were given a dispensation to undertake work on behalf of overseas railways or other organisations at home and abroad. The Workshops Division was restyled British Rail Engineering Limited (BREL).

As at BREL Headquarters, all the management staff in each works have clearly defined lines of authority. Table 8.1 shows the responsibilities of the Workshop Manager. Figure 8.4 shows the well-established BREL organisation, and Figures 8.5 and 8.6 the management and shop organisation of representative main works. Shop Superintendents are in charge of large workshops or more than one workshop; the grade of Chief Foreman is used in medium-sized workshops and Foreman in the smaller workshops where only one salaried workshop supervisor is considered necessary. Under the salaried workshop supervisors are highly qualified craftsmen who are designated as chargehands, each chargehand controlling a group of men, the number varying according to the volume and class of work involved.

TABLE 8.1   *Control functions common to all Works Managers in each main works within BREL*

1. Production Manager
2. Personnel and Administration Assistant
3. Works Accountant
4. Supplies Officer
5. Workshop supervisory staff
6. General works clerical matters
7. Workshop clerical staff
8. Estimating and control of expenditure
9. Detailed planning of manufacturing methods (materials and wages)
10. Jig and tool design and control
11. Issuing wages and material documents
12. Progressing manufacture of new locomotives, rolling stock and components
13. Progressing repair of locomotives and rolling stock
14. Progressing repair of locomotives and rolling stock components received from Motive Power Depots and Outstations
15. Examination before repair of locomotives, power units, rolling stock and components
16. Inspection of partly finished and completed work
17. Setting of standard times for payment by results
18. Authorising payment of wages for work done
19. Improvement in productivity
20. Installing and maintaining works machinery and plant
21. Workshop expenses
22. Control of works metallurgical matters
23. Control of works fuel efficiency matters
24. Control of internal transport
25. Training of graduate pupils, apprentices and all other grades
26. Safety standards
27. Statistical records directly connected with locomotive and carriage and wagon building and repairing

A major development in workshops headquarters organisation took place in 1984, when the BR Board decided to transfer all detailed design work to BREL. From the amalgamation of 1923 until nationalisation in 1948 design was the responsibility of the four CMEs. After 1948 the responsibility for design was vested in the Railway Executive and design and development staff transferred to the Railway Technical Centre, Derby. In 1962 design responsibility went to the British Railways Board, which assigned the function to its Chief Mechanical and Electrical Engineer, subsequently redesignated as Director of Mechanical and Electrical Engineering. The major development of 1984 involved two new fundamental principles:

(1) Fully competitive purchase of all future traction and rolling stock for use on BR, including a competitive commercial BREL which must be able to

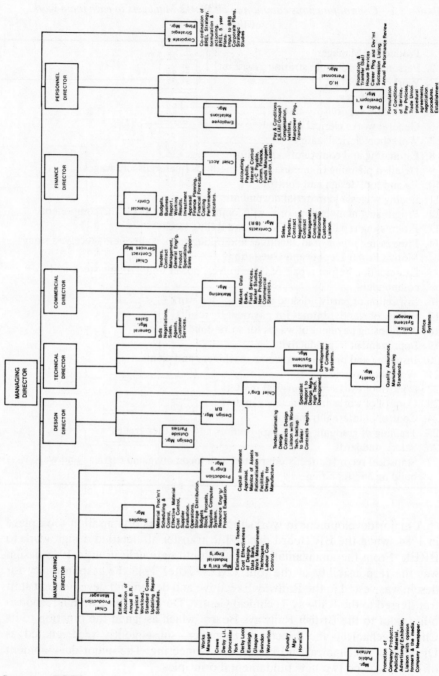

Source   BREL

Figure 8.4   *Management structure of BREL, 1984*

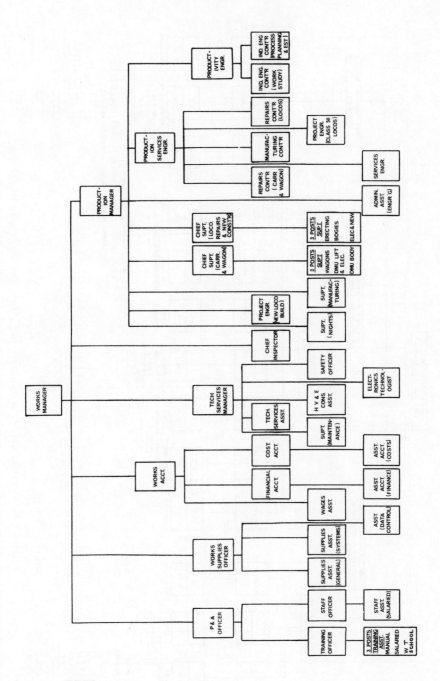

SOURCE   BREL

FIGURE 8.5   *Representative works organisation: Doncaster, 1981*

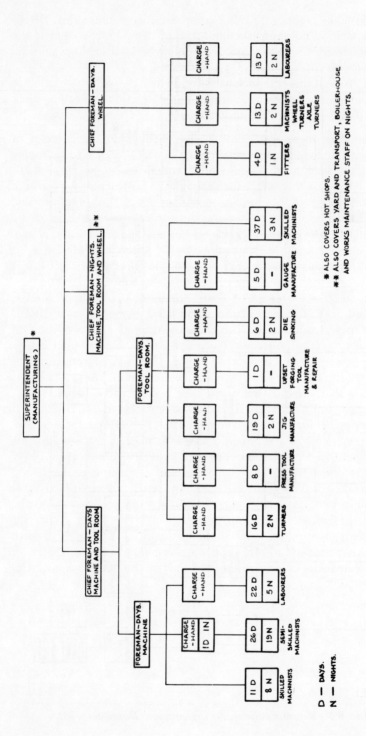

SOURCE BREL

FIGURE 8.6   *Organisation of the manufacturing shops, Shildon Wagon Works, 1983*

compete on equal terms with other companies. To achieve this, BREL must be capable in new construction terms of being independent of the Director of M&EE and all the necessary commercial disciplines must be seen to be observed;

(2) For BREL to fulfil this role, it must have its own design organisation in order to compete for design and construction of traction and rolling stock for both BR and any other administration.

The interpretation of these two principles has meant that the Director of M&EE is responsible for the conceptual design of a new vehicle to a strongly business-orientated specification. This leads, through an engineering specification, to the letting of a contract for design and construction with all the ramifications of strong contractual management which this implies. The Director of M&EE no longer does any production design or issues working drawings to BREL. Development work on designs and modifications in a post-warranty situation continues to be done by the Director of M&EE.

The effect of the changes on the manpower of the Director of M&EE was that about 200 staff, mainly drawing office staff who were engaged on production design, were transferred to BREL; and the Director of M&EE relinquished a number of senior engineers who filled the new posts in BREL to manage the new organisation. The changes resulted in the transfer of BREL Headquarters from the Railway Technical Centre, Derby, to St Peter's House, Gower Street, Derby, in order to provide increased accommodation. The advantage of the changes in a highly business-orientated railway scene is that they serve to sharpen up BREL's approach to costs and delivery.

It was announced in 1986 that BREL would be reorganised into two distinct business groups. The first group, comprising Crewe, Derby Locomotive, Derby Carriage and York Works, would concentrate on the aspects of business relating to competitive tendering for construction of new rolling stock, heavy overhaul and refurbishment. The second group, consisting of Eastleigh, Wolverton and Glasgow Works, together with the remaining repair activity at Doncaster, would undertake the lighter overhaul work in response to the maintenance requirements of the operating railway. This latter group was subsequently segregated into a separate subsidiary of the BR Board, known as British Rail Maintenance Ltd, whilst the wagon building facility at Doncaster was sold to a management consortium and operates under the name RFS Industries.

9 Production Planning and Control

The primary objectives of the main works of British Railways are to provide facilities and resources for the construction and repair of BR locomotives and rolling stock fleets at minimum cost, in accordance with quality assurance standards and specifications set by the Director of Mechanical and Electrical Engineering. Where manufacturing capacity surplus to the needs of these primary activities can be identified, it is a secondary aim of BREL to optimise the use of such resources by engaging in profitable private-party and export work. Miscellaneous work is also undertaken for all departments of BR, including such major items as the repair of mobile breakdown cranes.

At nationalisation in 1948 BR inherited 20 024 steam locomotives comprising 448 classes. There was great scope for rationalisation and this was effectively pursued by R. A. Riddles, who introduced twelve new classes of steam locomotives designed to run 100 000 miles between general repairs.

REPAIRS PROCEDURE

By far the greatest workload undertaken by BREL is the repair of locomotives, motive power units and rolling stock. In terms of man-hours and wages paid this commitment represents some 75 per cent of the staff employed in the main works, and the work undertaken in most of the works is entirely devoted to repairs. There is no comparable engineering organisation in Britain with the same expertise, and it is appropriate to consider the repair system first.

The statistics available for judging the efficiency of workshop organisation for the maintenance of stock can be shown under six main headings:

(1) Number and percentage of locomotives, carriages and wagons undergoing and awaiting repairs;
(2) Number of days on works under repairs;
(3) Number of days out of traffic for repairs;
(4) Mileage run related to classified repairs carried out and costs per mile;
(5) Number and percentage of casual repairs in relation to classified heavy repairs;
(6) Number of mechanical failures in service in relation to mileage run and costs incurred.

Economy and efficiency in the maintenance of locomotives and rolling stock of every type is always a matter of the greatest importance in the contribution

126

which the workshops make to the successful and efficient running of BR. There is no limit to the improvements which can be made, and no better index than costs per mile. Improved productivity is the measure of output per man-hour and must always be the watchword – as distinct from higher production, which is obtained by capital expenditure or more man-hours.

The shopping procedure for diesel-electric locomotives is organised on the unit exchange system of repair adopted by the Workshops Division and continued by BREL. A locomotive is considered for shopping purposes as comprising four distinct major units, namely: engine and generator, bogies, body and its auxiliaries, and steam generator. The period between each class of repair on each of these four units at each shopping of the locomotive is used as a separate standing order.

Procedure for locomotives requiring classified repairs

At the begining of each year a statement is compiled by the Shopping Bureau at each Regional HQ and issued to each Divisional Maintenance Engineer as well as to Regional Control, indicating the month that locomotives will be due for classified repair during the year and the class of repair which will be given to the body.

Six to eight weeks in advance of the date shown for each locomotive the Shopping Controller submits to the relevant Divisional Maintenance Engineer six copies of the shopping proposal report (BR 9419/3) showing against each major unit the abbreviation 'L', 'I' or 'G', indicating whether the unit is due for light, intermediate or general repair. The Divisional Maintenance Engineer arranges for the locomotive to be specially examined and indicates on the shopping proposal report the additional work which he considers should be carried out by the workshops when the locomotive is shopped. Five copies of the shopping proposal forms must then be returned by the Divisional Maintenance Engineer to the Shopping Controller within three weeks of receipt. The Shopping Controller considers the additional work requested and indicates his decision on the shopping reports. The five reports are then distributed as follows: one to the Mechanical and Electrical Engineer's Chief Inspector, one to the maintaining Works Manager, one retained in the Shopping Bureau and two returned to the Divisional Maintenance Engineer: one for his retention and one for reference at the depot (see Figs 9.1 and 9.2).

When these reports have been distributed the locomotives are 'in the pool' for workshops attention. Telephone contact is made weekly between the Shopping Controller and the Divisional Office or Central Maintenance Control to agree the date on which the locomotives will be required at the main works. Regional Maintenance Control makes the necessary arrangements for the movement of such locomotives to ensure their arrival on main works at the agreed time.

BRITISH RAILWAYS BOARD

SHOPPING PROPOSAL: LOCOMOTIVE–HAULED COACHING AND DIESEL RAILCAR STOCK

Region .... Depot .... Vehicle No..............
Date .... Parent Region .... Code ....
Where detained .... Date stopped ....

Build Particulars			Last Repair		Last Lifting		Shopping Proposal Date
Year	Works Built	Lot No.	Date	Classification	Date	Works No.	

WHEELS

Wear on tyre treads .... Condition of flanges .... Tyre thickness ......

GENERAL CONDITION

Brake equipment .... Body interior ....
Body exterior .... Trimmings:- First Class ....
Roof exterior .... Trimmings:-Second Class ....
Paintwork .... Heating equipment ....
Lighting equipment .... Lavatories ....
Damage (brief particulars) ....
Special defects ....
Reason for stopping ....

* I have stopped this vehicle for shop repairs.
* I have examined this vehicle and consider it fit to remain in service till .....
    * Cross out sentence not applicable.   Signed ....

FOR C.M.& E.E. USE ONLY

                            Week
To be sent to .... Commencing .... Repairs Required ....

To Shopping Bureau C.M.& E.E. Department .... Region	FOR WORKS USE Received .... Repairs given ...... Released .... Next due ....

....

BRITISH RAILWAYS BOARD

Vehicle No. .... Code ....
The above vehicle was despatched to .... Works.
On .... (date)
To Shopping Bureau
C.M.& E.E. Department
.... Region
....
....

BRITISH RAILWAYS BOARD

Vehicle No. .... Code ....
The above vehicle has been agreed for .... Works.
Please arrange for it to be labelled forthwith,
To Div. Mtce. Eng. (C&W)
.... Region.   Signed ....
.... Depot.   For C.M.& E.E. ....

SOURCE   British Rail

FIGURE 9.1   *Shopping proposal for locomotive-hauled coaching and diesel railcar stock*

BRITISH RAILWAYS BOARD

SHOPPING PROPOSAL: ELECTRIC MULTIPLE UNIT STOCK

Region..................... Depot..................... Vehicle No...............

Date...................... Unit No................ Description................

Where detained.................................... Date stopped...............

Build Particulars			Last Repair		Last Lifting	
Year	Works	Lot No.	Date	Classification	Date	Works/Depot

WHEELS	No.1		No.2		No.3		No.4		Last Turning
Wear	L	R	L	R	L	R	L	R	Date
TYRES									
FLANGE									
TYRE THICKNESS									

GENERAL CONDITION   MECHANICAL PARTS & COACHWORK

Brake equipment ....   Body interior ....

Body exterior ....   Trimmings:- First Class ....

Roof exterior ....   Trimmings:-Second Class ....

Paintwork ....   Heating equipment ....

Lighting equipment ....   Lavatories ....

Damage (brief particulars) ....

Special defects ....

ELECTRICAL EQUIPMENT

Collector gear ....   Motor generator sets ....
Air blast circuit breaker ....   Aux. compressor ....
Potential measuring device ....   Main compressor ....
H.T. Cable ....   Heating equipment ....
A.W.S. & A.P.C. equipment ....   Lighting equipment ....
Earthing switch ....   Battery ....
Transformer chokes ....   Battery charger ....
Transformer radiator ....   Transformer oil ....
Traction motors ....   E.P. brake equipment ....
Resistances ....   Jumper gear ....
Power equipment ....   Wiring ....
Control equipment ....
Oil pump ....   Special items ....
Fan motors ....

This vehicle requires Main Works attention for a Class .... Repair. To be sent to .... Works. Week commencing .... Signed .... for C.M.& E.E. .... Region.	FOR WORKS USE Received .... Repairs given .... Released ....

To E.T.E..............................   Depot............................Region.
Vehicle No...........................   Description............................
The above repairs have been carried out at .... Works. Date.......

Signed for Main Works ....
Signed for C.M.& E.E. ....

SOURCE   British Rail

FIGURE 9.2   *Shopping proposal for electric multiple unit stock*

The target number of days on works for a classified repair varies according to the class of engine, and the technique of network analysis makes a major contribution to determining this (see Figure 9.3).

Procedure for serviceable locomotives requiring unclassified repairs

When it is considered that a locomotive will not be able to continue to run until its normal classified repair, the Divisional Maintenance Engineer forwards five copies of the shopping proposal marked 'Special' to the Shopping Controller, detailing the nature of the defect.

The Shopping Controller then decides whether the locomotive shall be repaired in one of the regional maintenance depots, or receive main works attention.

In the first case the arrangements are made by liaison between the Shopping Controller and Regional Maintenance Control. In the second case the Shopping Controller endorses the shopping proposal, indicating what action shall be taken, and distributes the five copies as outlined above for classified repairs. The call of the locomotive to main works is agreed between the Shopping Controller and Regional Maintenance Control, which is responsible for ensuring that the locomotive arrives on main works at the agreed time. Regional Maintenance Control confers with the respective Divisional Maintenance Controls for movement to depot or main works for repair, whichever is applicable.

Inspection and classification

The inspectors in the works who carry out initial examination and finished work inspection are independent of the workshop supervisory staff. These inspectors authorise the work to be carried out by filling up pre-printed forms and then certifying that the work has been completed to the required standards. No single item is omitted. These same forms are then passed forward to the Works Accountant authorising payment to the men concerned. The forms serve a double purpose, indicating what work has been done and acting as a wages ticket.

Prior to the nationalisation of British Railways each of the four owning companies had different methods of classifying repairs. For example, soon after nationalisation the newly-appointed Railway Executive standardised the repair coding for carriages under ten separate headings, in descending order of the volume of work to be carried out. In recent years the carriage classifications have been reduced to six. All these codings were designed to maintain the rolling stock to a high standard when the vehicle was returned to service.

For wagon repairs there are only two classifications, namely heavy and light. Heavy repairs include lifting the vehicle, giving the body and underframe all the attention necessary, overhauling brakes and other fittings, as

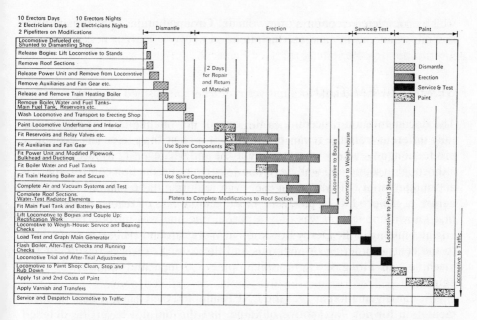

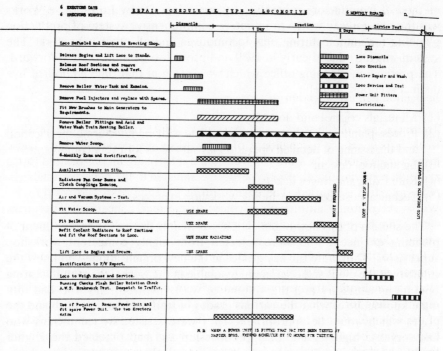

SOURCE   British Rail

FIGURE 9.3   *Overhaul schedules for Type 2 diesel-electric locomotive and EE Type 5 locomotive*

well as completely repainting the vehicle. Grouped under light repairs were any miscellaneous items requiring attention.

NEW MANUFACTURE

The documentation procedure in the case of new manufacture is fundamentally different from the repair procedure. It is clear that, to ensure economic production, any factory wherever it may be and whatever it produces requires a thoroughly sound and well-developed system of production control; there is an infinite variety of systems in use, each requiring to be tailored to suit the nature of the product or products. In the main works of British Railways the first known application was only a partial one and was introduced for new engine building in the Derby Locomotive Works around 1900. It was confined to the central ordering of materials and the issuing of wages tickets for the machine and fitting shop, in which some 800 men and apprentices were employed.

After amalgamation in 1923 the LNER adopted the Ormig system of documentation for new locomotive building, but this did not cover the detailed method of manufacture, operation by operation. Derby Locomotive Works was the first railway works to initiate a comprehensive system of production planning for manufacturing new locomotives and all other new work. The system was introduced early in 1939 and proved to be a major step forward. The production planning office which was set up at that time embodied five distinct sections, namely:

(1) Materials control and documentation;
(2) Process planning of manufacture, complete with manufacturing specification and the issuing of detailed operation layout sheets for every component;
(3) Jig and tool design;
(4) Rate fixing and wages tickets;
(5) Technical costs control including workshop expenses.

The success of this new organisation was mainly due to the appointment of planning engineers who were selected from highly competent workshop supervisors. They were the key grades in the new organisation, who knew the capacity of the plant and equipment available in the works, the manufacturing operations necessary and the volume of work involved, and who had intimate knowledge of what the various grades of staff could accomplish and the prices which would be appropriate. They were assisted by technicians who had served a higher grade of apprenticeship and had obtained the Higher National Certificate. The scheme, embracing all the relevant working drawings and documentation needed, was readily accepted by the workshop supervisory staff, who were relieved of much office work, and within a relatively short time the new system covered every item to be manufactured.

To assist in its acceptance the LMS in 1939 produced a film on production planning which was shown to all the staff at the various LMS main works and was well received. Over the next few years the system was extended, with beneficial results to all the LMS works, and it was in full operation by the time the railways were nationalised in 1948. When the BR Workshops Division came into being in 1962 the opportunity was taken to review the LMS scheme and, with relatively minor amendments to some of the forms used, it was extended to the sixteen BR continuing works where any new manufacture was undertaken.

The aim of production planning is to co-ordinate all the activities of the manufacturing organisation in each works to achieve the most efficient and economical means of production. Production planning comprises the organisation, planning and checking of materials, methods of manufacture, tooling, operation times, the handling of materials, routing, scheduling and coordination of inspection, and it is designed to ensure that the supply and movement of materials, operations of labour, utilisation of machines and related activities of all the factory departments, however subdivided or specialised, can be controlled in such a manner as to bring about the desired manufacturing results in terms of quantity, quality, time, place and cost.

The system is applied to the construction of new locomotives and rolling stock, the modification of locomotives and rolling stock, and the manufacture of new stores stock and non-stock items. The procedure covers all documentation required in the works from the time the relevant drawings and specification are received and has superseded all previous instructions relating to production documentation.

In the early 1800s the drawings issued to the workshops were sparsely dimensioned and were little more than sketches as compared with the sophisticated working drawings of today. In those pioneering days an enormous amount of detail design was left to the discretion of the skilled craftsmen, whereas by contrast all the drawings issued nowadays for the manufacture of any component stipulate working tolerances to thousandths of an inch or centimetre. Interchangeability was never contemplated when the early railway workshops emerged, whereas now it is highly relevant.

All modifications to individual locomotives and rolling stock are carefully monitored and recorded in the Rolling Stock Library at Derby, a key office which maintains the official records of all the stock and comes under the jurisdiction of the Director of M&EE at BR Headquarters in London. It will be appreciated that many different forms are required. Examples of the more important are shown in Figure 9.4 and the part to which they relate in Figure 9.5. All have their particular function but the key form is the 'operation layout sheet' which, *inter alia*, defines in detail the materials required and the method of manufacture, including the basic standard time allowed for each separate operation.

The piecework system in all BR main works was gradually discontinued from 1969 and times introduced (Pay and Efficiency Agreement dated

FIGURE 9.4a   *Works documentation: Material Ordering Schedule and Manufacturing Specificication*

SOURCE   BREL

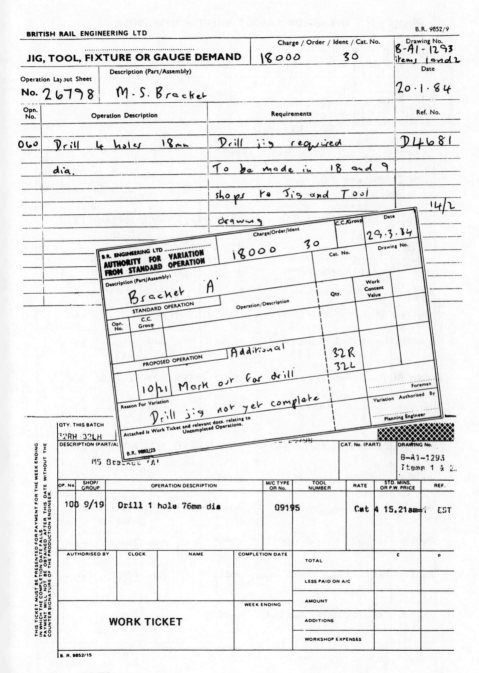

BRITISH RAIL ENGINEERING LTD

B.R. 9852/9

JIG, TOOL, FIXTURE OR GAUGE DEMAND

	Charge / Order / Ident / Cat. No.		Drawing No.
	18000	30	B-A1-1293 items 1 and 2

Operation Layout Sheet	Description (Part/Assembly)		Date
No. 26798	M.S. Bracket		20·1·84

Opn. No.	Operation Description	Requirements	Ref. No.
060	Drill 4 holes 18mm dia.	Drill jig required To be made in 18 and 9 shops to Jig and Tool drawing	D4681 14/2

B.R. ENGINEERING LTD ....

AUTHORITY FOR VARIATION FROM STANDARD OPERATION

	Charge/Order/Ident			C.C./Group	Date
	18000	30	Cat. No.	Drawing No.	29.3.84

Description (Part/Assembly)

Bracket 'A'

	STANDARD OPERATION	Operation/Description		Qty.	Work Content Value
Opn. No.	C.C. Group				

	PROPOSED OPERATION	Additional	32R 32L
	10/1	Mark out for drill	

Reason For Variation

Drill jig not yet complete

Attached is Work Ticket and relevant docs. relating to Uncompleted Operations.

Variation Authorised By .... Foreman

.... Planning Engineer

QTY. THIS BATCH						
32RH 32LH						

DESCRIPTION (PART/A....)

B.R. 9852/23

MS Bracket 'A'

		CAT. No. (PART)	DRAWING No.
			B-A1-1293 Items 1 & 2

OP. No.	SHOP/ GROUP	OPERATION DESCRIPTION	M/C TYPE OR No.	TOOL NUMBER	RATE	STD. MINS. OR P.W. PRICE	REF.
100	9/19	Drill 1 hole 76mm dia		09195	Cat 4	15.21 am=?	EST

AUTHORISED BY	CLOCK	NAME	COMPLETION DATE	TOTAL	£	p
				LESS PAID ON A/C		
			WEEK ENDING	AMOUNT		
WORK TICKET				ADDITIONS		
				WORKSHOP EXPENSES		

THIS TICKET MUST BE PRESENTED FOR PAYMENT FOR THE WEEK ENDING IN WHICH THE COMPLETION DATE FALLS. PAYMENT WILL NOT BE OBTAINED AFTER THIS DATE WITHOUT THE COUNTER SIGNATURE OF THE PRODUCTION ENGINEER.

B.R. 9852/15

SOURCE   BREL

FIGURE 9.4b   *Works documentation: Jig Demand, Authority for Variation and Work Ticket*

OPERATION LAYOUT SHEET – NEW WORK

BRITISH RAIL ENGINEERING LTD.

OPERATION No.	1	2	3	4	5		
COMMENCING DATE							
COMPLETION DATE							
OPERATION No.	6	7	8	9	10		
COMMENCING DATE							
COMPLETION DATE							

FINISHED DETAIL TO BE DELIVERED TO   18. SHOP.

QTY. THIS BATCH	BATCH No. OF	TOTAL QUANTITY	CHARGE/ORDER/IDENT		TOTAL QTY. (MATERIAL)	
32 RH '32 LH	1.	32 RH '32 LH	18000. —	30	4.	

DESCRIPTION (PART/ASSEMBLY)	CAT. No. (PART)	DRAWING No.	QTY. VEH.
M.S. BRACKET 'A'		B. A1. 1293	1.RH
		HAS. 1+2.	1.LH

DESCRIPTION (MATERIAL)	CAT. No. (MATERIAL)	SHOP
M.S. PLATE – 2500 × 1250 × 20. (BS. 4360 '43A)	12' 137700	18.

OP. NO.	SHOP/ GROUP	OPERATION DESCRIPTION	M/C TYPE OR No.	TOOL NUMBER	RATE	STD. MINS. OR P.W. PRICE	REF.	EST. TIME
A00		ISSUE MATERIAL.	—					
010	24'18	SHOT BLAST & PRIME	24018		CH+3.	C.N.R.		
020	18'6B	OP. CUT PROFILE.	18061	DP'TD. 4814	CAYH	12 MIN = 6	EST.	
030	18'3B	PUT IN PRESS BLOCKS (AS REQ'D).	18033		CAYH - 2	115 MIN = 1 S'U	EST	
040	18'3B	BEND AND SET.	18033	T.21389.	CAYH - 2	20 MIN = 6	EST.	
050	9'19	SET UP M'C (AS REQ'D)	09195.		CAYH	30 MIN = 1 S'U.	EST.	
060	9'19	DRILL – 4 HOLES 18 MM DIA	09195	D.4681	CAYH	6.21 WCM = 1	EST.	
070	9'19	INSPECT – 1ST OFF.	09195					
080	10'21	M.O. 76 MM DIA HOLE	10211		CAYH	5 MIN = 1 RH'1 LH	EST.	
090	9'19	SET UP M'C. (AS REQ'D)	09195		CAYH	30 MIN = 1 S'U.	EST.	
100	9'19	DRILL – 1 HOLE 76 MM DIA	09195		CAYH	15.21 SM = 1	EST.	
110	9'19	INSPECT – 1ST OFF AND INTO	09195					

OPERATION LAYOUT SHEET No.   26798

B.R. 9852/5

Source   BREL

Figure 9.4c   *Works documentation: Operation Layout Sheet*

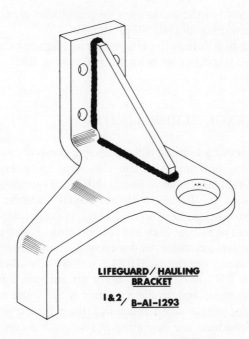

LIFEGUARD/ HAULING
BRACKET
1&2/ B-AI-1293

SOURCE   BREL

FIGURE 9.5   *Drawing no. B–A1–1293 of lifeguard/hauling bracket*

11 April 1969). The total time in which a task should be completed by a qualified worker at Standard Performance of 100 (BSI 3138) covers the basic time, plus allowances for contingencies which may arise, plus relaxation allowance. The last depends on the nature of the work and allows the operator some rest from the manual effort in carrying out the work: for example, a smith working at the anvil will require more relaxation than, say, an instrument maker, who can normally sit down to work. It also allows attention to personal needs. In contrast to the repairs procedure, all the documentation for new manufacture, including stock orders for manufacturing spare parts, emanates from the Production Office, a key office in every BR main works.

In 1982 BREL placed an order worth £2.5 million with ICL for a computer-based factory data collection and enquiry system. The first system was installed at Derby Locomotive Works early in 1982. It comprised a computer and associated peripherals connected to terminals throughout the works. Terminals record staff attendance and the progress of work, and more comprehensive enquiries can be pursued through visual display units and small printers in the offices. The new scheme gives supervisory and production staff a real-time system for minute-by-minute control and provides management with a more up-to-date picture at shop floor level than is possible by manual means. The whole system, which saves BREL some £3.5 million a year, supplements other computers used in the workshops for production planning and control, stock control, accounting and paybill production.

It is appropriate to conclude this chapter by highlighting the impressive role which BREL currently occupies as an integral part of BR.

BRITISH RAIL ENGINEERING LIMITED

British Rail Engineering Limited is the principal company manufacturing and maintaining railway equipment in the UK. Operating as a wholly-owned subsidiary of the British Railways Board, BREL is one of the largest engineering organisations in Britain, with an annual turnover exceeding £450 million and a 1986 workforce of some 23 000. It undertakes the overhaul of BR's extensive fleet of locomotives and rolling stock. It also produces most of BR's new locomotives, carriages and wagons and a growing range of equipment for other railway operators. BREL's unique manufacturing and maintenance role with BR enables it to obtain an unrivalled understanding of railway operators' needs and problems, a fact which more and more railway administrations appreciate when discussing their future requirements with BREL. BREL's products are operating in thirty-three countries on the five continents and its expanding product range is certain to increase interest in the company's quality equipment. A comprehensive product support capability is also available, covering field service, technical publications, customer training and the supply of a complete range of spares.

BREL enjoys the benefit of a very close liaison with BR's Research and Development Division – generally accepted as the most comprehensive and advanced technology unit in the railway world. Both headquarters are based in Derby and their special relationship ensures that BREL's customers have the benefit of the latest technological advances and most cost-effective design built into its products. (For an indication of costs see Figure 9.6.) It is from the concepts of BR scientists and designers that BREL has produced the latest range of railway equipment, which maintains BR's prominent position in the railway world.

Diesel and electric multiple units play a vital role in the operation of the world's railways. In Britain the multiple-unit concept is used extensively on rural, suburban and commuter routes, and BREL has supplied a new generation of electric, diesel and diesel-electric vehicles. The company has recently extended its diesel unit product range by developing two new vehicles to meet the economic demands of feeder services. These vehicles combine excellent riding qualities with low-cost efficient rail travel.

BREL is responsible for the manufacture and overhaul of the thousands of passenger coaches that operate on BR every day. Major advances in design and technology have enabled the company to produce the Mark III coach used on all BR's 125 m.p.h. trains, which have so revolutionised inter-city rail

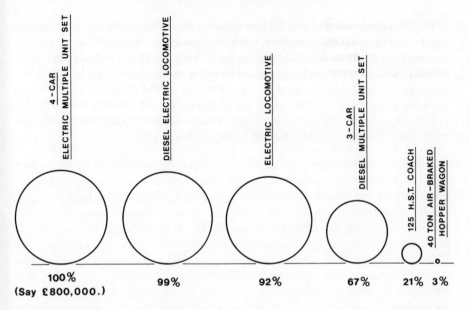

SOURCE BREL

FIGURE 9.6 *Approximate building costs, 1982, expressed as percentages of a 4-car electric multiple unit set*

travel in Britain. The successful Mark III coach has also been adapted to secure major export contracts.

BREL is the principal manufacturer of wagons in the UK. Its products include more than 10 000 high-capacity coal wagons which transport the bulk of Britain's coal from colliery to power station by the famous 'merry-go-round' system. BREL has made a major contribution to the productivity of BR's freight operations through the supply of more than 20 000 modern air-brake wagons. In recent years BREL has also supplied over 2000 wagons to railway operators in four countries. Of particular benefit to railway operators with a high proportion of curved track is the company's cross-braced self-steering freight bogie, and orders have been received from at least three countries for this equipment.

BREL's facilities are so comprehensive that there are few manufacturing operations which cannot be undertaken somewhere within the company. Consistent investment has also ensured that BREL has kept pace with the latest developments in production technology, and the company makes full use of modern computer-based techniques in design and manufacture, ensuring control of manufacturing costs, materials, management and work scheduling systems. The policy of training its own engineers and craftsmen ensures that BREL's skills are ideally matched to its construction and overhaul requirements.

BREL's expertise and production capacity are extensively employed in the highly demanding sub-contract market. Spares, components and general engineering equipment are supplied to a wide range of railway and non-railway customers. Vehicle suspensions, lifting frames, castings, fabrications, forgings and rail point clamp locks are some of the products supplied. A growing number of customers in many industries are finding that BREL's combination of traditional standards with modern production techniques provides value-for-money products of the highest quality.

10 Quality Assurance

Systems of quality control within general engineering practice are very much a twentieth-century development, gaining impetus in the second world war, yet only developing and coming into universal use recently. Pressure for improved quality and reliability appeared in the early years of the railways when locomotives were bought from contractors such as Robert Stephenson & Co., the Vulcan Foundry and Nasmyth, Gaskell & Co. The GWR and GJR (Grand Junction Rly) had similar experiences almost simultaneously: varieties of locomotives from different builders had high failure rates, particularly with crankshafts. These problems led to locomotive design and construction facilities being set up within the railways' own organisations at Crewe and Swindon. At Swindon Gooch produced lithographed detailed drawings, specifications and iron templates to send to contractors who built locomotives or supplied castings, forgings and other major components.

A few years later John Ramsbottom of the LNWR was sending standard patterns and gauges to contractors to ensure 'interchangeability of parts', although this was far removed from the modern meaning of the term. For example, centre-to-centre distances for connecting and coupling rods were not marked on Crewe drawings until 1859. Prior to this – and probably after – the finished machine rods went to the smithy to be 'jumped or lengthened' to fit the actual distances between wheel centres on locomotives being built.

Even if the interchangeability and reliability of components exercised the chief engineers in the 1840s to 1860s, there was little of the organisation which began to flourish 100 years later, such as finished work inspectors. The practice in most railway works – and probably at their main suppliers – was for each locomotive to be erected by small groups of men – normally one skilled man with perhaps an apprentice and a labourer or fitter's mate. This craftsman was held responsible for quality and, although dependent upon turners and machine operators for many components, he was in a strong position to object if defective material was supplied to 'his' locomotive. The arrangements were similar for repairs. For carriages and wagons it was much simpler: more men could work on a vehicle without getting in each other's way, and oversight of the finished product was simple for the chargehand or foreman to maintain. It was unusual for any progression to occur until after wheeling, so small groups could concentrate upon one vehicle at a time within their own area.

The lack of a good standard of interchangeability of components favoured the static repair position, particularly for locomotives. At the time of repairs large quantities of bolts, nuts, pins and brackets were kept in the pit marked for re-use so that no fresh fitting would be needed. With no guaranteed standard of reference sizes, or means of accurate measurement, there were no established standards of stepped sizes for worn components. Axle-boxes would be bored and then scraped to fit a specific journal; the brasses for the big ends of a connecting rod would need careful and tight fitting to the rod, and would be bored or scraped to fit the journal. If this was not done correctly the bearings overheated or a 'knock' was heard when the locomotive ran trial; the fitter, who attended the trial, would have no excuse for any failure.

The problem of accurate measurement and reproducible manufacture was not peculiar to the railway industry. Up to 1860 there were few measuring aids. Manufacturers like Maudslay and his former employee Joseph Whitworth devised their own forms and standards of screw threads for nuts and bolts. Many other firms with less experience made their own taps, adjusting their bolt threads to fit the nuts they had tapped. This lack of interchangeability between firms' products was apparent on all types of purchased vehicle. It was not until Whitworth's paper to the Institution of Civil Engineers in 1841 that a rational, universal system of screw threads and sizes was proposed. This covered the usual fractional British sizes in $^1/_{16}''$ steps for the smaller sizes, and a range of decimal sizes. More significantly it suggested that components in common use should be made to fit a *gauge*, not another component.

The inch was so ingrained in common thinking that the decimal idea had little support. The railways and the Royal Navy, however, were amongst the first organisations to adopt the new proposals; industry in general was slow to fall into line. Ten years later Whitworth had made his 'Millionth of an Inch Measuring Machine', but it was not until 1870 that it was known that John Fernie was using one at Derby Locomotive Works to manufacture gauges and templates based upon the Whitworth principles. This machine had a lengthened bed and could be used to measure bars up to an overall length of 100 inches. At Crewe a portable comparator measuring device also made by Whitworth, to a patent of James Cocker of Liverpool, was discovered recently. It measures material up to 2 inches in one-thousandth inch steps. Numbered 117, it is similar to one in the Science Museum dated 1857, and it may be that J. Ramsbottom introduced it at Crewe soon after taking charge in 1857.

Once a number of standard gauges were available skilled craftsmen using callipers could compare the size of a component to a standard with considerable accuracy. Not all gauges were prepared strictly to standard fractional sizes; for instance, rolled bar, like plate, was always supplied large by the contractors from a minimum of about $^1/_{32}''$ up to almost $^1/_{16}''$. It was thus difficult to thread a bar using solid dies and so the usual rolling size was chosen, from which basis the screw dies were made, and corresponding taps to a suitable oversize. Clearly the standards chosen by each works could differ. This variation was of no importance until with changes of policy, particularly amalgamations or rationalisation, locomotives were repaired at works other than their normal works.

The machining of wheels and axles to give interference of known amount also presented problems: there were no actual standard bores in wheels – they were only nominal. Therefore sizes were taken using callipers, the fit allowance (interference) was allowed for by some means and fresh callipers were set for the axle size required. To make this more difficult, early machines were ill-designed to take fine cuts or maintain a constant size. It needs little imagination to see the sort of fits resulting, all the more when a slight 'doctoring' of a surface could achieve the desired fit, aided by the choice of lubricant for the squeezing-in process. The declared aim was to achieve not less than 0.005" interference. In another procedure involved in the manufacture and repair of steam engine motion parts a single pin had to pass through and operate within a series of common brass-bushed holes. A long reamer, very finely tapered to parallel, was carefully worked through the whole assembly to match the pin, giving a close working fit, a procedure which was conceivably never surpassed.

In 1822 in America Eli Whitney is said to have made large savings by insisting upon complete interchangeability in manufacturing small arms, but as late as 1864 the US Car Builders Association reported on the diversity of screw threads in use. As a result the USA adopted the Sellars thread system, considered easier to produce than the Whitworth type, which remained the British standard until the publication of the International Standards Organisation data almost ninety years later. The US Car Builders Association also drew up a table for 'limit gauge' dimensions, and in 1883 Pratt & Whitney produced double-ended gap and stepped plug gauges to suit – the first record of limit gauges used to control the vital sizes of components. In 1901 the Engineering Standards Committee was set up in Britain but before it could report on a system of limits and fits John Walker Newall published a set of standard tables of limits, providing for force and three grades of running fits, the basis for this set of standards being the 'hole'.

Over the years most railway works developed their own sets of standard fixed gauges dominated by the plug and the ring gauge, available to the production shops from the toolroom stores. When special measurements were needed components were taken to the tool or gauge room for checking by micrometer equipment. The well-known hand micrometer was first made by L. S. Starrett to the 'Palmer' design in about 1870 in the USA but it did not become a general tool for use in the workshops until the first world war.

The advantages of the Newall system were taken up at the L&YR's Horwich Works, by examining all components for new work and repairs to establish the tolerable and desirable sizes to be achieved during their manufacture. Drawings were suitably endorsed and a comprehensive set of gauges provided for all the L&YR locomotives and rolling stock, starting in about 1920. This development was so important to the whole industry that it is worth describing in detail.

The fund of experience available to designers, workshop supervisors and running maintenance engineers was directed to establishing the most desirable 'fit' that should exist between any two members, in accordance with size, function, efficiency, cost and permissible tolerances. The 'hole' was adopted as the standard and the fit allowance allocated to the 'shaft'. Many component holes were made by circular tools, such as drills and reamers, each subject to wear, so the distribution of tolerances was allocated as two-thirds to the hole, prolonging tool life. Tolerances were defined as 'high' or 'low' acceptable dimensions, measurable by 'Go' or 'Not-go' gauges available for use on the shop floor. Gauges were made for each case, with job identification and gauging dimensions stamped upon them. They were made in the tool-room to tolerances of 10% of the total allowable, applied as a minus for high and a plus for low dimensions. The system was extended to include acceptable progressive repair sizes. For three classes of locomotive 2000 gauges were needed. Following the 1923 amalgamation the Horwich scheme was adopted by all LMS main works, though the changes were tardily accepted in the early stages.

In 1924 BS 164 was issued, closely resembling the Horwich system, but including a more comprehensive set of sizes. Twenty years later an LMS committee recommended adopting the Horwich scheme, expanded to include a wide range of renewable bushes and 'transition' or push fits. It took some years to complete the study, amend the drawings and make or purchase the gauges. At Crewe Locomotive Works alone some 11 000 gauges were needed, mainly of the limit type, which included about 6 per cent of 'specials'. After nationalisation the system became standard for all BR workshops, including the preparation of drawings showing the degree of fit required.

During the first world war most of the workshops, assisting in the war effort, had acquired sets of the Johansson gauge blocks, invaluable for checking standard measuring instruments. During 1918 Zeiss received orders for a total of 10 000 micrometers and similar instruments, followed two years later with the Optimeter for gauge inspection and three years after this with the Interferometer to compare works gauge-blocks with the Johansson standards. The principal toolrooms of the railway works were provided with these, and during the second world war a large staff was allocated to assist. With the introduction of the Aeronautical Inspection Directorate (AID) pressure was put on the works to provide more accurate measuring equipment, including optical devices on jig borers, and to replace visual comparators with the new Talysurf surface-textured measuring instruments. The use of Matrix thread-grinding machines was also supplemented for the production of all forms of thread taps.

In the inter-war years efforts were made to introduce greater accuracy in locomotive construction, particularly in the squareness of cylinders, frames and axle-box horn guides, because of the need to reduce tolerances in bushes and eliminate the numerous stresses on engine framing which had caused premature cracking. This was achieved at Swindon by introducing optical alignment equipment which gave highly accurate information, enabling corrective action to be taken. Special grinding machines with oscillating traversing heads were used to make the horn guides accurate. A supplementary drilling jig was introduced on which the boiler could be placed with smokebox attached, and the securing holes to match the cylinder casting saddle accurately drilled on the true centre-line of the engine frame. The improvement in efficiency and useful running life of the locomotives was outstanding. Frequently mileages exceeding 180 000 between heavy repairs, with one intermediate repair, were attained as a result. At about this time Doncaster Works also adopted optical measuring facilities for accurate locomotive construction.

With the creation of the Workshops Division in 1962 all toolrooms were brought into line. A new system was introduced for checking gauges periodically against works master standards, in turn periodically checked against master standards held in selected works. Equipment was brought up to a common high standard and the rooms refurbished to provide clean conditions. The master standards in every BR works now have National Physical Laboratory Certification.

The above account illustrates how the railway workshops have led or kept pace with developments in the technology of metrology and demonstrates the growth of quality assurance. While this system was developing there was growing activity on another front: in the materials used for locomotives and rolling stock, rails, signalling equipment and bridges. Up to about 1870 the main engineering materials available were wrought iron, cast iron, gunmetal and shear steel for springs, copper for fireboxes and timber. Understanding of their metallurgy and characteristics was acquired slowly. For most of the nineteenth century the manufacture of wrought iron, cast iron, steel and copper was based on a combination of experience, practice and observation, rather than scientific knowledge. Component failures due to defective or badly manipulated materials were not uncommon. Most main works set up their own foundries for iron or brass, facilities to recover scrap wrought iron and rolling mills to convert it into usable bar. The first was probably Wolverton, followed by Crewe, Gorton, Derby Locomotive, Swindon and St Rollox. By 1864 Crewe was using one of the first Bessemer steel processes in the country to produce rails, and later all other steel products for LNWR locomotives and rolling stock. Horwich followed suit. Inevitably works tended to use their own 'recipes', each strongly defended against others, despite their similar purposes.

As early as 1840 far-seeing engineers prepared specifications for the manufacture of wheels, tyres, axles and cylinders to achieve some control over the domestic 'recipes' from whatever source. This was strengthened by the formation in 1869 of the Association of Railway Locomotive Engineers (ARLE) composed of Locomotive Superintendents and CMEs. Concern over the variety of specifications for what were basically the same components led to a request to G. J. Churchward of the GWR to put forward a comprehensive standard set of specifications and test procedures, after studying all those in use on the railways. The report was accepted in 1903, following which Churchward and Holden were appointed to a newly-formed BSI Committee, later the British Engineering Standards Association (BESA), where their work led to the publication in 1906 of BS 24 covering the most important steel components used for locomotives – the axles, tyres, springs and drawgear. Early action had also been taken on other aspects of the control of materials.

In 1864 the LNWR set up at Crewe a chemical laboratory to 'control' its new Bessemer steel-making process. A young engineer was selected – normal LNWR practice – to work with a professor of chemistry at Manchester University for a year, and returned to Crewe with such enthusiasm that he delved into the chemistry of boiler feed water, oils and coal. This laboratory was the forerunner of many others set up by the main railway companies for all manner of analyses and operations concerning engineering materials and purchases of coal, oil and other materials. This led in turn to establishing a 'classification' of freight, and studies of 'dangerous goods' and of goods damaged in transit. The chief chemists soon emulated their superiors, forming standardisation committees, some closely linked with the Railway Clearing House operations. The present smaller number of chemical laboratories are grouped together as the Scientific Services Section of BR's Research and Development Division, continuing to provide a broad scientific service to all branches of BR including the main works. Items such as the production of glass-reinforced plastic components, problems of component or vehicle cleaning and air pollution by various processes receive attention. Chemical analyses of any item can be supplied by the Central Analytical Laboratory.

In an effort to obtain reliable raw materials, castings and forgings, each Superintendent or Mechanical Engineer also had his own inspection service. This practice, certainly of early origin, was the means by which the chief himself would follow up his own enquiries. It is probable too that the inspecting engineers were young men with the responsibility of examining all new locomotives on order for the opening of the various lines. Long before any common standards were defined the works found it necessary to set up their own mechanical testrooms. One need which arose was to anneal and re-test wrought-iron chain. The first railway reference is to a 100-ton capacity hydraulic chain-testing machine from Ransome & Pooley, installed in the Swindon testhouse in 1874. Supplied with piped water at 800 pounds per square inch from the new accumulator, it had a supplementary handpump to generate 1500 pounds pressure when full power was required. In 1891 a Buckton tensile testing machine, supplied with 1500 pounds per square inch of water pressure, was also installed and both have continued to give service whenever required. Several other similar machines for tensile testing were installed at about the same time at other works.

W. Dean set up a chemical laboratory as well as a testhouse for materials between 1871 and 1892. It is known that J. Aspinall and H. G. Ivatt worked in Crewe testhouse, and Fowler and Gresley in the Horwich testhouse, and in 1899 Stanier was appointed a materials inspector at Swindon. In 1915 W. A. Lelean, of Rendell, Palmer & Tritton, the last-named at one time employed in Swindon testhouse, gave Paper No. 35 to the Institution of Locomotive Engineers, describing the work of an inspector of locomotives under construction. Other equipment such as that used for the Izod test, Wohler fatigue test, oil test, welding test and file test was installed, and Brighton Works installed an Amsler machine.

Following the 1923 amalgamation the LMS set up a comprehensive central inspection and test system to deal with major purchased components, becoming in 1928 the Central Materials Inspection Bureau (CMIB) under W. Treadgold with HQ in Derby Locomotive Works and subsidiary offices at Glasgow, Crewe and Horwich. There was no mechanical test facility at St Rollox. The CMIB established new principles and dealt with works-produced as well as contractors' items; it also produced all LMS materials specifications.

By the 1930s the four group companies (and the London Passenger Transport Board) had materials inspection departments. In 1951, after nationalisation, these were merged under T. W. Brown at Derby, again with the title of Central Materials Inspection Bureau, and with responsibility for inspecting purchased locomotives and rolling stock, an arrangement which has continued into the 1980s. In 1970 the then Inspection Division, under the Chief Mechanical and Electrical Engineer at BR Board HQ, assumed a defined responsibility for inspection and acceptance of all new manufacture in the workshops. With the need for greater utilisation of equipment, higher productivity and increased competition, the requirement for greater division of labour was seen and various steps were taken, including the introduction of 'belt systems' (Chapter 6).

Munitions work during the second world war brought ordnance inspections and the AID with a preference for delegating inspection to approved contractors' staff. Many railway finished work inspectors gained this approval, becoming familiar with rigid systems of quality control, higher degrees of precision and in some cases statistical techniques for assessing quality.

From 1945 to 1970 inspection reverted to the pre-war CMIB system but from 1970 there were three separate inspectorates concerned with new construction: (1) internal works finished work inspectors, (2) inspectors responsible to the Materials and Inspection Division and (3) resident inspecting engineers responsible to the Regional Chief Mechanical and Electrical Engineers. This three-tier system did not work very smoothly, and the compromise which emerged was to amalgamate the BR Board's and Chief Mechanical and Electrical Engineers' functions into a new Quality Assurance Division, responsible for defining the essential standards of quality and liaising with all parties including designers. It was an updating of the intentions of inspection which had operated for over 100 years, aimed at bringing quality at all stages of production fully up to the standard of a progressive engineering industry. The responsibility for the day-to-day achievement of quality was firmly placed at the point of origin, on the internal BREL inspection teams: the works inspectors were to be wholly responsible as in the AID system.

The BRB Quality Assurance Division continues to maintain the testhouses, control quality of bought-in material, provide chemical advice and generally give assistance to resolve local quality problems. Within each works the Quality Assurance Engineer is responsible through the Works Manager to the BREL Quality Manager, with the constant aim of meeting all the requirements of BS 5750. In 1981 the Institution of Mechanical Engineers set up the

Pressure Vessels Quality Assurance Board to give its stamp of authority to manufacturers, including BREL, engaged in the production of pressure vessels to British Standards.

The work undertaken in the railway workshops is rightly classed as heavy engineering, and it is fair to say that the quality assurance standards observed within those works are as favourable as any to be found elsewhere in a comparable industry.

11 Machinery and Plant

The number and variety of cutting and forming machine tools currently in use in the various machine shops of the main works for the repair and construction of locomotives, carriages and wagons or other aids to production is so great that it is difficult to visualise the dearth of facilities at the beginning of the railway age in Britain. It is appropriate to consider some developments in machinery and plant as well as the materials used since that early date, and also to indicate the importance of the railway engineer in optimising the combined influence of design, materials, tools, machinery and technology.

In the earliest days of the railways the industries placing demands upon the emerging machine-tool manufacturers for heavier and better equipment were the textile, stationary steam engine and railway locomotive constructors. For all of them the dialogue between brilliant engineers who emerged from virtual anonymity rapidly extended the development in Britain of the Industrial Revolution. The principal influence on railway engineering was the availability of materials, which were limited to wrought iron, cast iron, brass, copper and also wood. Wrought iron could nevertheless be fire-welded, and it was therefore possible for a craftsman using a smith's fire and a hammer to fashion pistons, motion, framing details and the various components of wheels and axles, and to make and fit boiler plates. Water and steam pipes were a different matter for, unless cast, they were made from rolled plate, scarfed and fire-welded or, if made of copper, brazed. The crafts of coal-wagon building and coach building were available for wooden wagons or carriage bodies, as well as for the manufacture of the heavy timber stiffener fitted between dual locomotive frameplates. In many early railway works the smithies occupied up to 30 per cent of the space.

The tools and machines available to the craftsmen were as important as the materials. Tool steel for hammer faces, hand chisels, files and scrapers, or for use in machines, was produced by heating pieces of good quality wrought iron for a long period in a closed box packed around with charcoal; this was called 'blister steel'. It was then converted by hammering into 'shear steel' and this material was hardened by heating, quenching in water and tempering after controlled heating. Such material was available from suppliers in Newcastle and Sheffield where, from about 1760, the Huntsmann practice of melting broken pieces of 'blister steel' yielded the superior 'cast crucible steel'.

Whilst machine tools such as the lathe, drill and planing machine were already in use, those which existed were very small and light, and they were usually manually or foot driven, for there is no known record of power supply from a waterwheel in a railway works. Small stationary steam engines were just beginning to be manufactured for general sale at the beginning of the railway era. The development of machine tools for railway purposes, whilst conforming to the nature of the work required, was also strongly influenced by the limitations imposed by the tool, which had – and still has – a limit of load which it is able to withstand without early failure. The early machines, whilst they may have been dimensionally large, were structurally no more than adequate to support the loading potential of the tools. The old machines were lightly built by modern standards; this is particularly noticeable with the 'H' framing of planing machines.

In the first railway works at Shildon, where repairs such as replacing broken wheels occurred within a few months of opening, the lifting was carried out by screw-jacks and the wheels were removed from, and replaced on, the axles by means of heavy hammers swung against the wheel boss. When building the locomotive 'Royal George' in 1827, at the earlier Shildon Works, Timothy Hackworth had secured a lathe of 4-foot swing which was too small for the cast-iron wheels, so they were made as a centre, with a wide ring pegged to it.

It has frequently been said that the greatest invention ever made was the wheel, and certainly for a railway, however high the cost of manufacture, the wheel is indispensable. The history of the railway wheel's manufacture and maintenance methods dates back to the 1820s. The variations in design are diverse, early types consisting of cast iron, or wood spokes and felloes fitted into cast-iron centres with wrought-iron tyres shrunk on, or wrought-iron spokes cast into iron centres, or all wrought iron, all of which had ceased to be manufactured by the early 1900s. There was one exception when in 1848 the Carriage and Wagon Superintendent of the former London & South-Eastern Railway patented the 'Mansell' wheel following experiments at Ashford Works. This wheel had an iron – later steel – centre with a ring of machined and balanced hardwood blocks sandwiched tightly between the tyre and centre. There were improvements to this design in the 1860s when various workshops commenced manufacture under licence, the last being produced about 1939. The 'Mansell' wheel possessed resilient features and suppressed noise; hence it became the standard for carriages for a long period, and it was also used for some tenders.

It became common practice for the early main works to make their own wheels using their iron-founding facilities and substantial forging plant for wrought iron. About 1890 a complete layout for making wagon wheels was introduced in Derby Carriage and Wagon Works. The plant was supplied by Cravens of Manchester and included a producer gas-fired reverberatory furnace, and a small overhead travelling crane with rope drive and wall-mounted steam engine to transfer molten metal. A unique item was a press designed and built in the works. The wrought-iron spokes were successively held while hot, with hot pieces of iron forming the rim, and were then hydraulically pressed together, achieving a 'fire-welded' joint. The ring of spokes, attached to the rim, was laid flat over a mould for cast iron to be poured to form the boss.

The machining of wheels, which initially presented a problem at Shildon, continued to exercise the ingenuity of railway engineers. Early difficulty was experienced in handling a diameter of around 5 feet but by 1840 wheels of 10-foot diameter had been supplied. Whilst these locomotives soon disappeared, the 8-foot diameter wheel for passenger working was established, and there are indications that a double faceplate wheel lathe supplied by Whitworth to handle this diameter was installed between 1843 and 1846.

The question arises as to when the first wheel lathe was made, and by whom. A sales brochure from Nasmyth, Gaskell & Co., with pencilled date 1839 and certainly not later than 1842, refers to a powerful lathe adapted to turn locomotive engine wheels – under 7 feet in diameter – with a self-acting slide rest. Joseph Beattie of the London & Southampton Railway, later CME, London & South-Western Railway, applied in 1840 for a Patent No. 8741 (confirmed in June 1841) for an improved lathe to enable a workman to turn two wheels at the same time. This patent included the provision of two geared faceplates for the attachment of both wheels, each faceplate being driven by a pinion from a common jackshaft. A number of machine-tool manufacturers subsequently acknowledged their machines as conforming to Beattie's patent, adding the phrase, 'thus overcoming torsion in the axle'. Unless extreme care was taken, considerable damage could occur in turning wheelsets on either of the Nasmyth lathes, when the wrought-iron axle or, worse still, the crank axle was transmitting the torque to the wheel furthest from the driving faceplate.

The most prolific supplier of machinery to the early workshops was Whitworth, who set up his engineering workshop in Manchester in about 1834. He recognised the need throughout the growing industry for machines generally, small and large, and began to construct them on a stock basis. He was the largest exhibitor at the International Exhibition in 1861 when, inter alia, his Patent Railway-Wheel Turning Lathe with four cutting tools was shown. These lathes, of several sizes, turned wheels from 3 feet to 10 feet in diameter!

Few of these four-tool versions were installed in railway works, but large numbers without the rear tools were purchased. Records have been traced of 22 firms contributing their products, in addition to a few made at Horwich and a further 26 at Swindon in 1885–98. Dozens of lathes were actually installed at Derby Carriage and Wagon, Gorton and Horwich Works. The reasons for the existence of so many wheel lathes are threefold: (1) the volume of new wheels made, (2) the frequency of repairs and (3) the very long turning-cycle time. Tyres frequently returned to the works at very short intervals, usually well below 50 000 miles, and the low performance of tools and wheel lathes was less than adequate. The 'underfloor' wheel lathe, thought to be of continental origin, was first made in Britain by Maclea and March of Leeds and supplied in 1860. Two identical lathes were made at Swindon (1900) and by Cravens (1934/7), all for use in the running sheds.

There was another item, the crank-axle, used for inside cylinder locomotives, which taxed the skills of both private manufacturers and railway companies. It was large, heavy and unbalanced, and was produced either by 'pile welding' wrought-iron strip on to a shaft, itself made by forging bars together, to form the crank throws, or by making two half-lengths, each with a single throw, before joining them by fire-welding in the centre. So frequent were the failures of these crank-axles that dummy inside frames with bearings to support the member were fitted to the locomotives. For the heavy forging work in making such axles, some manufacturers used heavy tups hauled up by ropes over pulleys by up to 12 men, and one employed a friction device to engage a long tailpiece on the tup to lift it.

The machine which had the most far-reaching effect upon the railway construction industry was the steam hammer, invented by James Nasmyth in 1839, but not patented until 1842 and first produced in 1843. A very significant development was the delivery from the Bridgwater Foundry, Patricroft, of a 10-hundredweight steam hammer, despatched in 1845, and another of 25 hundredweight in 1846, which made possible the efficient forging of axles and wheels for the first locomotives to be built in the Swindon Works. By 1858 Nasmyth had delivered 29 of these hammers to the railway workshops; ultimately 4 were purchased, including the largest of 4 tons capacity. Two of 3½-ton size were supplied in 1870/1 to the Lancashire & Yorkshire works at Miles Platting, but both were transferred to Horwich in 1886. The steam hammer became so important to the economy of the country that by 1877 there were 36 manufacturers; relatively few were made by the railways. Between 1865 and 1981 B. & S. Massey supplied 145 to the railways. From 1874, 107 drop stamps were supplied (the first to Ashford) and from 1905, 105 pneumatic hammers were supplied (the first to York). The heavy steam hammer revolutionised the manufacture of wheels in particular, forging the spokes into the boss in a thorough manner. It also made possible the forging in one piece of the large crank-axle. During the process the cranks were kept in the same plane, and when complete, the centre portion of the axle was made hot; one crank laid upon the hammer anvil was securely held in that position, while a large 'spanner' fitted to the other crank enabled the men to twist the central shaft to obtain the 90° set between each crank. The proof of this is seen on the driving wheels of the 'Lord of the Isles' in Swindon Museum or on the larger pair of wheels outside the National Railway Museum at York, the evidence being the twist in the slag lines on the central portion of each.

How to remove the large block of metal between the crank webs was solved by the installation of the largest Whitworth slotting machine then existing. This is shown by an early engraving with the comment that the only attention required during machining was 'to keep up a supply of soft-soap and water to cool the tool'. A precise description exists of such a machine installed in Gorton in 1847 and it was this machine, No. 20, which was still in use in 1893. The design was unique: the slotting motion was achieved by means of a reversible screw-driven ram carrying the tool, having a stroke of 26 inches. This was before the adoption of the reciprocating slotting device. The machine had a light though large structure and the process must have been comparatively long.

At Crewe Works an alternative machine was introduced for the same purpose by John Ramsbottom, having a large, wide disc carrying up to 120 cutters inserted into both sides on the periphery. This, by slowly revolving, cut away the metal between the crank webs before final lathe-turning. The basic design predated the inserted tooth milling cutter by almost 50 years. A standard machine of this type was marketed by Cravens in the 1880s. To overcome the hard manual labour involved in the fitting or removal of wheels James Nasmyth marketed a screw press for this work. Early hydraulic presses also existed and were supplied to Doncaster early in the 1850s. It is salutary to consider the engineers' ability in the mid-nineteenth century to prepare patterns, to cast, to machine and fit up a wheel press, to deliver and install the machine, probably with its own pump, within a period of three months for the sum of £210. Another form of hydraulic press was devised at Ashford Works by Mansell in order to compress the wood blocks for his patent wheels. These instances are only a limited selection to illustrate the principles and application of energy by hydraulic means, originally demonstrated by Bramah, who had also used the hydraulic accumulator idea half a century before Sir William Armstrong used and patented the idea to operate cranes connected to high-pressure water mains.

Apart from the forge and associated production machines, two important facilities were required in some form in every railway works, namely the traversing table and the overhead travelling crane. Traversing tables vary from 20-foot wagon types to 60-foot carriage types, and a 200-ton pit table for locomotives as at Crewe. Included within this wide range are variants, such as the one formerly in the Cowlairs Works at Glasgow, which actually climbed a gradient from the lifting shop floor to the body shop, 1'-6" higher. Another specialised traversing table was installed during the 1964/5 reorganisation at St Rollox, Glasgow, which as well as being capable of traversing could also lift the coaches with four synchronised electric jacks, thus saving space and movement within a restricted area. There is a strong possibility that the first traverser in any railway works was that provided in the 'engine shop' at Swindon. It had two roads and was manually moved from end to end of the traverser way with a cranked handle, long shaft and gearing to each side.

Locomotives were moved manually or with the assistance of pinch-bars from the pits on to the table. About 1850 the first works traversers were provided with power both to traverse and to haul vehicles on or off by means of a winding drum with ropes. The power unit was a small steam engine with vertical boiler, either on the table or as a permanent tractor unit running on two of the traverser way rails. Many have been made within the works, some have been modified to electric drive, and at least one of these is still used in Derby Carriage Works.

It was David Napier – supplier to I. K. Brunel of three hydraulic presses for the new goods yard at Bristol (1842) and three hydraulic traversing frames to transfer wagons from one road to another at Cheltenham, Bristol and Swindon (1845/8) as well as three wheel presses in the Swindon Works –

who built the two cranes for Swindon, one in 1844 and the other two years later. Longitudinal travel was achieved, as for the traverse, by means of a cranked handle attached to a long shaft with gearing at each end engaging one of the travelling wheels. For the cross travel of the lifting crab a spoked handwheel similar to a ship's steering wheel was geared to one of the travelling wheels of the crab, the senior craneman having control of this wheel. The lifting unit was situated within the cross-travel carriage, as was an inverted hydraulic cylinder with a lifting eye attached to the lower end of the piston rod. Small hydraulic pumps drew water from an adjacent tank and a long lever, centrally mounted, enabled two men to raise any desired load by manual pumping. A release valve lever for lowering was provided under the control of the cross-travel operator.

The crane structures were of timber strengthened with wrought-iron tie-bars, each rated at 25 tons; the first, of 57'-2" span, was fitted with new timbers in 1887 and continued in service until the rebuilding of the erecting shop in 1914. The second, of 44'-6" span, used in the millwright's shop, lasted until 1908. The price for these remarkable cranes was less than £800 each, so the GWR must have made a good bargain. It is also remarkable that for the first portion of the new west-end erecting shop basically similar hydraulic cranes were installed as late as 1903, using oil as the compression fluid and each having two 25-ton crabs. These were Swindon-built steel structures with three throw pumps and electrically driven. One was still in use in 1982, still driven by its Swindon-built motor, and their cost was £1500 each.

Apart from the two Napier cranes there is no record until about 1860 of any overhead travelling crane in any other railway works. For the purpose of heavy lifting the alternatives were large jib cranes, movable or fixed, or fixed trestle type hoists, either form being equipped with winding drums and multiple blocks on the beam. In the works yard the latter or sheer-legs were normally used, but whatever the type it must have been hazardous to undertake the removal from or fitting of a boiler into an engine frame.

Whilst the travelling crane was an immense step forward, for a long period there was only one hoist block, so that the wheeling of an engine required great care because of the height that one end had to be lifted. Nevertheless cranes of this type were still in use in some small locomotive erecting shops in the early 1940s. A variant on the lifting practice for engines existed at a very early date in Derby Locomotive Works, where lifting took place across the turntable, with two fixed hoists and tackle arranged overhead at each end. It was usual for these fixed hoists to be of wood. The Napier type of crane did not spread to other works, probably because it was not convenient in the through-type shops; Swindon had traverser-type shops with engine pit roads at right angles to the craneway, so that one crane could service a whole bay without interference to any other locomotive in the bay.

By 1858 the LNWR had only three engines exceeding 21 tons weight, but the future clearly indicated that there must be considerable increase in the size and hence the weight of new types to be built. This coincided with an extension of workshop facilities planned for Crewe, where John Ramsbottom applied his patent – based on experience of textile plant drives – to the design and construction of powered overhead travelling cranes with cotton rope drives. His workshops were equipped with crane tracks supported by hollow circular cast-iron columns, to carry wood-framed structures with supporting wrought-iron tiebars, these in turn having cross-travel carriages with an integral geared lifting crab. The three motions – long travel, cross travel and hoist – were derived from a steam engine frequently existing for machinery drives, via grooved pulleys which carried ⅝″ diameter, 1½-ounce cotton rope the entire length of the craneway, closely below the roof supports. A take-off pulley diverted the rope to drive the crane gearing, under the control of an operator travelling on a platform on the crane. The rope could run at speeds up to 5000 feet a minute and, by an inverse mechanical advantage of up to 3000 to 1, could engage a very slow lifting speed.

By 1864 a number of cranes had been erected with lifting capacities of 4 and 6 tons and up to 20 and 25 tons with a maximum clear span of 40 feet. In an erecting shop a rope life of 8 months was normal. The same rope-driving principle was applied to operate 4-ton 'walking' cranes for a wheel and heavy turning shop. This type had a long two-wheel carriage which ran on a straight rail in the shop floor, supporting a vertical crane post carrying a 360-degree 8½-foot radius jib, whilst at the top were rollers which ran between two guide members attached to the roof structure and took any thrust when lifting off rail centre. This was a most effective lifting device for heavy components to and from machines which could be arranged in line with the rail for progressive manufacturing operations. The two cranes at Crewe, which had a hoist speed of 9 feet/minute and travel of 80 feet/minute, were the forerunners of many such cranes throughout railway works, although now cranes are fitted with electric drive. Whilst larger works such as Crewe and Swindon made many cranes during the next 40 years, private manufacturers such as Cravens made rope cranes in great numbers; for example, 20 were supplied around 1890 to Gorton Works with capacities from 5 to 30 tons.

When electricity for power supplies became available, from the early 1900s, the opportunity was taken to eliminate many of the old stationary steam engines in the shops in favour of electric motors. Similarly the rope-driven cranes were provided with electric motors, generally one for each motion individually, and several works such as Horwich made their own motors for the purpose. Horwich Works at first fitted single motors but soon found it more economic to use smaller individual ones. Not all the rope-driven cranes survived at this juncture, the weight of new types of locomotive exceeding the capacity of all except the largest in the erecting and boiler shops; hence at a number of works cranes of 50, 80 and 100 tons were installed. At Swindon four 100-ton cranes having two 50-ton crabs and a supplementary light lift with fast hoist were supplied by Ransomes and Rapier at £8000 each in 1920, and during the late 1970s these were fitted with new control gear.

For carriage works the lifting problem has been less critical, with capacities of 15 tons for each of two cranes performing the lift during the early part of this century. They have given way to pairs of cranes each of 25-ton capacity, an important part of the lifting procedure resting upon two long vertical arms suspended from the cross-travel crab, and each of these arms having a horizontal claw at the base which is located beneath the coach body at the lifting point. This device enables a safe and easily positioned set of lifting tackle to be used which will not damage the coach. In one special case St Rollox Works at Glasgow has the lifting facility for coaches, in the form of four electrically-operated jacks, engaging under the lifting point while the vehicle is still on the traversing table. The method is unique, but the principle of lifting by four electric jacks stems from earlier manual types made at several works and has become common for diesel or electric multiple-unit train sets which can be lifted in regular positions. Early equipment was foreign, from Geiger, but many sets of jacks supplied by Matterson's have remained in use, having been installed during the main works reorganisation. The four jacks can be electrically synchronised.

In the wagon works the smallness of the vehicles forming the bulk of the fleet has meant that the quickest possible method for lifting is by the manual use of simple equipment. The ancient screw-jack principle was the simplest and was used for single-end lifting, with one jack either in the centre of the end-frame or at the end corners, the time for removing bearings or a wheelset being only a few minutes. The introduction by some works of the hydraulic accumulator, feeding a system of high-pressure mains, led to the adoption of a simple fixed lift or jack under the end-frame of a wagon; this was a safer but more restrictive method of lifting than the use of the screw-jack, and reduced the manhours formerly involved.

With the availability of compressed air on ring-main systems from the 1920s, air lifters were introduced at a number of works; these were also used singly. As these jacks were coupled to a valve on the main by a flexible rubber pipe, the system gave greater flexibility for the positioning of the wagons, thus saving time, and the air jack was much faster in operation. Apart from instances when the wagon repair activity during some reorganisation within a works was transferred to a shop having overhead cranes, such expensive provisions were never considered necessary. However, during the major reorganisation of the workshops in the 1960s, and bearing in mind the larger-capacity all-steel wagons which were being introduced for specialised traffics, such as the hoppered high capacity of 40 tonnes colliery to power station working which had a tare weight of some 13 tons, the need for improved lifting facilities was apparent. To meet this requirement, and to increase the efficiency of the lifting procedure and enhance safety, sets of four electrically-driven screw-jacks by Matterson's were introduced at a number of works. One installation was placed at Shildon, where most of the heavy repair to wagons was concentrated.

An examination of the gradual evolution of general production machinery must include the sources of power. For a long period the waterwheel held the dominant role, but there is no evidence that any railway works had such an installation. The emergence of the rotative steam engine had been under the sole control of James Watt until 1800 and his was a low-pressure engine. Trevithick in 1804 showed the potential of the high-pressure steam engine, and in the following 30 years great strides were made by a few adventurous engineers in the development of stationary steam engines, some on the condensing principle, but many more simply using high-pressure steam, whilst the boiler manufacturers probed the design requirements to make matching equipment. Thus by 1838 it was possible for railway works to be constructed in the most suitable positions to maintain the locomotives and rolling stock of their particular railway. Even so the totally inadequate roads for the carriage of fuel, building materials, iron and raw materials caused almost every works to be located near a canal or navigable river.

There is limited knowledge of the sources for supply of stationary steam engines. The first known, about 1843, was one with 21-inch diameter cylinders from Stothert, the builders also of the first two locomotives 'Arrow' and 'Dart' to run from Bristol to Bath, whilst another came from Harvey of Hayle and had 30-inch diameter cylinders. At Gorton there were stationary engines in 1893, the first from Goodfellow in 1848 with 15¼-inch diameter by 28-inch stroke cylinders taking steam at 70 pounds per square inch from a locomotive-type boiler. Others with 18-inch diameter by 30-inch cylinders came from Robinson (Rochdale) and Garforth (Dukinfield). Of particular interest were steam engines Nos 1 and 2 shown in the machinery schedule at Derby Carriage and Wagon Works, which came from the nearby locomotive works and had locomotive cylinders and motion and large flywheels. These drove underground line shafting with belts through the floor to the sawmill machinery, an arrangement modelled on that at Swindon Works, from where the first superintendent had come to Derby.

The stationary steam engines used in large numbers in the larger works came from many sources but with the facilities available within those works records show that a high percentage were within the works and were designed in various forms and sizes – vertical, inverted, single, duplex, compound, condensing or non-condensing. In most instances the steam supply came from converted locomotive boilers. Line shafting ran for long distances, changes in direction being made usually by using bevel gearing, one gear being cast iron and the other having inserted wooden teeth to reduce noise and give flexibility. The customary light machine shop had a spectacular appearance with a conglomeration of rapidly-moving belts disappearing into the dimly-lit roof, accompanied by the click of the joints passing over the pulleys. Below the patchy illumination of gas flares supplied from a small internal gasworks there was continual flickering from the belt interference. For about 60 years, until the incandescent gas mantle came into use, such lighting had to be endured.

Before any major changes in the field of machine tools there was a far-reaching development in boiler-making following a general application of the hydraulic accumulator, with ring mains supplying high-pressure water to any point required in the workshop for a whole range of fixed or portable presses for flanging or riveting (see Fig. 11.1). The introduction of hydraulic power to the railway works came about 1880 and gave rise to new techniques using the ductile properties of iron and later steel to form material precisely, thus eliminating a great deal of smith-forging and fire-welding. The longitudinal seams of boilers were frequently fire-welded which, whilst demonstrating a high degree of perfection in the art compared with modern practice, now appears no less than frightening. Boiler explosions on locomotives and particularly stationary plant in England were frequently as many as 100 per year. The reason was not confined to failure of fire-welded seams, but Fairbairn was commissioned to report upon these disasters, and in the long run inspection of boilers on a regular basis became statutory. Insurance was also introduced.

While changes were taking place in the supply of power, there were also developments in machine tools, which were slow at first. Besides the early Whitworth tools, other firms such as Sharp, Roberts and Nasmyth Gaskell were suppliers to the railways. Basic forms were used until the availability of improved cutting tools brought about major redesign, involving structural strengthening, wider speed ranges, greater accuracy and improved bearings. Some early specialised machines were devised at individual works, such as at Swindon, where a cylinder-boring machine with travelling tool was made in about 1851 (see Fig. 11.2). Others with two tool bars which could face each end followed. Nasmyth devised a segmental grinding machine with inserted blocks of Yorkshire stone, and this may have led to the design of Ramsbottom's slidebar grinder of about 1854.

Difficulty was experienced when reconditioning slide-valve faces or the bores of cast-iron cylinders, which were firmly attached to the engine frames, especially the twin-cylinder inside types. Hand rectification involved the use of conventional files, valve rubbers (curved or flat) and scrapers, and was both onerous and time-consuming. Ramsbottom devised a portable machine which, when attached to the cylinder studs, supported a long reciprocating arm carrying a cutting tool; this was fed across the valve face and would make it level. This item became universal for use in all locomotive works and major motive-power running depots until the end of the steam era. When compressed air was available an air motor gave continuous drive. For the cylinder bores a simpler portable machine was used. The abrasive used for lapping or polishing was older than the locomotive, the material being a powder from Turkey or the island of Naxos. It was used on leather-covered wheels stuck with glue for polishing, and at a later date emery was the standard material for the polishing of connecting and coupling rods.

The introduction of large-quantity production of mild steel by the Bessemer and shortly after by the Siemens-Martin process, in which Crewe Locomotive Works took a leading role, was first applied to rail, then sections and then plate, all being achieved by 1865. Castings in steel followed, and Webb at Crewe had the brilliant idea of placing wheel-moulds on a rotating table for part of the pouring operation, thus achieving centrifugal casting and better-

HENRY BERRY & Co. LIMITED, HYDRAULIC ENGINEERS 53

HYDRAULIC RIVETTERS

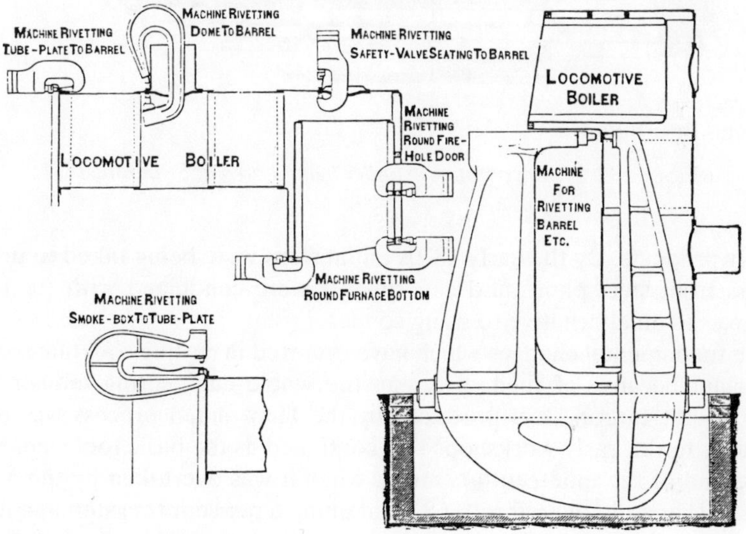
Machine Rivetting Tube-Plate To Barrel
Machine Rivetting Dome To Barrel
Machine Rivetting Safety-Valve Seating To Barrel
Locomotive Boiler
Machine Rivetting Round Fire-Hole Door
Locomotive Boiler
Machine For Rivetting Barrel Etc.
Machine Rivetting Round Furnace Bottom
Machine Rivetting Smoke-box To Tube-Plate

Application of Hydraulic Rivetters to Locomotive Boilers.

CROYDON WORKS, LEEDS, ENGLAND

Source Henry Berry & Co. Ltd

Figure 11.1 *The application of hydraulic riveters to locomotive boilers*

Source   British Rail

Figure 11.2   *Locomotive cylinder being bored at Swindon, 1851*

quality products. By the early 1870s initial steps were being taken to produce boilers from steel plate, and experiments were conducted with steel inner fireboxes as an alternative to using copper.

The fundamental changes which have occurred in cutting-tool materials are important because of their effect on the whole engineering industry. The crucible-cast carbon steel produced by the Huntsmann process was readily available to the early workshops and continued as the basic tool steel almost to the end of the nineteenth century, when it was overtaken by the Mushet tool steel, first discovered in 1868, containing 6 per cent tungsten and a small quantity of manganese. This new type of steel, with an air-hardening property following heating to 1000°C, had a remarkable potential to cut material some three times more quickly than the type of steel previously used. The Mushet steel was used soon after its discovery for machining Bessemer steels (first introduced on the railways in 1861) and the alternative product about 1866 from the Siemens open-hearth furnace. By the 1880s these new materials were rapidly beginning to replace wrought iron, especially in the design of locomotives. There had been several trials of tyre steel, and some locomotive motion details supplied by Krupp's from the mid-1850s must have created difficulty in machining. Ten years earlier Daniel Gooch had discovered the same problem when trying, and failing, to machine his 'steeled' tyres: that is, tyres with a segment of steel rolled on to the wrought-iron tyre-bar. As a result of the changes in engineering material and tool steels, a new range of machine tools were designed with greater power and rigidity for economic manufacture.

The next important change in cutting tools followed the development of high-speed tool steel, in about 1900. It was the result of adding some 18 per cent tungsten and smaller quantities of other alloys to cast steel. This coincided with two other developments: firstly the design of feed mechanisms was strengthened, and secondly replacement of belt drives by electric motor direct drive provided much-needed power. Metal removal rates were doubled or trebled. Initially many of the new machines had an imposing array of gears and shafts replacing the cone pulleys. These collected dirt and required regular oiling, and they presented a continual safety hazard. By the end of the first world war more powerful machines were available, usually designed with enclosed gearing and automatic lubrication by oil bath.

This development not only revolutionised the normal cutting procedures for metals, but also made it practicable for the manufacture of multiple-edged milling cutters to become the foundation for an entirely new generation of machines such as the milling machine, which is probably the most versatile feature of a modern machine shop. To match the new material, which only began to reach this country from about 1900, there was the need to sharpen the cutting edges. Charles H. Norton had been working on the problem of making superior grinding wheels and had just introduced bonded wheels of carborundum, the hardness of which was greater than that of high-speed steel. These early artificial grinding wheels were far from satisfactory, but when used with care they satisfied the immediate need.

New possibilities appeared as a result of the development and introduction of milling machines. The potential of the grinding machine for high-speed precision production of a wide range of components from pins and bushes (pre-hardened) to axle-journals, axle-box seatings, vacuum-brake piston rods and locomotive slide-bars was also realised. In the toolroom precision grinding was applied in the manufacture of reamers and screw-taps, including the very long ones used to tap boiler crown-stay holes in one operation through outer and inner fireboxes. The production of precision gauges also became an important function. The milling cutter, and the machine to use it, opened wide the practicability of making dies in specially toughened steels, thus enabling the use of drop-stamping for the manufacture of large items such as draw-hooks, spring-hanger bolts, brake-hangers and a multitude of other items for use on locomotives, carriages and wagons. So great was the demand for these items that large new layouts with either single or multiple batteries of drop-stamps appeared in the early 1900s in several railway works. These included Shildon (which became the only plant), Derby Carriage and Wagon, Eastleigh, Gorton, Swindon Locomotive (heavy) and Swindon Carriage and Wagon Works (light).

Further change was introduced with the marketing in Britain of 'Widia', a metallic base material produced by powder metallurgy, initially as dies for wire-drawing in the 1920s. The material was sintered under high pressure and contained – besides a major amount of tungsten carbide – other carbides such as cobalt, designed to give greater toughness whilst retaining great hardness.

The practice of brazing small pieces to the cutting end of a tool-bar was replaced by high quality pre-set tooling with throwaway 'carbide' tips which ensured complete interchangeable accuracy. For efficient use 'negative rake' machining became necessary.

The introduction of tungsten carbide tip tooling became the springboard for yet another more powerful type of machine with non-wearing slideways and bearings supported by efficient lubrication. These new machines formed the basis for self-measurement in the automatic operation of the cutting tools and heralded the sophisticated introduction of the numerically-controlled machine tool. Whilst only small selective use was made of tungsten carbide tips, most heavy-duty machining had been carried out for a long period using several superior grades of alloyed high-speed tungsten tool steel. It was, however, a considerable time before the first numerically-controlled machine tool was installed in a railway works, and this occurred during the early stages of the workshops reorganisation of 1962.

By the 1930s the large DC electric motors, which at about the turn of the century had replaced the steam-engine line-shafting drives, had themselves been replaced, many self-contained new machines having taken the place of older types particularly after heavy first world war usage. Similarly after the second world war considerable numbers of new machines were installed. The situation remained fairly static until a number of special lathes were provided to remachine plain journal wagon wheel sets to accommodate roller bearings, and at about the same time some new wheel lathes from Cravens, having the first electric copying devices, were introduced on production work. This form of copying was known on the railways as the system of copying used on Keller dic-sinkers for milling operations.

When in 1963 the workshops modernisation plan reduced the number of works to 16, action had to be taken to deal with major re-equipment of the continuing works. Quadruple-frame slotting and drilling machines and a wide range of boiler-making drills, riveters and heavy flanging tools were no longer required. In the carriage and wagon field extensive development of welding techniques had eliminated the need for solebar drilling machines with multiple heads on 60-foot long beds. An unexpected situation arose from the modernisation plan as a result of all the retained works being made into an independent contractual maintenance organisation, responsible for the achievement of annual budgeted repairs at contracted costs. The customer – that is, the railway regions, through their Regional Chief Mechanical Engineers, and the design engineers at BR HQ – began to set new standards of dimensional accuracy for components and performance, involving much more frequent replacement and the provision of more accurate machinery. The workshops were able to use this development to advantage in the achievement of much greater production rates by using the pre-set tungsten carbide tooling on a whole range of modern machines. Many sequentially-controlled machines were installed, the sequences being set up by means of plugs or switches, principally for the vast quantities of turned bolts, pins and bushes required.

Initial steps were also taken to evaluate the use of numerically controlled drills, mills and lathes.

Whilst it was anticipated that special grinding equipment would be required only for the repair of journals and crankpins of the small diesel railcar underslung engines, it was also necessary on the large Sulzer diesel locomotive units. These had been manufactured from steel castings and plate, the welding on which failed in numerous areas, and hundreds of cylinder blocks and crankshaft housings for these large engines needed complete rectification. The distortion from rewelding made it essential to remove all studs, clean up all machined faces and cylinder bores and completely remachine the whole unit. Large plano-milling machines or the Innocenti types of machine were used and the crankshaft bearing housings rebored with new machines from Giddings, Lewis and Fraser, dimensional control being maintained using digital readout.

The form of wheel lathes did not change greatly until the arrival of high-speed tool steel, when new machines would be more robust yet because of the use of tougher grades of steel, particularly for locomotives or motor-bogies on electric multiple-unit Southern Railway vehicles, there was little hope of increasing the speed of turning. A further factor was the higher speeds of trains: heavier braking produced harder tyres and only too frequently 'glass-hard' or 'shelled' areas, which broke the cutting edge of the tools. No increase in power above the usual maximum of 30 horsepower was of advantage.

The German railway works and wheel lathe manufacturers had collaborated in the process of reconstruction after the second world war and, in experimenting with the Krupp 'Widia' (tungsten carbide cutting material) they had found it possible to machine worn tyres more quickly using robust machines to eliminate 'chatter' and more powerful electric motors. The London Midland Region of BR took the initiative to obtain machines for trial purposes from Maschinen Fabrik Deutschland, Dortmund, the delivery and installation passing into the hands of the newly formed Workshops Division. Before any trials could be effective the urgent reorganisation of the workshops took uppermost priority; the total number of machines from Maschinen Fabrik Deutschland was increased to four and tenders were issued to British machine-tool makers. The machine-tool manufacturers responded and substantial orders were placed, notwithstanding that these would come straight from the drawing board. For experimental purposes a 'Portal' type wheel lathe was ordered in 1964.

Over an extensive period the performance of all the new machines of the copying type for automatically forming the whole tyre profile, by electric or hydraulic sensing, needed more consistent maintenance than the usual plant, but showed great improvement over the former wheel-turning achievement. British firms ceased to compete, and as the first German manufacturer was outpriced, new machines giving complete satisfaction have come from Hagenscheidt. Close co-operation between this firm and BREL has resulted in gratifying technical developments. In one instance a suggestion from the railway that it was practicable to control automatically the setting of the cutting tools by sensing the greatest amount of wear sustained by either wheel was developed by the firm with alacrity, and it has become possible for the tools to be automatically set during 1¼ free revolutions of the wheelset, so that all operator measurement and its inherent errors no longer exist. The power input for these new machines has reached 120 horsepower, and the centring and gripping devices for the wheels have also been improved. By the end of 1983 BREL had 9 Hagenscheidt wheel lathes.

The development of improved welding techniques, in conjunction with new designs of bogies for carriages, involved the construction of the main frames from a number of fully-welded closed box frames, itself a fine achievement in welding techniques, and it also created the need to use large plano-milling machines capable of carrying the whole bogie. The same principles have been applied to locomotive bogies, resulting in the provision of machines from Noble and Lund as well as Asquith which can carry a bogie of 26-foot length on the table. Dummy tables are also in use for setting up the next bogie to be machined. Associated with this project many different shapes of plate are needed, most with welding preparation machined all round. For this purpose at BREL's request the Wadkin Machine Tool Co. devised a means of linking a series of automatic cramps holding a plate, such that each one in turn will release and move out of the way as the cutting tool passes by, then returning to grip the plate again, with the numerically controlled system.

Experiments were carried out in 1968/70 with a 'Robot' welding machine specially designed to embrace and envelop approximately 20 by 4 by 3 feet in order to weld mild-steel assemblies, using operator-simulated movement input to the small computer storage control system, and the experiments demonstrated a potential for such applications. In 1981 a production robot welding machine was installed in the York Carriage Works for use on carriage underframe subassemblies. Many of the early numerically controlled (NC) machines, with their great variety of control systems, were replaced, having given more than 10 years' service. A high degree of standardisation of makers' control systems from a small number of sources has been achieved, and almost all have the facility of manual input or modification of the programme. These are designated computer numerically controlled (CNC) machines. Drawings have been simplified to assist programming, and bolts, pins and corresponding holes have been limited to a smaller number of standards, so limiting tool changing and increasing cutting potential on these expensive machines. Since the installation of a Huron milling machine at Derby Locomotive Works and a Burgmaster drill at Crewe Locomotive Works in 1964, both equipped with NC systems, and after allowing for the displacement on life expiry of many others purchased up to 1970, the total of NC machines in use in 1983 had reached 111, of which 61 were furnished with CNC systems, these having been purchased since 1975.

Amongst the lathes are some of a new generation in which the headstock gearing was eliminated in favour of direct drive of the spindle by DC motor, with virtually infinite speed variation throughout the range, electronically obtained by varying the field flux through the control system. The justification for these machines, all of high cost, does not rest solely upon improved production rates for given components and operator manpower reduction. The package includes fewer tools, material savings from reduced wastage particularly of plate, reduction of production scrap, and stocks of material and manufactured articles in store. Improved dimensional accuracy also greatly reduces fitting and assembly times, and eventually fewer machines will make it practicable to reduce workshop capacity with consequent savings in heating, maintenance and other overhead charges. There is an increasing need for a new breakthrough in cutting performance to reduce further the costs and time for machining; in addition any developments which could totally eliminate machining for no greater cost must never be overlooked.

Some of the prominent machine installations in the main works since 1979 are as follows:

(1) A Trumpf sheet-metal punching and machining centre with plasma-arc cutting of up to 12 mm steel plate.
(2) CNC lathes, vertical boring and turning lathes, machining centres, milling machines, bridge-type drilling and milling machines, laser gas cutting for steel plate and inspection machines.
(3) Specialised machines costing from over £¼ m up to £1 m including:
    (a) Boromill Machining Centre for bogies, table 2.25 m × 7 m with automatic tool store and changing. Kongsberg, NC.
    (b) Milling machine, bridge-type, Wadkin, for bogies, 1.7 m × 4.6 m, table, CNC with automatic cramp release, for complete contouring of plate.
    (c) Gas cutting machine, Hancock, 2.5 m × 6 m, cutting area, underwater using plasma-arc, with supplementary part programming facility for 'nesting' of maximum number of cut components per plate, also post-processor for bogie milling and machining centre machines.
    (d) Inspection machine, L.K. Tool Company (Aston-on-Trent), NC with readout, with bed of two granite beams, supporting two granite columns with cross-slide and probe holder, giving travelling coverage 28' × 10' over items such as complete locomotive bogie.
(4) Robot welding machine, 6 axis, CNC. Languepin, coverage 0.7 m × 6 m × 1 m with operator teach-in facility.
(5) Paint-spraying machine, 6 axis, Tralfa. Robot CNC, Tralfa.

This is an impressive list and clearly demonstrates that the main works of BREL are alive to the range of modern equipment which has become available to them.

12 Specialised Activities

INTRODUCTION

Most of the specialised activities of the main works developed before the 1923 amalgamation, including the manufacture of steel castings or ingots for forging, rolling mills for bar sections or plate, and nails at several works. After amalgamation a few of these activities continued and remained in operation until the 1960s. Design changes, such as the use of reinforced plastics, have resulted in new activities to meet the new demand as well as to provide a valuable development source. The variety of specialised activities is divisible into two groups: the larger group concerns those activities necessary to facilitate the construction or repair of locomotives, carriages and wagons, whilst the secondary group consists of those activities serving other departments of the railway.

IRON

There is only one substantiated instance of iron manufacture, which was at Crewe, where a number of furnaces were used to convert pig iron into wrought iron. Rolling of iron was more common: many of the early workshops installed merchant rolls for the conversion of parcels of iron into the great variety of sections of bar and angle needed for the construction or repair of all vehicles. No evidence has been found of plate rolling in iron, although it was common practice to form pieces of plate by hand hammer and later under steam hammers.

Wheels were the most fundamental requirement of all. From James Nuttall's 'Sketch-book' we have information on some of the methods used for the manufacture of wrought-iron wheels, including tyres and spokes with rim but with cast-iron boss (1833). The first all-wrought-iron locomotive wheel was made in 1836, the same year in which a bossing hammer, friction-roller lifted, was made at the Viaduct Foundry, Newton-le-Willows. This foundry was leased by the LNWR in 1853 and purchased in 1860, subsequently becoming Earlestown Works, where wheels for wagon production were made.

At two other works the manufacture of locomotive wheels and crankshafts in wrought iron took place. An 1846 plan of Swindon Works includes one area where wheels were made within the very large forging section; a document of about 1850 carries illustrations of several aspects of wheel manufacture including a crankshaft forging on the table of a large slotting machine. Wagon wheels were also produced there, as Swindon built new wagons. The other works was Crewe, where in 1847 there were 60 forge fires and anvils, 12 of which were engaged upon wheel centres. A new plant to manufacture wagon wheels in large numbers was established about 1890 at Derby Carriage and Wagon Works.

Two works set up rolling equipment for the supply of wrought-iron rail to the Civil Engineering Department at Crewe (about 1854) and Swindon (in 1861). At Swindon a large amount of bridge rail which was too light for service was available for conversion, involving the use of a large steam hammer to shingle large piles of cut pieces of the rail after furnacing, followed by cogging down and converting into rail. The output from Crewe in 21-foot lengths was 150 tons per week.

BRICKWORKS

Clay suitable for the manufacture of building bricks was found at the sites of Crewe and Swindon Works, and each exploited the situation, with Crewe producing as many as 5 million bricks annually by 1880.

STEEL

Soon after Henry Bessemer had patented a process for making large quantities of mild steel reasonably cheaply, the LNWR Locomotive Superintendent, J. Ramsbottom, became involved in experiments at Crewe, with the result that in 1861 the first lengths of steel rail for trial were made. Experiments were made on the 'steeling' of the top of wrought-iron rail, the subject of an earlier patent by D. Gooch, and tyres and plate were also rolled in steel. As a result of the success attained a new steel plant was completed at Crewe in 1865, containing four 6-ton Bessemer converters, three furnaces and a cogging mill to reduce the steel ingots to billets. New rolling mill equipment added to the output potential, which then included locomotive frameplates, boiler plates, tyres and merchant sections as well as rail. The first trials of rail on the main lines were conducted at Crewe Station in November 1861.

Ramsbottom introduced an innovation when making the plate-rolling mill at Crewe. He found that using the complete cylinders with motion and reversing gear from a steam locomotive was sufficiently powerful to drive the mill-train without a flywheel, and the inertial reduction allowed rapid reversal of the mill by using the reversing lever. A royalty of between £1 and £2 was paid for every ton of steel produced. Four years later two 5-ton open-hearth furnaces were installed; together with other plant which included a 30-ton duplex horizontal steam hammer and several heavy conventional steam hammers, they provided forge capacity to match the steel-melting output, which rose to about 80 000 tons annually.

An increase in rail output was achieved in 1875 following the installation of new open-hearth furnaces and works-built rolling mills powered by Corliss type 1200 horsepower Wilson gas-driven engines from Hick Hargreaves of

Bolton. Rail output is recorded as 30 ft × 75 lb (1876), 30 ft × 90 lb (1887) and 60 ft × 95 lb (1893) at a rate of 10 000 tons per annum. A plant renewal in 1924 replaced ten melting furnaces by two 40/45-ton acid plants and two 60/70-ton basic Siemens-Martin open-hearth type plants. The steel foundry contained three 10-ton furnaces and a Tropenas converter for steel casting work, which included wheel centres, locomotive cylinders and many other items.

The L&YR decided to provide a steel plant and forge in the new works to be built at Horwich. Ramsbottom, who had retired in 1871, was engaged as the works consultant. When the works opened there were two Siemens-Martin 20-ton regenerative furnaces with Tropenas converters for steel-casting work. Similar furnaces were installed in the forge as well as a 30-ton duplex horizontal steam hammer, an 8-ton and two 5-ton hammers, a 30-inch cogging mill, a 14-inch merchant mill, an 8-inch guide mill and a tyre mill, all these machines being driven by electric motors for the live rollers. The furnaces were supplied with gas from Wilson type producers and output reached 12 000 tons of steel per annum.

Following the 1923 amalgamation the Crewe steel plant was rebuilt (1925–7) with a potential of 84 000 ingot tons a year, and the Horwich plant was closed in 1932. The slump of 1929–32 resulted in the cessation of steel-making. The melting plant, reopened during the second world war, supplied ingots for conversion into ships' plate at the rate of 5000 tons a month during 1943–5. A small amount of steel-casting activity has continued in the iron foundry at Crewe, the furnaces being replaced by two small Secci type plants supplied with pulverised fuel in 1934, and in the 1960s by two 4-ton electric carbon arc type plants which have continued in service in the 1980s.

At Swindon the upsurge of new construction of all types of vehicle following the changeover from broad gauge to narrow gauge ensured the retention of the rolling mill, which was found to be most economic because it involved the recovery of scrap wrought iron. The plant continued for over 120 years and was only disbanded under the workshops reorganisation plan in 1962.

DROP-STAMP FORGING

This activity commenced as early as 1874 at Ashford, but the larger sites for heavy locomotive components were at Crewe and Swindon, together with intense production at the carriage and wagon centres of Derby, Shildon and Swindon, in addition to some at Eastleigh and Wolverton. This means of production came into existence mainly between 1903 and 1912, and some plant additions were made during the 1914–18 war and in 1932–5.

The 1962–5 reorganisation brought about the cessation of most drop-stamp forging, although Derby continued for a few more years, and following re-equipment of the Shildon plant in 1970–2 all such work was concentrated at Shildon, which had the largest continuous history of drop-stamp forging in the railway works of Britain. After the concentration and reorganisation the facilities at Shildon included 9 drop hammers from 15 hundredweight to 5 tons and one counterblow type of 4 tons, 5 forging hammers of 10 to 30 hundredweight, 11 trimming presses, 12 temperature-controlled and 4 un-controlled furnaces, 5 hydraulic presses and 5 forging machines. A separate heat-treatment shop existed for normalising or oil-quenching, with 5 furnaces served by a mechanical charging machine.

CONTINUOUS CASTING PLANTS

Almost all main works possessed an iron foundry which manufactured a variety of cast-iron items for new construction or repair of railway vehicles, as well as an extensive range of components for maintenance purposes. Items such as cast-iron axle-boxes, firebars, brake blocks and chairs for main line use were ordered in large quantities.

Work in the foundries was labour-intensive and heavy, the atmosphere was generally polluted and dusty, and both working conditions and productivity needed improvement. In 1932/3 at Eastleigh a mechanised foundry was installed, which provided for automated moulding, sand supply and conditioning, casting and knockout with final cooling conveyor. In the Scottish works at Cowlairs and St Rollox automated sand and moulding conveyors were built around existing moulding plant, with cooling conveyors for the removal of the castings. The total output of the three plants at Cowlairs, St Rollox and Eastleigh – engaged on brake block manufacture up to 1962 – was approximately 12 000 tons, representing a quarter of all brake blocks produced in railway workshops. During the same year a further 25 000 tons was produced in the large-scale mechanised foundry at Horwich.

Horwich was chosen because there was adequate space available in the old forge and steel works, and by the end of 1951 the first portion of the new foundry commenced working with an ultimate annual target of 51 000 tons of chairs and base plates and 17 000 tons of brake blocks. The plant consisted of two units for rail-chair and one unit for brake-block manufacture, with a fully automated sand preparation and conveyor system, moulding box conveyor, knockout and cooling line and one unit independently provided for brake blocks and for chairs.

By 1955 the total output had risen to 99 000 tons and all the other foundries ceased to make these types of castings. Approximately 500 men were em-ployed in the Horwich plant and by the early 1970s, when renewal of much of the mechanism became urgent, the wastage of staff was almost 50 per cent a year. Tenders were sought for a more highly-mechanised plant where the teams of three men on each of the 14 pairs of moulding machines could be eliminated; a fully-automatic central moulding machine with a minimum output of 120 moulds per hour was specified and achieved on test.

In recent years, with the light baseplate replacing the heavy chair, the light brake block displacing the large steam locomotive type, and a greatly reduced mileage being run on BR, the Horwich plant has been reduced to single-shift operations. The rationalisation of the foundries in the main works in 1962 resulted in only three of the continuing works having a foundry: the steel foundry at Crewe, the iron foundry at Horwich and the brass foundry at Swindon.

SIGNALS AND SIGNALBOX MECHANICAL EQUIPMENT

On the advice of F. W. Webb the directors of the LNWR established in Crewe a workshop to manufacture signal posts and arms, locking frames, signal levers and facing point locks. The activity commenced in 1873/4 and in 1876 Webb introduced his standard locking lever frame, which by 1885 was installed in some 50 per cent of the LNWR's signalboxes. Statistics show that the following totals had been produced by that date: signal posts 7785, signal arms 11 542, locked facing points 1629 pairs and signal levers 26 500, with the largest locking frame containing 144 levers. In 1891 Crewe supplied the largest signalbox in the country, comprising two locking frames with a total of 288 levers. The output in 1953 was 21 frames (15–125 levers) and 500 steel signals.

FILES

About 1857 the monthly consumption of files used in Crewe Works and bought at 57 different prices amounted to 1847. Subsequently many files were made at Crewe and Horwich, the former continuing into the 1960s. At Horwich in the year 1905 a production of 14 000 files was achieved.

POINTS AND CROSSINGS

The manufacture of points and crossings for the permanent way involves a large amount of heavy planing. At Horwich, for each of the years 1905/6, expenditure amounting to some £10 000 was incurred, indicating that about 200 units were called for annually. Steel point and crossing rail machining lasted until the end of the 1940s at Crewe. At Swindon a workshop was erected in 1898 to manufacture the GWR's requirements, not only of machined units but also of complete layouts, which included a large number of timbers (see Plate 12c).

LAUNDRIES

These were an unusual activity to be found in any heavy engineering factory. Three works which each had one, though for quite different purposes, were Crewe, Swindon Carriage & Wagon and Wolverton Carriage & Wagon. At Crewe a laundry was provided to clean sponge-cloths used by staff for both personal and job cleaning. At Swindon a much more elaborate plant was set up to deal with sleeping-car bedding, carriage carpets, upholstery and curtains, welders' and other heavy-duty protective overalls. At Wolverton there was a somewhat smaller laundry mainly catering for the bedding and linen used on the Euston–Glasgow service. All were closed by 1952.

WOLVERTON BATTERY SHOP

This shop manufactured a complete train-lighting system. The system embraced an enclosed watertight dynamo, a field regulator, a voltage switch and a large group of batteries slung below the vehicle. The field regulator, which was a complicated unit with over 20 carbon contacts, was necessary because of the wide variation in armature speed derived from the wheel. This equipment was made in the works, from the dynamo castings to the batteries, Best Lowmore Iron being used to make the pole pieces.

The Wolverton train-lighting system became the standard for LNWR coaches, and from 1923 the standard for the LMS. From 1950 the new BR Mark I carriages were fitted with more modern batteries, Types BRA 1 and 2 having 15 or 23 plates with capacities of 235 amps and 365 amps respectively at 5-hour rating. With the introduction of the BR Mark IIA, B and C vehicles in 1964, the first move away from the Wolverton train-lighting system came about, with the decision to use alternators and a rectifier in place of the dynamo.

GLASS-FIBRE REINFORCED PLASTICS

During the search for an improved design of carriage door for use on Southern Region suburban stock, a door-slamming machine was made for quick comparative testing. Trials were made of doors built up by layers of epoxy resins with laminations of woven glass fibre in suitable shaped moulds, and considerable improvements in door life seemed to be possible. Two moulds were used, one for the inside and the other for the outside, and the two half-sections were finally joined using glass fibre and resin. These experiments commenced at Eastleigh in 1955/6.

At the same time the manufacture of diesel railcars had commenced at Derby Carriage Works, involving the development of a multiple curved canopy at the end of each vehicle. Trials with a wood mould into which layers of resin and sheets of woven glass fibre were pressed resulted in a most successful new manufacturing practice which extended to many items on carriages and later on locomotive cabs. A most useful tool was an air gun which chopped straight bundles of glass fibre and blew the short lengths on to successive layers of resin, so achieving easy coverage of involved shapes and a rapid build-up of thickness. The development of this process led to the manufacture of ducting, gangway ends, partitions and even complete lavatory compartments in a selected range of colours (see Plate 12a).

TRACTION MOTORS

Several works in the early 1900s produced electric motors for internal use during the period of expansion when demand on the private electrical industry outstripped supply. Principally these were direct current machines, although some wound for alternating current were made to standardised designs within the works concerned, and Crewe, Derby Locomotive, Horwich and Swindon Works are known to have been involved. Most of these were of small output range, from 1 to 10 horsepower, but some machines up to 50 horsepower were also made. Probably the most important development was at Horwich, where the complete requirement of traction motors – each comprising steel carcase, field windings, armature, commutator, pinion and gearwheel – was supplied for the electric multiple-unit trains used on the Manchester and Bury line. Only the soft iron for the core stampings was purchased.

Throughout the years it became a common saying that the railway works could make anything, and this was true for almost every essential of railway engineering. Significantly, from time to time and particularly after the workshops became an entity controlled separately from the railway regions, it was necessary to prove the point – and at costs which were *cheaper* than those obtaining in the trade!

The 'Princess Royal' Class 7P 4–6–2 passenger tender locomotive No. 6200, built at Crewe, 1933.

Steam locomotive No. 44 765 under test at Rugby Locomotive Testing Station, jointly controlled by the LMS and LNER and running at up to 100 m.p.h.

8a.   The General Drawing Office, London Road, Derby, in 1938.

9a.   Control board for diesel main-line locomotives under and awaiting repair: Chief Production Mana[...]
Office, BREL HQ, Derby, 1984.

10a. *(left)* Dynamic balancing machine, Derby Loco. Works.

(right) Materials testing house, Swindon Loco. Works, showing Ransomes-Pooley 100-ton hydraulic testing machine, 1874 *(right)*, Izod Test *(foreground)* and 100-ton Buckton testing machines *(left)*.

10c. *(left)* Setting up Loke-Lynn Zeiss optical centring and collimating equipment for a 49xx Class locomotive at Swindon.

11a. Bridge-type plate-edge milling machine (Wadkin) with CNC system also controlling the sequential release of cramps for passage of tool and recramping, Derby C. & W. Works.

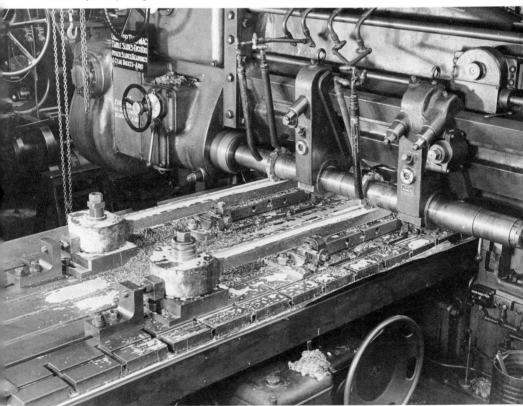

11b. Connecting rod fluting on heavy plano-milling machine, Derby Loco. Works, 1965.

(right) Large diesel-engine crankshaft grinding machine (Schmalz), Derby Loco. Works, 1966.

11d. (left) Drawing down shaft of drawbar hook under a steam hammer, Derby C. & W. Works, c. 1940.

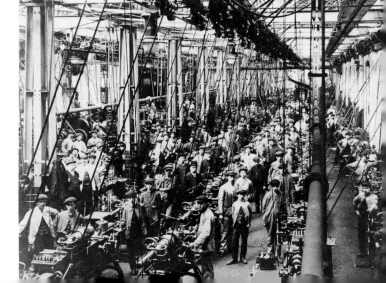

(right) Machine/fitting shop with many lathes, Darlington Loco. Works. The multiplicity of belt drives, pulleys and overhead shafting is typical of 1910.

11f. 100-ton overhead electrically-driven travelling crane with two crabs and auxiliary light hoist, Swindo Loco. Works, 1920.

11g. Unique design of electric traverser, carrying the coach supported on 4 screw jacks, installed during 1965 reorganisation of St Rollox Works.

Arch steam hammer, Rigby type, forging a bogie centre, Darlington Loco. Works, c. 1910.

Erecting shop, Darlington, c. 1910, showing a cotton rope-driven overhead travelling crane and (*left foreground*) a portable cylinder boring machine.

12a. Polyester moulding of top end of a corridor coach, Derby, 1970.

12b. Stockrail planing for switch component, Swindon Loco. Works, 1962.

Track layout with curved crossings being assembled, points and crossings shop, Swindon, 1962.

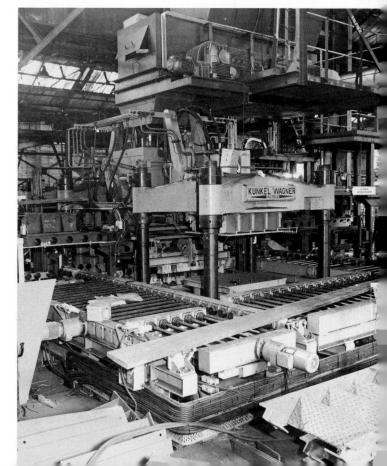

High-pressure moulding machine (Kunkel/Wagner) in the modernised mechanised foundry, Horwich Loco. Works, 1975.

13a. *(right)* 2nd world war Covenanter tank, designed and produced in railway workshops.

13b. *(left)* Train of rail-mo[unted] Howitzers built for 1st [world] war, reconditioned fo[r 2nd] world war service.

13c. *(below)* Repair layou[t for] Lancaster bombers.

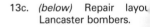

13d. *(above)* Women lathe operators, 1st world war.
13e. *(top right)* Shell production unit, Horwich Loco. Works, 1st world war.
13f. *(bottom right)* Conversion of passenger carriage to multiple ambulance coach, Derby, 2nd world war.

14a. Derby Litchurch Lane Works Training School: preparing a carriage and locomotive for permanent exhibition in the National Railway Museum, York. M7 tank locomotive (1897) and LMS coach No. M598 (1937).

14b. General view of Derby Litchurch Lane Works Training School.

New trainees allocated to plate and sheet metal work, the first apprentice training school on BR, Derby, 1947.

Official opening of Crewe Works Training School by Lord Robertson, 1955: (*left to right*) H. G. Ivatt, R. A. Riddles, CBE, and Sir William A. Stanier, FRS.

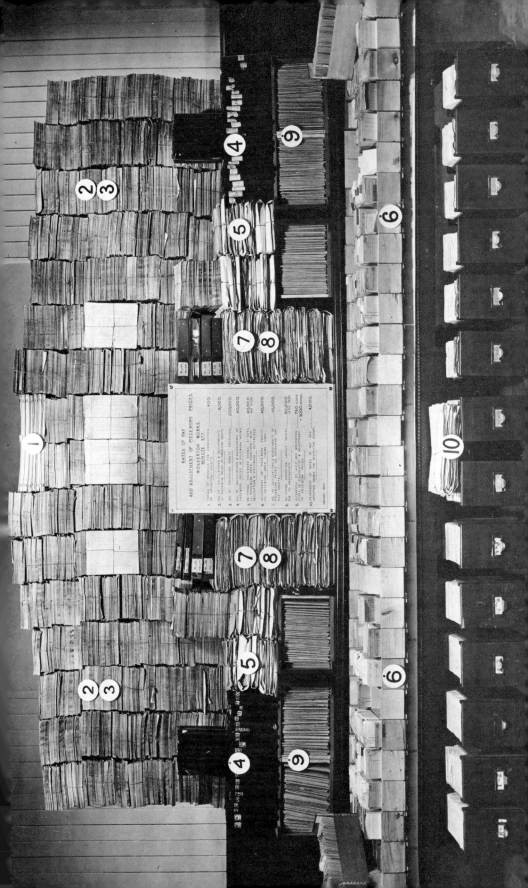

RATES OF PAY
AND ADJUSTMENT OF PIECEWORK PRICES.
WOLVERTON WORKS
MINUTE 671.

1. TONS OF OPERATIONS 400.
OF OPERATION SHEETS.

2. No. OF CALCULATIONS & ADJUSTMENTS 6,000.
OF OPERATION SHEETS.

3. No. OF OPERATION SHEETS PRODUCED. 200,000.

4. No. OF CALCULATIONS & ADJUSTMENTS OF 40,000.
PIECEWORK PRICES IN PIECEWORK BOOKS. PER YEAR.

5. PICTORIAL WORKMEN BOOKS - SETS. 40,000.
DESCRIPTION & PIECEWORK REFERENCE.

6. ADJUSTMENT OF PIECEWORK PRICES. 10,000.

7. No. OF OPERATIONAL ADJUSTMENTS OF 50,000.
PIECEWORK PRICES ON OPERATION DAY. 2,780 ITEMS.

8. RE-TYPING OPERATION LAYOUT SHEETS. 750 ITEMS.
DUE TO AMENDMENTS. 2,500 HOURS.

9. ALTERATION OF H.I.C. AND WOLVERTON 4,000.
OF PIECEWORK PRICES.

10. ADJUSTMENT OF RATES OF PAY AND
CHANGING UNDER THE WHITE COUNCIL.

JANUARY 1950.

Carriage built at Derby Litchurch Lane for export to Guinea Bauxite Mines, Kamsa, West Africa.

Class 87/0 BR B–B AC electric locomotive No. 87 012, 'Cœur de Lion', built at Crewe in 1973 with a continuous rating of 5000 Rail HP and top speed of 100 m.p.h., here on a trial run near Stonebridge Park in experimental livery and fitted with the BR/Brecknell Willis pantograph.

13 The Railway Workshops in Two World Wars

The main works are not always associated with their war-time record, yet their collective achievements had no equal in non-governmental establishments throughout the two world wars. The works provided the railways with the means to transport troops, evacuees and war materials under difficult and often – in the second world war – dangerous conditions. They also manufactured huge quantities of war products of all kinds, which greatly furthered the war effort of the country. The challenge of those international crises demonstrates the adaptability and skills of Britain's railway engineers.

At the outbreak of the first world war in 1914 the network of 120 railway companies was taken over by the Government under the Regulation of the Forces Act 1871, and was managed as a single system under the instructions of a newly-appointed Railway Executive Committee. Throughout the war the various independent railway companies undertook to assist the war effort to the limit of their capacities. With new building of locomotives, carriages and wagons reduced to a minimum, workshop staff became available to undertake war contracts of many types. Additional staff, including many hundreds of women, were employed. The extensive workshops of the leading railway companies, equipped on a scale to meet most of their normal requirements, gave employment to skilled artisans and other workers totalling over 78 000.

The co-ordination of the railway workshop activity to aid war production became the responsibility, under the Railway Executive Committee, of the Railway War Production Sub-Committee, whose members were the CMEs of a number of the larger railways. The first indication that the railway works should be used for the production of military requirements had come within a month of the declaration of war. In September 1914 the War Office asked the Railway Executive Committee whether the companies could urgently supply 12 250 ambulance stretchers of standard War Office pattern. A meeting of Carriage and Wagon Superintendents was convened and 11 railway companies agreed to divide the work between them. The first deliveries were made within 10 days and each company continued to supply a stipulated number per week, ranging from 100 to 500 until the whole 12 000 had been delivered. General service artillery wagons for the Artillery Section of the War Office were supplied at a rate of at least 400 per week from the beginning of December 1914 until the end of January 1915, a total of 9300 from 22 railway companies. The companies also converted 500 railway vans for Government use, and the total number of ambulance stretchers was raised to 25 195. The type of work involved was similar to some of the normal activities of a carriage and wagon works.

More unfamiliar requirements were nevertheless undertaken almost from the very commencement of hostilities, the earliest consisting of gun carriages for 8-inch howitzers, with the guns supplied by ordnance factories and the wheels by contract firms. Even by the end of December 1914, 12 finished howitzers had been turned out by Swindon and 11 by Derby. A wide range of forgings and stampings were made and machined, together with components for guns of various calibres and also rifles. A few works even had lathes with a long bed length where gun barrels could be rough-turned before they were sent to the specialised ordnance factories for finish-turning and rifling. Numerous contracts were accepted for Admiralty work, including mines and parts of paravanes, the latter being towed on steel-wire ropes from the bows of a ship and designed to deflect enemy mines out of a ship's path so that they could be cut loose from their anchorages and destroyed.

There was some demand for trains of special rail vehicles, partly for home defence and partly for overseas service. A number of carriage works built ambulance trains composed of vehicles adapted from standard passenger carriages and parcel vans, and these saw service at home and in France. Five trains were supplied to the US Army for use on the continent, and a special ambulance train was constructed of carriages converted to a gauge suitable for operation in Egypt. A few armoured trains were built in locomotive works; the locomotive and hauled vehicles were protected above the waistline by armour plate.

The contribution of the railway works in the production of shells formed an impressive part of their record of performance. The initial demand was for 6-inch high-explosive shells at the rate of 1000 per week, and by the end of 1917 a record output in one week of 5796 had been achieved. In all a total of 614 769 6-inch shells were produced. The works were also able to produce 62 141 forgings for other firms to machine and finish. At Darlington a plant was installed for the production of 18-pounder shrapnel shells, of which 1 064 665 were supplied. Additionally 26 654 shells of 4·5-inch calibre and 9500 bombs of various sizes were manufactured.

A vast number of component parts associated with shells were undertaken and supplied to the shell-filling and -arming factories. These consisted of some 3½ million fuses, 4½ million adapters, nearly 5 million copper driving bands and about 1½ million gaines. At one stage the demand for the last was so great that each day's production in the railway workshops was sent off to Woolwich the same night by special messenger. Initially these components were produced using the normal railway workshop machine tools and equipment, but as the demand grew certain shops were cleared and equipped specifically for the special requirement. For example, Derby Locomotive Works, which could produce 3000 fuses per week on pre-war machines, assembled an exceptionally fine plant of automatic lathes and other machines to produce 30 000 complete fuses per week. This provided employment for 550 women and girls, reflecting part of the great contribution made by girls and women who during the war took on all sorts of tasks normally undertaken by men.

In June 1915 Woolwich Arsenal had on hand a collection of 750 000 18-pounder brass cartridge cases which, after being fired at the front, had been sent back to England to be reformed. The railway companies agreed to guarantee the repair of a minimum of 50 000 per week, but offered to raise the number to 75 000 if necessary. By August the number had been raised to 89 000, but even at this rate there were still 500 000 fired cases awaiting refurbishment at Woolwich. Eventually 8 railway companies arranged to install cartridge-reforming plants to provide a total weekly output of 102 000 cartridges. One of the problems was that a number of cartridge cases had developed a split, and although initially these were scrapped Swindon devised a brazing technique which was adopted by other works, thus saving many cases. Altogether more than 33 million shell cartridge cases of four different calibres were reformed and nearly 2 million brazed.

The selection of the 2–8–0 freight locomotive by the Forces Railway Operating Division seems to have been the right choice. This simple and robust locomotive was most successful, and those built for the Railway Operating Division had a number of features which facilitated maintenance overseas, including the case-hardening of all nuts and bolts so that components could be removed for repair and replaced repeatedly. A total of 600 locomotives were built, some at Gorton but most by outside contractors, and after the war many of the locomotives were handed over to the four amalgamated railways formed in 1923 and continued to operate for several years.

The considerable technical problems involved in war production requirements presented a challenge to the railway workshop engineers. Most were resolved quickly with the help of advice from armament experts. The main problem, common to all production factories, was the matching of capacity to demand. The works had a duty to keep the rail vehicles in running order and were at the same time being pressed to accept urgent contracts. The works of 32 railway companies (out of the total of 120) had been involved in war production. By 1918 the railways were in a run-down condition and the need for rationalisation was even more apparent. The fact that railwaymen of all the companies had worked closely together during the war made the 1923 amalgamation more acceptable.

By the 1930s pioneer work on progressive planned systems in the workshops, both for vehicle construction and repair, had been introduced, and new plant including modern machine tools and woodworking machinery was being installed. The works were therefore in a sound condition to assist once again when war threatened. In an atmosphere of growing tension in Europe the Minister of Transport in 1937 held preliminary discussions with the four General Managers of the railways, and in 1938 the Railway Executive Committee was appointed, composed of the four main-line General Managers and the General Manager of the London Passenger Transport Board.

In the second world war the contribution of the railway works was even more substantial than that made in the first war. The work undertaken covered a much wider field, and the quantities of war material produced were quite remarkable. The problems were also greater, mainly as a result of enemy action. The works were fortunate that relatively little bomb damage was experienced, but damage to the rail system affected delivery of production material. The railway works were involved in the production – and sometimes the repair – of aircraft, tanks and armoured fighting vehicles, guns and gun mountings, shells, bombs and cartridge cases, bridge sections, landing craft, assault boats and submarines, together with many miscellaneous components, forgings, stampings and castings.

Although the works did not construct complete aircraft, they were heavily involved in the production and repair of wings and the repair of fuselages. In 1938 Eastleigh produced 1475 conversion sets to enable Blenheim bombers to be operated as fighters. The LMS works were the pioneers in aeroplane wing manufacture, and by 1940 Derby Carriage & Wagon Works was producing 10 pairs a week. Two years later the output was doubled, and by the end of hostilities over 4000 pairs of wings had been completed. The plan to mount a massive airborne landing in Europe, after the D-Day invasion of the French coast, called for a fleet of gliders to operate in conjunction with the parachute troops in the dropping zones. In association with outside contract firms the LMS and LNER formed a group to produce sections of Horsa gliders at Wolverton, Doncaster, York, Cowlairs and St Rollox. Eastleigh and Lancing turned out 200 Horsa glider tail units.

One of the most valuable contributions was in the repair of aircraft. The railway works had gained considerable experience of this activity, and although the article to be repaired was very different from those usually handled in railway workshops, the organisation for a repair undertaking could be very similar. C. E. Fairburn, the Chief Mechanical and Electrical Engineer of the LMS, was appointed Controller of a Hampden Bomber Repair Organisation involving both the locomotive and carriage and wagon works at Derby and also contract firms at Loughborough and Nottingham. The supply of spares for the whole group was controlled from Derby, where 2½ million parts were produced. Damaged aircraft were stripped down and rebuilt and, when beyond economic repair, parts worth reconditioning were recovered for use as replacements. Repairs were carried out at Derby on wings and fuselages, which were then transported to the Nottingham contractor for assembly. Whitley bombers were repaired at Wolverton and Spitfire fighters were repaired at Barassie, where after ground testing they were flown off from the adjacent golf course at Troon. The works at Derby, originally laid out for the repair of Hampden bombers, were adapted for other aircraft including Lancasters. Many smaller contracts were undertaken for the Ministry of Aircraft Production, including aero-engine parts, such as 200 000 bearing shells for Rolls-Royce Merlin engines produced at Cowlairs and 140 000 petrol cocks from Gorton.

The LMS contribution is shown in Figure 13.1. Its achievement in the manufacture of armoured fighting vehicles was outstanding. As early as 1938 work had started at Crewe on a prototype tank designed by the Derby LMS

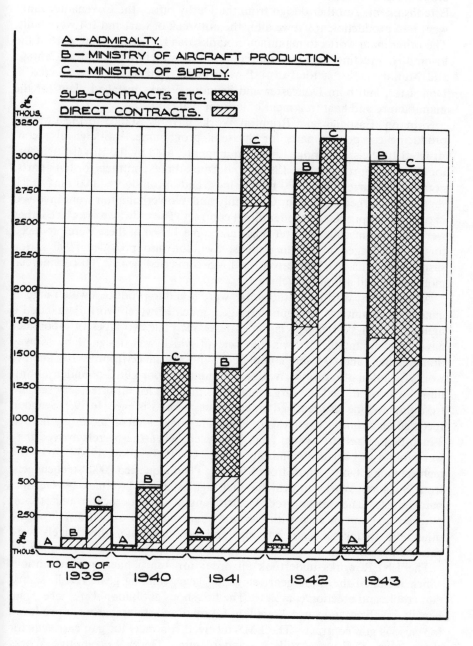

A — ADMIRALTY.
B — MINISTRY OF AIRCRAFT PRODUCTION.
C — MINISTRY OF SUPPLY.

SUB–CONTRACTS ETC.
DIRECT CONTRACTS.

SOURCE   British Rail

FIGURE 13.1   *The growth of LMS expenditure under the Railways General Manufacturing Agreement, 1939–43*

drawing office in collaboration with the Fighting Vehicle Research and Design Establishment. Another design from the Derby office, the Covenanter tank, went into production at Crewe after the outbreak of war, and 161 were built. The other main works to manufacture tanks was Horwich, where part of the locomotive erecting shop was utilised in the construction of Cruiser, Centaur and Matilda tanks; a total of 481 were built. Tank hulls were erected at Doncaster, and both Doncaster and Swindon Works installed plant for the manufacture and heat treatment of armour plate.

Swindon, Eastleigh and Brighton Works gave assistance to the LMS by producing component parts for the tank programme. Eastleigh also constructed 100 Scissors Bridge Layer Equipments, used by the Royal Engineers for bridging short gaps. The LNER undertook direct contracts for tank parts, notably 350 turrets and 1700 turret rings, and at Shildon 54 000 tank track shoes were forged. Swindon, Caerphilly and Wolverhampton were involved in component production under direct contract. The railway works tyre lathes were ideal for machining turret rings, and some 12 000 of these were produced for firms engaged in building tanks. Swindon also provided 8000 spring suspension units. At Wolverton the LMS converted nearly 700 commercial motor vans into armoured vehicles.

As in the first world war, the works were asked to produce a wide range of guns, gun mountings and gun carriages, much of which work demanded a high degree of skill and precision. The GWR built two types of 6-pounder naval gun mountings at Swindon, one of which was designed by railway draughtsmen, and 400 were completed. With assistance from LNER and SR works Swindon also produced 30 sets of multiple four-gun 2-pounder mountings. Swindon turned out large quantities of items for all three services and from time to time also received urgent requests for assistance. In 1939 Swindon received an Admiralty request to design and make a recoil mounting for 100 3-inch gun barrels to be sent from Woolwich; when the barrels arrived they were found to bear the Admiralty stamp 'GWR Swindon, 1915'! In 1940 a high-ranking infantry officer from Salisbury Plain requested 2000 'steel cudgels' from Swindon Works to arm his men against possible attack by German parachutists. The works used 14-inch lengths of superheater unit tubes, plugged one end of each with a round-head rivet and drilled a hole at the other end to take a leather thong, and two days later the cudgels were collected by the army.

The LNER works undertook an order for 4-inch naval gun mountings which included the firing gear, elevating gear, training gear, recoil, sights, gun cradle and erection complete. The hot shops at Shildon were once again heavily involved and some ¾ million forgings and stampings were produced for various gun contracts. The LMS received contracts for gun carriages for three types of Royal Artillery standard guns. Derby Locomotive Works produced 500 carriages for 25-pounder field guns and 250 carriages for 17-pounder anti-tank guns, whilst Wolverton, with help from Crewe, Derby and contract works, constructed carriages and limbers for 9·2-inch heavy guns.

Eastleigh manufactured 1500 anti-tank gun barrels and, assisted by Brighton, built 240 sets of multi-barrel rocket projectors, a type of equipment which was used in anti-aircraft defence and also produced by Doncaster.

Again the railways were directed to establish plants for the manufacture of shells and some remarkable performances were achieved, notwithstanding considerable disruption resulting from changes of policy. Swindon set up two plants, of which one was transferred to the USA before it had reached full production and the other was closed after producing 64 000 shells. At Wolverton two out of three shell-forging and machining plants were also transferred to the USA, the remaining plant producing over ½ million shells of three calibres. The LNER installed a shell-forging and -machining plant at Dukinfield but, like Swindon and Wolverton, its productive capacity was never fully utilised. Horwich was more fortunate with plant installed for the production of 20-mm Oerlikon shells, machined from lead-bearing steel bar, and 6·3 million of these were completed. The LNER plant at Dukinfield manufactured 1¼ million cartridge cases for various types of shell and reformed 5½ million, while at Horwich 3½ million cartridge cases were reformed. The GWR works machined and assembled nearly 60 000 high explosive bombs for the RAF ranging in size from 250 to 4000 pounds.

The works also dealt with a host of other Government contracts, many far removed from normal railway business. Swindon built 34 landing craft and superstructures for 50 midget submarines, and Eastleigh produced 250 landing craft, 6 fuel tenders and 24 harbour launches. Wolverton built 8442 assault boats and the LNER works constructed bridge pontoons, motor dinghies, steam launch boilers and Balsa rafts. A vast number of bridges were damaged or destroyed by enemy action, and the works were engaged in a programme to provide replacement bridge sections of War Office design, composed of interchangeable parts, including the production of jigs and fixtures which were supplied to outside contract firms. The output of steel forgings and drop stampings was greatly increased and the steel melting furnaces – closed in 1932 – were reopened for the production of steel billets.

During the second world war the LMS Class 8 freight locomotive, many of which were built by contract works, was adopted as a standard for overseas service. The works were heavily involved in giving assistance to the American Transportation Corps in connection with their 2–8–0 locomotives and special vehicles, and in a number of cases the works handed over space and facilities to the American units to operate. R. A. Riddles, who had been the LMS Mechanical and Electrical Engineer for Scotland, was appointed Director of Transportation Equipment at the Ministry of Supply, in which capacity he was responsible for the design of the standard Liberation 2–8–0 and 2–10–0 locomotives, which were built in contract works but were transferred to the UK railways after the war and maintained by the railway works.

The railway works can certainly be proud of their achievement in the war years. Tribute must be given to the staff who had responsibility for planning the ever-changing production requirement, and to the staff of all grades,

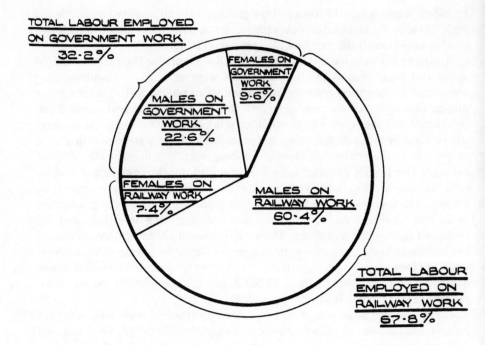

TOTAL LABOUR EMPLOYED
ON GOVERNMENT WORK
32·2%

FEMALES ON
GOVERNMENT
WORK
9·6%

MALES ON
GOVERNMENT
WORK
22·6%

FEMALES ON
RAILWAY WORK
7·4%

MALES ON
RAILWAY WORK
60·4%

TOTAL LABOUR
EMPLOYED ON
RAILWAY WORK
67·8%

SOURCE   British Rail

FIGURE 13.2   *Peak percentage of full-time railway workshop staff employed on Government work in the 2nd world war*

including a great number of women (see Fig. 13.2), who worked long hours, often on three shifts, under difficult conditions and with little rest before undertaking some additional duty such as firewatching or home guard. A remarkable example of devotion to duty occurred at Lancing Carriage Works, where on a visit shortly after the fall of Dunkirk in 1940 General (later Field Marshal) Montgomery revealed that the enemy had detailed aerial photographs of the works. It was Montgomery's contention that the Germans intended to land on the adjacent beaches and utilise the factory for the maintenance of their mobile equipment. The fact that there were many bombing raids in the area but never on Lancing supported his theory. He gave instructions that vital parts of all machines should be painted red and, in the event of an imminent landing, should be removed and placed – together with all maintenance documents – on a goods train with an engine in steam day and night for dispersal inland at short notice. From that date until the end of the war either the Works Manager or his assistant slept in an old Pullman car at the works to take charge of such an operation if necessary.

Tribute must also be given to the railway contribution made in 1939. The first four days of the war saw the successful completion of one of the most remarkable mass passenger transport movements in railway history. Over

600 000 civilians, mostly children, were evacuated from London in 1577 special trains, and more than 700 000 civilians from 17 other major centres in England and Scotland were moved out in a further 2246 trains. There were also endless troop-laden trains moving in various directions. This historical achievement stemmed from the main works, which over the years had produced the locomotives and carriage stock to make it possible, enabling colleagues in the operating and motive power departments to plan and carry out the train movements with the highest efficiency and success. It was a railway achievement without parallel, and even today could not be equalled on the roads.

Some years after the war, during the 'Cold War' of the early 1950s, an interesting contract for the production of 50 Flail tanks was carried out by Horwich Works for the Ministry of Supply. This invention had been used in the war for the destruction of mines by deploying a rotating drum on arms in front of the tank, beating the ground with balls on chains. With only some 450 horsepower to drive the vehicle and rotate the drum, the original tanks could only flail to a depth of a few inches. By 1950 it was known that mines could be effective at a depth of two feet, and the flail to be built at Horwich required some 1000 horsepower for deep flailing in addition to 450 horsepower for driving the tank. These machines were designed by railway staff at Derby and based on a reworked Churchill tank hull and a Rolls–Royce Meteor engine for flailing. Once again railway engineers were able to show that they could tackle complicated design and production problems and take them in their stride.

14 Training of Staff

In recent years staff under training in the main works have been divided into eight distinct categories consisting of craft apprentices, craftsmen, workshop supervisory, clerical personnel, administrative personnel, technicians, technologists and professional engineers, and management.

CRAFT APPRENTICES

At the time when the first railway workshops were built there was little, if any, formal training of the trade apprentices who were destined to become the craftsmen of tomorrow. As elsewhere, the customary practice was to place the young apprentice with a craftsman and hope that the former would acquire the craftsman's skills by watching and assisting.

As early as 1845 the first Railway Institutes were established by several of the developing railway companies. Their original aim was to provide scientific instruction for the working classes and thereby stimulate interest in the technical and theoretical aspects of the great industrial changes which were taking place in Britain at the time. At first there was no rush to attend lectures except, perhaps, when a prominent visiting lecturer was engaged. In the case of Crewe a young man named Warren Mand Moorsom, son of Admiral C. R. Moorsom (1792–1861, Chairman of the LNWR from 1860 to 1861 and an engineering graduate of Trinity College, Cambridge) started in Crewe Works as an engineering pupil in 1864. He entered fully into the life of the town and his interest in popular education is evident from his record of work in connection with the Crewe Mechanics' Institute. In 1870 Ramsbottom made him manager of the rail mill in the locomotive works, a post which he held until his departure from Crewe in 1876.

It was not until after the turn of the century that careful consideration was given to the development of a planned system of workshop training for trade apprentices. It was clear that there is always a sizeable volume of repetitive and relatively simple work which has to be carried out on a regular basis in engineering workshops. Such work properly falls within the scope of apprentices rather than fully skilled craftsmen. It scarcely makes sense to arrange otherwise. At the same time there were two fundamental principles which required to be fulfilled:

(1) The flow of work must be maintained to fulfil the needs of production;
(2) The apprentice requires adequate and varied experience in order to become fully proficient in all the branches of his trade.

The Progressive System of Workshop Training, called progressive because it was largely self-organising and the apprentice automatically progressed from section to section, was devised in 1932. This novel system was based on simple mathematical principles and was first introduced throughout Derby Loco-motive Works to the advantage of some 500 trade apprentices. The system took into account three basic factors, namely:

(1) The number of apprentices for whom there was useful work to be done on each section of the shop;
(2) The relationship of this number to the total number of apprentices in the shop;
(3) The total time to be spent in the shop.

To ensure continuity of work – important from the point of view of both the railway and the apprentice – it was necessary for the period of training provided on each section of the shop to be made directly proportional to the number of apprentices employed on the section compared with the total number of apprentices in the shop. When these principles were put into practice the situation which arose, say, in a small shop of three sections, all of which were suitable for apprentices, would probably be as shown below:

Section	Level of skill required	No. of apprentices required	Period on section (months)
A	Elementary	5	$5/10 \times 60 = 30$
B	Intermediate	3	$3/10 \times 60 = 18$
C	Advanced	2	$2/10 \times 60 = 12$
Total		10	60

If it were considered that 2½ years was too long on elementary work – which of course had to be done, and the volume of which work involved a normal complement of five apprentices – then this period could be shortened if additional work could be made available for them on Sections B or C. With a greater volume of advanced work diverted to the senior apprentices in this shop and, say, four apprentices accommodated instead of two apprentices in Section C, the following revised schedule would apply:

Section	Level of skill required	No. of apprentices required	Period on section (months)
A	Elementary	5	$5/12 \times 60 = 25$
B	Intermediate	3	$3/12 \times 60 = 15$
C	Advanced	4	$4/12 \times 60 = 20$
Total		12	60

This was a very satisfactory arrangement, with the training periods well balanced and the flow of work ensured. It was a scheme which readily appealed to the shop supervisory staff, and so far as the apprentice was concerned he knew from the outset what had been planned for him. With continuity of production apprentices were being given the best 'on the job' training the works could offer. Sometimes the men had to be won over to ensure smooth working. The Progressive System of Workshop Training was subsequently extended to all the main works of the LMS, and indeed within a few months following nationalisation in 1948 the British Transport Commission issued instructions for all regions to adopt the scheme.

Whilst the fundamental principles of this enlightened scheme were logically sound, the LMS, after eight years' experience of the scheme, still considered that the apprentice applicant straight from school might be destined, after a relatively short interview, to follow a trade for which he was not entirely suitable. Accordingly in 1940 the LMS carried out a three-month experiment at Derby with some 20 apprentice applicants who, in a separate workshop, underwent both theoretical and practical instruction. The LMS was encouraged

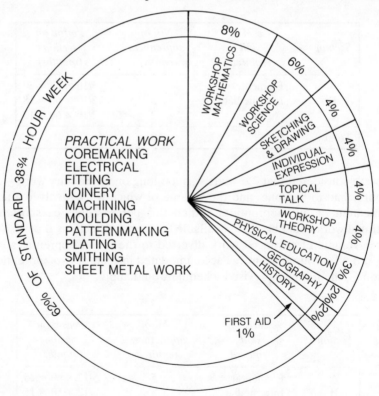

Source British Rail

FIGURE 14.1 *Relationship of practical and theoretical instruction in the works training schools (12-month course) from 1947 to 1962*

by this experiment and followed it up with another batch of 20 new trainees. It became crystal clear that a total period of 12 months was necessary to ensure a good grounding in basic skills: the first 4 to decide the trade and the next 8 to give both theoretical and practical experience in the appropriate trade before transfer to a workshop (see Fig. 14.1) .

Accordingly the LMS approved schemes for a Works Training School at each of its seven main works, the first one being officially opened at Derby by the LMS Chairman, Sir Robert Burrows, in 1947. Six more LMS schools followed and at nationalisation in 1948 the British Transport Commission authorised similar training schools for each of the main works of the other five regions of BR, as well as a similar apprentice training school for London Transport at its Acton Works, where all London underground trains are maintained and serviced. There were 10 well-equipped Works Training Schools for apprentice trainees situated within the main works at Crewe (see Fig. 14.2), Derby (2), Doncaster, Eastleigh, Glasgow, Horwich, Swindon, Wolverton and York. All had modern equipment and classrooms.

Until 1960 a boy would normally leave school at 14 or 15 and serve an apprenticeship to a particular trade until he was 21. Since that time the school-leaving age has been raised to 16 and, as all apprenticeships throughout BR now terminate at 20 years instead of 21, the apprenticeship is of only four years' duration. The first of these four years is spent in the Works Training School and at the end of the first four months the Chief Instructor decides on the trainee's most promising trade (see Fig. 14.3) and ensures that his further training in the school follows the right course. Over the years these schools in BR works have come to be recognised by the Engineering Industry Training Board – the Government-sponsored body – as well as by other organisations as setting an example throughout the industry.

HIGHER-GRADE APPRENTICES AND PUPILS

Towards the end of the nineteenth century there emerged a few far-sighted pioneering schemes to provide a limited number of opportunities for career development. In the *Daily News* of 18 August 1891 it was reported that Sir Richard Moon, late Chairman of the LNWR, had transferred £2000 of North-Western 4 per cent debenture stock to University College, Liverpool, to be used for scholarships, exhibitions or prizes for young men employed in each of the LNWR main works at Crewe, Wolverton and Earlestown who were desirous of pursuing the study and practice of engineering. The fund, known as the Sir Richard Moon Scholarship Fund to commemorate Sir Richard's long connection with the railway, was applied at first to create two scholarships each of the value of £10 per year and tenable for two years.

At the turn of the century the Great Eastern Railway works at Stratford, East London, devised an internal industrial scholarship training scheme which was probably the first of its kind in the country. Stratford Works had

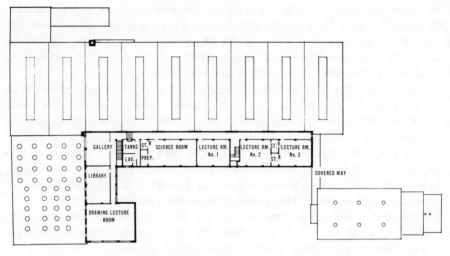

FIRST FLOOR

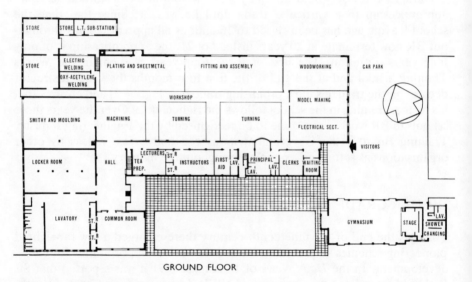

GROUND FLOOR

SOURCE   British Rail

FIGURE 14.2   *Plan of the Crewe Works Training School, the largest on BR, with accommodation for 300 apprentice trainees*

its own Mechanics' Institute and to its credit kept it alive as a teaching establishment, with part-time day and evening classes taught by qualified members of the staff, until the outbreak of the second world war, when the premises were requisitioned for use by an air-raid precautions organisation.

The first important development in training for higher-grade apprentices and pupils took place in the railway workshops at the beginning of the

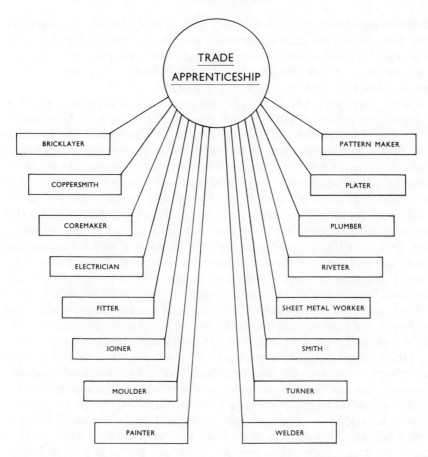

SOURCE   British Rail

FIGURE 14.3   *Principal trades taught in the locomotive works*

twentieth century. Some of the larger railway companies introduced small numbers of young men as premium apprentices, special apprentices or privileged apprentices on merit, and a still smaller number of graduate pupils. They were boys with higher education than those who became trade apprentices and some were admitted by the payment of a single premium. Their basic training was directed towards an overall workshop training with a view to their developing into professional engineers rather than craftsmen to particular trades. It was said by Sir William Stanier that Beethoven had to learn the scales before he could compose his world-renowned music! And so it was with the embryo engineer, if he was to have a solid practical basis for his future career. His close working association with the men on the shop floor taught him a great deal about human nature, for which contact there is no substitute and which experience would help to equip him for a managerial post. The railway companies concerned with these higher grades had well-established internal schemes when amalgamation took place in 1923. The works at Crewe, Derby, Doncaster, Eastleigh, Glasgow, Horwich, Stratford and Swindon were probably the most prominent.

It is not surprising that some engineers who received their basic practical training in the railway workshops subsequently attained to high distinction in other fields. Lord Hinton of Bankside was one such individual, the man who more than any other gave Britain the world lead in the peaceful development of atomic energy. Christopher Hinton was born of humble origin in Wiltshire, where he attended grammar school, and became an engineering apprentice in the Swindon GWR workshops at 16, maintaining contact with his railway contemporaries throughout his life. He threw himself into his work with that concentrated enthusiasm which became so familiar in his later atomic energy days. On completion of his apprenticeship at Swindon he won a scholarship to Cambridge and took a degree in mechanical sciences at Trinity College. He joined ICI and at 29 was chief engineer at the Alkali Division, Northwich, Cheshire. Besides his brilliance as a technologist and engineer, which places him in broadly the same historical class as Watt and the Stephensons of the eighteenth and nineteenth centuries, he was an outstanding administrator and a far-seeing and persuasive contributor to policy committees.

At the conclusion of the second world war a scheme was initiated by one of the railway companies for the interchange of junior technical staff and graduates between the railways and prominent firms manufacturing electric traction equipment. These exchanges, which were usually for six months, widened knowledge of electrical manufacture and design for selected railway staff, whilst their opposite numbers from the manufacturers gained experience in the maintenance and operation of the equipment in service. Formal agreements were made enabling the exchanges of staff to operate in a systematic manner. The scheme worked admirably.

With nationalisation in 1948 a review of all the higher-grade training schemes took place. All premiums were abolished, the grade of pupil was confined to engineering graduates and the grade of engineering apprentice was introduced for students with school certificate successes in a minimum of four subjects, two of which had to be in mathematics and English. Few engineering concerns other than the railway workshops could offer such a wide diversity of practical training, embodying both new and repair work. During the past twenty years, however, there has been a dramatic change in the relative proportions of these two grades: engineering apprentices (currently designated technician trainees) have dwindled to a trickle, whilst the admission of engineering graduates has increased at least tenfold.

The main reason is not hard to find. For 600 years there were just two universities in England, at Oxford and Cambridge; it was not until 1832 that Durham University was founded. London followed four years later, Manchester in 1880 and Birmingham in 1900. With the turn of the century the pace quickened a little, Liverpool, Leeds, Sheffield and Bristol opening by 1909. Between the two wars only Reading opened its doors, so there were 10 universities by 1945. Then came the post-war Robbins report (1961–4) with its laudable aim of improving the nation's educational standards by the provision of many new universities, making a total of 45. Polytechnics (around 30) and Colleges of Higher Education (some of which are called Institutes) total around 100, all of which, like the universities, provide tertiary education. Perhaps it has become too easy to win a university place; the lack of well-educated younger men entering the engineering industry direct from school as engineering technicians could prove to be a major setback.

The graduate will probably undertake a high proportion of non-practical workshop training and his course will be planned to include more remote training, with perhaps a variety of appreciation courses, the contents of which would be far better absorbed after a substantial and intensive course of basic workshop practice. Few former graduates in control of large numbers of workshop staff, rather than the designers and research personnel, depend on their academic training. It is a problem which has to be solved by the engineering industry in close collaboration with the Department of Education and Science, the universities and the relevant professional institutions.

Technician trainees

Previously designated engineering apprentices, technician trainees are selected from students who are about to leave school, providing they have:

(1) GCE passes at least at ordinary level in English, mathematics, a science subject (preferably physics) and one other subject, at Grade A, B or C, or CSE Grade 1 equivalent; or
(2) Scottish Certificate of Education passes at the ordinary grade in the subjects specified above.

Provision is also made, as hitherto, for craft trainees in BREL to be appointed as technician trainees, providing they have reached an appropriate academic standard. Students should be not more than 18 years of age at entry, but this age may be exceeded where students are already serving a craft apprenticeship.

The BR engineering sponsored studentship scheme

Candidates who wish to take a three-year full-time university course are required to undergo one year of practical training with BR before they enter university, to return for 10 weeks of practical training during each summer vacation and to undertake about 6–9 months of further practical training after they have completed their last year at university and obtained an engineering degree. This is known as the 1–3–1 sandwich scheme and the training with BR is apportioned as shown below for those who intend to follow a career in mechanical and electrical engineering:

Basic workshop practice in mechanical and electrical engineering	3 months
Construction and repair of locomotives or other rolling stock in a main works	6
Diesel and/or electric locomotive and rolling stock maintenance experience in a service depot	3
Design appreciation	3
Regional M&EE headquarters	1
Special courses	2
Objective training (aimed at probable first appointment)	6
	24

TRAINING CENTRES

BREL Training Centre, Derby

During the second world war the LMS organised regular courses for the workshop supervisors at each of its 7 main works, and the value of these courses was well established several years before nationalisation. When British Railways Workshops Division was formed in 1962 (reconstituted as British Rail Engineering Limited in 1970) it was decided to adapt a suitable office block located in Derby Locomotive Works as a headquarters training centre with lecture rooms and syndicate rooms for the training of workshop supervisors of various grades. Table 14.1 shows courses run here between 1965 and 1982.

Railway Engineering School, Derby

This was formerly the LMS School of Transport at Derby, opened in 1938, and originally catering mainly for the needs of the operating and signalling and telecommunications departments. This impressive purpose-built residential training centre, to which a new wing was added in 1956 to meet the needs of diesel-electric traction, provides training in technical subjects for members of the Mechanical and Electrical Engineering Department and the Signals and Telecommunications Department of BREL; hence the adoption of its new name in 1976. Courses are of 1–4 weeks' duration and are in progress throughout the year from basic to advanced levels.

The resources of the school allow up to six different courses to be taught simultaneously. On average 10–12 students are accepted for each course, thus allowing adequate individual tuition, especially in practical work, with considerable emphasis on practical fault-finding in the more advanced courses. The employment of practising engineers as instructors ensures that the courses remain practically orientated and avoids undue academic bias. The mechanical and electrical engineering courses are attended mainly by all levels of technical

TABLE 14.1 *BREL specialised courses in industrial engineering for workshop supervisory staff and associated grades, 1965–82*

Type of course	Duration	Approx total no. who have attended	Grades of staff attending	Remarks
Industrial Relations	1 week	750	Management Staff Reps Reps of Management Artisan Clerical Up to MS 3	
Supervisory Management Training	4 weeks	640	Supervisory/ Substantive/Acting/ Temporary	Candidates may elect to sit NEBSS exam. then proceed to Training Centre for final two weeks and examination.
NEBSS	2 weeks	300		
Introductory	1 week	70	CAT 4 to Workshop SB	Introduced to assist those who need training assistance in calculating. The student may elect to be considered for a future course. It is NOT a pass/fail situation.
Industrial Engineer Foundation	5 weeks	40	CAT 4 to Workshop SB	Industrial Engineering restructured.
Industrial Engineering Method Study	3 weeks	12	Workshop SB	
Industrial Engineering Estimating & Planning	1 week	30	Workshop SB	
Network Analyses	1 week	150	Workshop SB to MS 1	
Basic Work Data	2 weeks	20	Workshop SB and Workshop SC	Successful students receive certificate from PERA.
Industrial Engineering Practitioner	8 weeks	360	CAT 4 to Workshop SB	Now replaced by separate courses as above.
Statistics	1 week	80	Workshop SB to MS 1	
Spoken Word	2/3 days	30		For those who are required to give 'short' sessions to works staff. e.g. Fire Precautions, First Aid.
Use of Visual Aids	2 days	10		Complementary to the Spoken Word course.

SOURCE   BREL

and workshop supervisory staff. As newly-developed rolling stock comes into service the engineering school devises a training programme to deal with its maintenance.

The Work Study Training Centre, Watford

In 1956 the British Transport Commission, under the chairmanship of Sir Brian Robertson, appointed a Director of Work Study to provide an internal management consultancy service to all divisions of the BTC, totalling 750 000 employees. To assist in this work the wartime headquarters of the LMS at The Grove, Watford, Hertfordshire, was placed at the director's disposal and converted as the training centre for management staff. The first Principal was Arnold G. Kentridge and the Senior Instructor P. Corbishley. Regional schools were provided for practitioner training in method study and work measurement.

PROFESSIONAL ENGINEERING INSTITUTIONS

The Institution of Mechanical Engineers and the Institution of Electrical Engineers are the two most important professional institutions to which senior management within BREL turn their attention. The former has a special attraction because it has a separate Railways Division; regular meetings of the division are held and papers read at the Institution, which is located in Birdcage Walk, London, as well as at its four Regional Centres in England and Scotland. There are various grades of membership and any established engineer is permitted to use the letters CEng, MIMechE or FIMechE, whichever is appropriate.

The word 'engineer' is frequently used indiscriminately. In broad terms a *chartered engineer* is concerned with the progress of technology through innovation, creativity and change, the development and use of new technologies, the promotion of advanced design and design methods, the introduction of new and more efficient production methods, the generation and pioneering of new engineering services and management methods. The *technician engineer* is in general concerned not with promoting change but with maintaining and managing existing technology at peak efficiency; he provides the most satisfactory service possible from existing resources, and exercises firm control and management within defined and regulated conditions.

From 1984 all applications for corporate membership of the Institution of Mechanical Engineers are subject to rules requiring candidates to attend a professional interview in addition to satisfying the pre-existing requirements of obtaining an academic degree in engineering and passing the examination set by the Institution.

For over half a century the overall training standards applicable to the various grades of staff employed in the main works of British Railways and its predecessors have taken second place to none in the British engineering industry. Systematic training was practised in many works in their very early days, and over the years, with the conscious desire to improve safety standards for both passengers and staff as well as to improve efficiency and productivity within the works, well-devised training schemes have been introduced. Most of this training is now carried out in well-equipped BR training establishments which form an integral part of the organisation. Selected professional and technical staff as well as workshop supervisory staff also attend specialised courses organised by various outside authorities. BR is very much alive to all that is needed to keep management staff and other key grades in tune with an ever-changing technology.

15 Industrial Relations

The importance of good industrial relations in any industry can scarcely be overstated. British Railways and its predecessors have, over a very long period, brought relationships between their employees and management representatives at all levels to a commendable standard. For many years after the railway era began there were no trade unions. The first affecting railway staff was established in 1871.

There are many early minutes of the various Railway Companies Committee Meetings, as well as other sources, which make revealing and informative reading. At the New Shildon Locomotive Works (later to become the Shildon Wagon Works) of the Stockton & Darlington Railway the rules provided, among others, for the following punishments:

Any workman leaving his work without giving notice to the clerk or the foreman to be fined 1s. 0d.

Any workman swearing or using abusive language to a shopmate to be fined 1s. 0d.

Should any workman leave his work for the purpose of drinking in working hours, he will be considered as having forfeited his situation.

Those seeking employment on the Great Western Railway in 1837 were required to write these words: 'Zealously strive to excel. Industry is commendable. Perseverance deserves success. Quietude of mind is a treasure.'

A strike of sixty Irish labourers employed on the Glasgow & Ayrshire Railway, which began on 30 July 1838, was unsuccessful. The contractors in this instance resisted the demand for a wage increase and quickly replaced the Irishmen with Scotsmen! Since these early days fundamental and enlightened changes in practice have become firmly established. In short, BR today can unequivocally be classified as a good employer.

AGREEMENTS ON WAGES AND HOURS

To trace the history of industrial relations in the railway workshops one has to go back to a period just before the first world war. Until then each of the 120 individual and independently-owned railway companies had made their own agreements with their workshop staff. None was more important than the weekly rates of pay paid to the various grades comprising skilled, semi-skilled and unskilled workshop staff. At that time there was no consistency in the rates in operation on the different railway companies. The trade unions were asking for district rates, that is, the rate agreed upon or recognised by organised employers and workers in different trades and industries in particular localities.

194

On 7 April 1920, at a time when the railways were still working under Government control, a letter was sent to the Federation of Engineering and Shipbuilding Trades and also to the National Union of Railwaymen by the Negotiating Committee of General Managers, which was then acting for the Ministry of Transport. In the letter it was stated that the railway companies generally would be prepared to concede the principle of district rates to the men employed in their various shops on the clear understanding that the men would be debarred from any railway privileges, except perhaps such privileges as they obtain today under the privilege ticket arrangement.

At a meeting of the joint committee on 5 November 1920 certain heads of arrangement were adopted in which it was recorded that the craft unions and the National Union of Railwaymen assented to the principle of grouping places at which railway shopmen were employed and fixing railway rates for the different classes of railway shopmen in each group. Protracted negotiations between all the parties followed this provisional agreement and differences were revealed upon which it was found that no agreement was possible. The parties concerned (see Appendix, Table A.2) referred the matter to the Industrial Court.

It transpired that some 600 workshops, running sheds and depots throughout England and Wales had to be considered, involving approximately 1500 different classes of railway shopmen and the rates of pay and conditions of about 110 000 men. The case was of an extremely complex character. Representatives of the parties were heard at the Industrial Court in February 1922 and the court's decision was set out in Schedules A, B, C, D and E of Industrial Court Award No. 728 dated 8 July 1922. These determined six area rates (for London and five classes of town) and enumerated all the various grades of skilled, semi-skilled and unskilled workers. There is no doubt that the award of 1922 will always be recognised as an outstanding judicial decision in the long history of the railway workshops.

This agreement was in operation until 1948, when the rates of pay of railway shopmen underwent another far-reaching change following the appointment of a railway management committee. The rates for the five classes of town were eliminated, a considerable number of grades eliminated and the basic rates of all the grades retained revised, with some of the war wage consolidated, whilst ensuring that appropriate differentials were maintained for each grade. The committee had been set up by the four main-line companies in 1947 and its recommendations were approved at a meeting of the Railway Shopmen's National Council on 25 May 1948 (RSNC Minute 577), only five months after nationalisation. It was a major development and was well received by the senior officers of all the technical departments.

The third and current agreement applying to basic rates for workshop staff was introduced on 11 April 1969 under the title of 'Pay and Efficiency Agreement'. It is doubtful whether any other major industry comparable with the workshop staff of British Railways has operated successfully with only three major agreements over a period of sixty years. This enlightened agreement between the BR Board and the Railway Shopmen's National Council reduced the number of grades to a mere twenty, with eight basic rates. The determination of the basic rate of pay is independent of any system of payment by results. The basic rate is the accepted measure for comparing and contrasting different grades of craftsmen.

The highest-paid craftsman in BR main works has been, and appropriately continues to be, the patternmaker. He is not only a highly skilled craftsman, but he regularly has to interpret working drawings of intricate castings of various metals and redraw full-size sectional views to produce both patterns and coreboxes, whilst making due allowance for the shrinkage of the different metals.

The Pay and Efficiency Agreement provided for work measurement, as understood in the field of work study and industrial engineering, to supersede the piecework system, a most decisive step which has been beneficial to the staff and the railway industry. RSNC Minute 577 was a landmark in the railway shopmen's rates of pay. It was the first complete revision of base rates and piecework prices since Industrial Court Award No. 728, and was recognised as involving the largest administrative task undertaken at the main works since that time. Plate 15a shows the documentation involved at Wolverton Carriage and Wagon Works, where 40 000 registered piecework prices had to be revised. All the main works had developed similar systems; at Crewe Locomotive Works the number to be revised was no less than 150 000, involving four times as much documentation as Wolverton. Following the replacement of the piecework system with the introduction of BSI standard minutes in 1969 this amount of clerical work when basic rates of pay are changed will never arise again.

Even before the Pay and Efficiency Agreement of 11 April 1969 applicable to railway shopmen the first pay and efficiency agreement was applied to workshop supervisors as from 31 October 1968. This was concluded between the British Railways Board, Amalgamated Engineering and Foundryworkers' Union, Association of Scientific, Technical and Managerial Staffs, Confederation of Shipbuilding and Engineering Unions, National Union of Railwaymen and Transport Salaried Staffs Association, for improving the pay and efficiency of workshop supervisory staff. Table 15.1 show rates of pay for clerical, supervisory and professional and technical staff in 1982.

Of all the aspects of dealing with organised labour, perhaps only second in difficulty to rates of pay and overall earnings comes hours of work. In the railway workshops weekly hours of work were changed from 54 to 47 in 1918, to 44 in August 1947, to 40 in February 1966 and to 39 from 1 January 1982, thus keeping in line with the engineering industry generally.

The machinery of negotiation for wages staff employed under shop conditions in the main works of BREL is still based on an agreement made between the former railway companies and the trade unions on 15 August 1927, as subsequently amended. This provides for elected Shop Committees and Works Committees. In the event of a Shop Committee not resolving a

TABLE 15.1 *Rates of pay, 1982*

	Rates of pay (£ per annum)
Clerical staff (max.)	
Clerical Officer, Grade	
1 (18 and over)	4 117
Clerical Officer, Grade 2	5 120
Clerical Officer, Grade 3	5 646
Clerical Officer, Grade 4	6 564
Clerical Officer, Grade 5	7 484
Workshop supervisors	
Minimum	5 363
Maximum	7 612
Professional and technical staff (max.)	
Technical Officer	5 911
Senior Technical Officer	7 936
Principal Technical Officer	8 510

matter which has been raised, the item is referred to the Works Committee, which normally sits under the chairmanship of the Works Manager.

SUPERANNUATION SCHEMES

Pension Funds have a long history on the railways. The LNWR, for example, established a superannuation fund as early as 1853, whilst the GWR Locomotive and Carriage Department Sick Fund Society was established as long ago as 1844 and is still paying pensions. For well over fifty years there has been a railway history of joint control of the pension schemes by employer and employee. Indeed this policy can be traced back to the nineteenth century in relation to the older sick pay and death benefit societies. The policy of joint control or participation has been further developed in the modern railway pension schemes.

The gradual amalgamation of the many railway companies into the present unified system has been paralleled in the railway pension fund field. Following the amalgamation under the Railways Act 1921 each of the four new railway companies set up a superannuation fund for the benefit of its salaried staff, and these funds absorbed the superannuation funds of the pre-amalgamation companies. In 1970 these four superannuation funds were amalgamated into one fund, the British Railways Superannuation Fund.

In the field of pensions for wages staff progress was less uniform. Pension schemes for wages staff did exist under the pre-grouping companies but these varied considerably from company to company; in many cases these arrangements and the differences between them continued unaltered after the 1923 amalgamation and even after nationalisation in 1948. An industry-wide pension scheme was started by the British Transport Commission in 1954, but the first comprehensive pension fund for railway wages staff was the British Railways (Wages Grades) Pension Fund established in 1967, to which large numbers of railwaymen were transferred.

The three main bodies established to look after the pension schemes are the Joint Working Party on Pensions, the Trustees and the Management Committees. Each of these bodies has a clearly-defined area of responsibility. The Joint Working Party on Pensions is the forum in which representatives of the board (the employer) and the five main railway trade unions (representing the members) meet to discuss changes in the pension schemes. The trade unions represented on this body are the Associated Society of Locomotive Engineers and Firemen (ASLEF), the British Transport Officers' Guild (BTOG), the Confederation of Shipbuilding and Engineering Unions (CS&EU), the National Union of Railwaymen (NUR) and the Transport Salaried Staff Association (TSSA).

The Trustees have delegated very wide investment responsibilities to Investment Committees. There is a separate Investment Committee for each of the pension schemes. One half of the members of each committee is appointed by the board and the other half is nominated by the main trade unions involved. There is also a separate Management Committee for each pension scheme. One half of each committee is appointed to represent the members (and pensioners) of the scheme, the balance being appointed by the board.

The Management Committees ensure that the correct contributions are collected and the correct benefits paid in accordance with the rules. As the whole reason for the existence of the schemes is to pay benefits to members and their families, it is essential that these benefits are paid accurately and on time. This is an enormous task in which the committees are assisted by a secretary and his staff who are members of the Corporate Pensions Department at Darlington. This department is staffed by experienced administrators using computerised systems.

The railway pension schemes are amongst the biggest in the country and the figures in Table 15.2, extracted from the 1980 accounts, indicate the scale on which they operate.

HEALTH AND SAFETY

The first piece of factory legislation was the Morals and Health Act 1802, almost a quarter of a century before the opening of the Stockton & Darlington Railway. It provided for the ventilation and cleansing of cotton mills and factories, and stipulated the clothing, hours of labour and religious education of apprentices. In 1878 the Factory and Workshop Act appeared. Besides

TABLE 15.2   *Railway Pension Funds, 1980*

Fund	Number of pensioners	Number of members	Market value of invested funds
British Railways Superannuation Fund	44 000	71 000	£1 032 000 000
British Railways (Wages Grades) Pension Fund	40 000	152 000	£430 000 000

consolidating earlier legislation, this Act increased the minimum age of child labour in textile factories to 10 and made provisions for holidays and breaks in the working day.

An important development in 1893 was the first appointment of women inspectors. Up to 1937 the only parts of the Factory and Workshop Act which applied to men were those respecting sanitation and safety, such as cleanliness and ventilation, means of escape in case of an outbreak of fire, the fencing of machinery and regulations in regard to dangerous trades. Greater stringency in these respects came in the Factory and Workshop Act of 1895 and still more in the codifying Act of 1901.

The Factories Act 1961 lays down general principles for the health, safety and welfare of factory employees. The Act applies only to premises which come within the statutory definition of a factory, though this includes many varied types of premises such as shipyards and dry docks. It would be impracticable to exhibit copies of an Act having 160 sections and 4 schedules, but factory occupiers must display at principal entrances to their premises, in places where it can be conveniently read by employees, a prescribed abstract of the Act.

Legislation for preventing accidents to railway employees dates from 1900. The largest remaining gap was filled when office workers were covered by the Offices, Shops and Railway Premises Act 1963, which applies to all office premises, shop premises and railway premises where persons are employed to work.

The Health and Safety Executive falls under the aegis of the Minister of Employment and has wide-ranging responsibilities, including control of the Factory Inspectorate. By 1972, HM Factory Inspectorate, which was responsible for enforcing the 1961 Act, had over 700 inspectors. The Health and Safety at Work Act 1974 set up a single inspectorate, the Health and Safety Executive, to take over the functions of all previous inspectorates. Factory inspectors are authorised to visit BREL works at all reasonable times, and in general it can be said that all the main works enjoy a high reputation in meeting the standards required.

STAFF SUGGESTIONS

The first recorded railway staff suggestion came from Leonard Brierley, a Birmingham railway employee, on 22 April 1846. He wrote to his London & Birmingham HQ at Euston Square urging them to construct the first train restaurant cars, for which he enclosed his own blueprint drawings. The first dining car went into railway service 33 years later – on the Great Northern's Kings Cross to Leeds route in 1879.

The first official railway staff suggestions scheme started in 1913. Up to 1949 the regions had their own individual schemes but subsequent arrangements stem from the unified scheme formed in 1949, revised in 1969 (WASP Scheme) and amended in 1981. The objectives of the BR scheme are twofold. It is primarily an industrial relations instrument with the object of encouraging the co-operation of the staff in maintaining progress and development and seeking generally to further the interests of BR. Its secondary objective is to achieve reductions in the cost of processes and operations, and it offers financial incentives to staff to participate (see Table 15.3).

BRITISH RAIL FIRST AID ORGANISATION

The British Rail First Aid Organisation is conducted in England under the auspices of the St John Ambulance, in Wales under the Priory for Wales and in Scotland under the St Andrew's Ambulance Association. Organisation is on a regional basis, with the General Manager as President, the Chief Personnel Officer as Chairman and a Group Medical Officer as Medical Adviser. The administration of the Regional First Aid Organisation and its activities is undertaken by the Regional First Aid Secretary, who is responsible to the Chief Personnel Officer.

Each region is divided into appropriate districts, with District First Aid Secretaries appointed in an honorary capacity by the Chief Personnel Officer. District Secretaries are responsible to the Regional First Aid Secretary for activities within their respective districts.

First aid training is undertaken within classes and elected members form class committees. These committees meet voluntarily as necessary to discuss local matters and may make recommendations to the District First Aid Committee. British Rail has a legal responsibility to provide first aid equipment and, in certain circumstances, trained personnel at premises under its control.

BRITISH RAIL STAFF ASSOCIATION

The British Rail Staff Association was created in 1952, four years after nationalisation, to integrate into one organisation, for the benefit of all staff

TABLE 15.3 *BR Staff Suggestions Scheme showing BREL in the context of BR regions and BRB Headquarters for 1980*

Region	Number of staff at 31.12.80	Number of suggestions received	Number per 100 staff %	Suggestions adopted						Interest awards						Total amount paid £
				By Region		By HQ Committee (includes wider application)		Total		By Region		By HQ Committee		Total		
				No.	£	No.	£	No.	£	No.	£	No.	£	No.	£	
Eastern	46 898	665	1.4	44	1 280	10	697	54	1 977	91	560	41	257	132	817	2 794
London Midland	49 471	896	1.8	79	2 978	13	1 640	92	4 618	136	880	38	373	174	1 253	5 871
Scottish	18 939	120	0.6	8	165	—	—	8	165	41	253	4	28	45	281	446
Southern	29 617	667	2.2	50	1 823	7	276	57	2 099	61	559	21	130	82	689	2 788
Western	23 157	573	2.5	35	343	3	715	38	1 058	91	595	21	132	112	727	1 785
Total (regions)	168 082	2 921	1.8	216	6 589	33	3 328	249	9 917	420	2 847	125	920	545	3 767	13 684
BREL	36 255	244	0.7	47	4 717	15	2 004	62	6 721	64	536	48	417	112	953	7 674
BRB headquarters	8 394	199	2.4	—	—	4	1 100	4	1 100	—	—	30	218	30	218	1 318
Grand total	212 731	3 364	1.6	263	11 306	52	6 432	315	17 738	484	3 383	203	1 555	687	4 938	22 676

nationally, the existing sports clubs, institutes and social clubs which had been established under the former main-line railway companies and had received widely different levels of support from the companies. This enabled everyone who became a member to have access to a wider range of activities nationally on payment of a standard subscription.

Previously the clubs and institutes had served mainly local needs and interests, with relatively little inter-club and inter-regional contact. The establishment of a central fund assisted in the development of inter-area, inter-regional and international competitions and other events designed to strengthen the sense of a wider social community of railway people. Clubs and institutes which had been set up by or in close association with the main workshops were identified with the region in which they were located for BRSA purposes. This practice has continued since the formation of BREL, that is, BRSA members employed by BREL vote through area and regional councils and conferences.

The aims and objectives of BRSA are: 'To develop social, recreative and cultural activities amongst BR staff and their families, to foster the spirit of fellowship, and to do everything possible to further the prestige of British Railways.'

There are opportunities for members to participate in international events with representatives of the staff associations and social clubs of railways abroad. Apart from sport and recreation BRSA has a good traditional record of helping retired employees and widows to keep in touch, and of supporting the railway charities generously, especially those for children and for people suffering ill-health.

In 1981 the association had 127 000 members who are or were employed by BR and certain other transport undertakings formerly covered by the Railway Executive immediately after nationalisation, but now separate from BR, such as BT Docks and NCL. Despite the contracting size of BR over the years, the membership of BRSA has remained fairly constant, reflecting the strength of continued interest in the original concept of a railway community.

16 Financial Control

The conditions under which the engineering industry is now carried on are vastly different from those existing a generation ago. The railway industry in Britain is no exception, and this applies especially to the service provided by the main railway workshops, in which very large sums of mainly public money are involved, with a turnover of £440 million in 1982. The common practice in industry today is to provide a firm tender, and in BREL, whether the product is for BR or for outside customers, a firm price has to be quoted. One of the chief elements in the cost of production is the cost of labour, and improved methods of manufacture are constantly under review.

At the time when most of the main railway workshops came into operation a century ago, the system of keeping accounts was primitive compared with present-day accountancy practices. Early financial records are no longer available because the scanty records which were prepared would have been destroyed after the usual retention period of 50 years, but there is plenty of evidence to show that the system of railway accounts was already much improved by the beginning of this century.

Between amalgamation in 1923 and nationalisation in 1948 important developments in railway accountancy took place. Each of the four main-line companies introduced its own system for ascertaining the cost of locomotives and different classes of rolling stock, whether new or undergoing repairs. Individual costing of classified locomotive repairs in the main workshops, as well as in the motive power depots, was introduced by the LMS in 1927, and this far-seeing system was extended to all six regions of BR in 1949, when approximately 10 per cent of the locomotive stock was included. The classes selected were those of modern design likely to remain in service for a considerable number of years, involving separate wages and material documents. The use of individual costing figures has proved extremely valuable in providing justification for the premature breaking up of unsatisfactory locomotives and other stock. Initially the main problem with individual costing was the overhead cost of producing a multiplicity of documents, but for many years computerised documentation has increasingly come to the aid of the engineer and the accountant.

For all new manufacture the documentation for material costs and direct wages emanates from the Works Production Office in each works. For locomotive and rolling stock maintenance work the equivalent documentation is produced by the Initial Examiners in the shops concerned, the pre-printed worksheets which the examiners use forming the actual wages tickets which are passed to the Works Accountant for wages computation.

After the formation of BR Workshops Division in 1962 the accounting system was refined to provide statements of accounts, individual accountability and control of costs, which corresponded more and more closely to

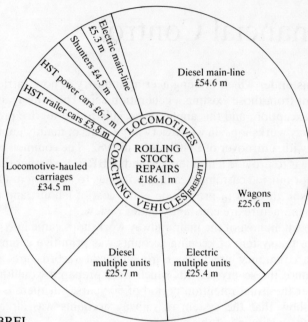

Source   BREL

Figure 16.1   *BREL expenditure on repair of BR rolling stock, 1979*

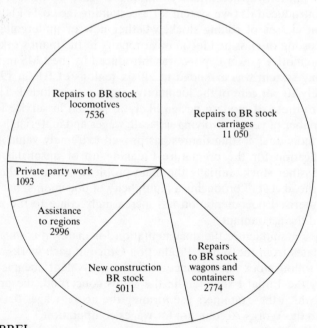

Source   BREL

Figure 16.2   *BREL manpower utilisation (wages paid staff), 1979*

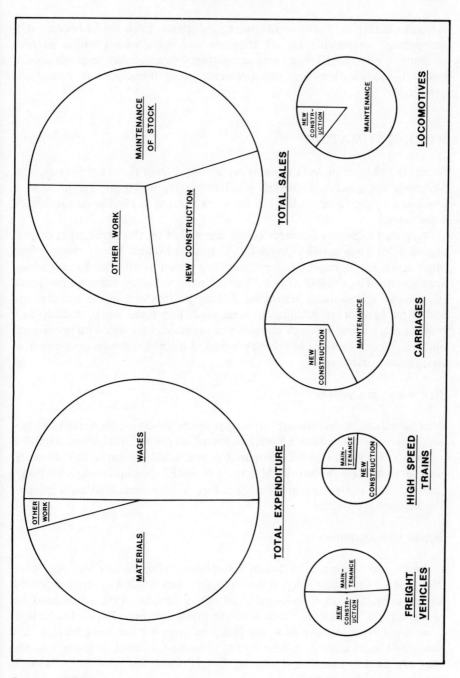

Source   BREL

FIGURE 16.3 *Proportions of BREL expenditure and sales income in different areas, 1980, with sales further analysed within 4 categories*

systems existing in other manufacturing industries. Each works became self-accounting, responsible for all activities and costs arising within its own confines. Under BREL the same accountancy practice has been continued, but with modifications and improvements being introduced as considered beneficial.

WORKS ESTIMATING

Material and level of work content are assessed from the drawings supplied. Materials are priced at current purchase rates, whilst the labour cost is evaluated by group or trade from the work content at current or anticipated wage rates.

Overhead expenses (indirect costs) are added by the application of percentages for each activity or trade to estimated direct labour costs, whilst other costs, for example delivery costs, are added to total works cost where appropriate. To calculate work for outside parties, selling expenses and profit (to achieve an adequate return on the capital invested in the activity) are added by percentage addition to total cost. For some work, notably new power units and rolling stock construction, estimates are based on previously-built vehicles or sections of vehicles, updated for major design or component changes and price levels.

New works procedures

New works schemes consist of new projects involving new layouts, new equipment or workshop improvements of any kind, for which capital is required. They are carefully prepared as and when they arise at each works and submitted by the Works Managers to BREL headquarters, where they are vetted by the Technical Director before further consideration is given by the Managing Director.

Repair documentation

Vehicles are inspected by Initial Examiners, who identify the operations required for the repair. Depending upon the classification of repair required, certain operations are mandatory whilst others depend on the actual condition of the vehicle. The Initial Examiners' pre-printed sheets – Repair Instructions – are used as an instruction to the group to carry out the work and are then submitted to allocate the labour cost to the repair account. In some instances they are used to calculate labour bonus payments, but in other cases this is based on vehicle output.

Materials are also identified by Initial Examiners, and Demand/Issue Notes are prepared to draw the material from stores. These notes indicate job chargeability by the use of a cost allocation code.

Production planning documentation (new manufacture)

Each new job, from a complete locomotive or vehicle to a component, is deduced from the working drawings into individual operations. The key document is the Operation Layout Sheet produced by experienced planners. From this document individual labour operation documents are also prepared in the Production Office as instructions to the relevant group of men to carry out the work. These documents are forwarded to the Works Accountant when the job is complete – both for payment in respect of bonus calculation to the individual or group, and for production and cost control purposes. A computer-controlled machine loading and material scheduling system has recently been introduced into the works to facilitate tighter financial control over these activities.

Demand/Issue Notes for the materials required are also prepared from the Operation Layout Sheet as instructions to draw the materials from stores.

Workshop expenses

These include all shop charges incurred in the provision of services, labour, materials and equipment which are necessary to operate a works and are not chargeable directly to a manufacturing account. They are often referred to as production on costs or overhead expenses. Whenever items can be charged directly to a manufacturing order this is preferable: for example, the original cost of a jig is debited to the first order and not to workshop expenses. To obtain the overall cost of any productive work it is necessary to add overhead expenses, or workshop expenses, to the direct wages. A statement is prepared each 4-weekly period, giving a total of 13 statements per annum for each cost centre. There is an approved budget figure for each item of expenditure and this is shown against the actual expenditure, with a column of figures showing the credit or debit amount involved and an overall total for each cost centre (see Fig. 16.4). Workshop expenses are classified as variable or non-variable, each individual item having its own distinctive number in the computer.

The works are divided into cost centres usually representing an activity, and each of the large works, such as Crewe Locomotive Works and Derby Litchurch Lane Works, has over 20 cost centres. Workshop expenses are all costs associated with the cost centre. There are four main types of cost centre at each works, with a varying number of individual cost centres depending on which costs cannot easily be identified with the job, repair or process carried out there, that is, costs other than direct wages and materials. The main types are:

(1) Administration;
(2) Services;
(3) Maintenance;
(4) Production.

BRITISH RAIL ENGINEERING LTD - _____ WORKS

SUMMARY TRADING, PROFIT AND LOSS ACCOUNTS - FOUR WEEKS ENDED _____ 198_

	PERIOD						AGGREGATE					
	BUDGET	ACTUAL	VARIANCE FROM BUDGET			BUDGET	ACTUAL	VARIANCE FROM BUDGET				
			TOTAL	PRICE	VOLUME			TOTAL	PRICE	VOLUME		
	(a)	(b)	(c)	(d)	(e)	(f)	(g)	(h)	(i)	(j)		
	£000	£000	£000	£000	£000	£000	£000	£000	£000	£000		
SALES												
11 REPAIRS TO ROLLING STOCK												
12 MODIFICATIONS TO ROLLING STOCK												
13 CONSTRUCTION OF ROLLING STOCK												
14 SUNDRY SERVICES TO REGIONS												
15 SUPPLIES TO REGIONS												
16 SERVICES TO OTHER WORKS												
17 SUPPLIES TO OTHER WORKS												
18 OUTSIDE PARTIES												
29 TOTAL SALES												
31 LESS COST OF SALES												
TRADING PROFITS /LOSSES/												
41 REPAIRS TO ROLLING STOCK												
42 MODIFICATIONS TO ROLLING STOCK												
43 CONSTRUCTION OF ROLLING STOCK												
44 OTHER SERVICES TO REGIONS												
45 SERVICES TO OTHER WORKS												
46 OUTSIDE PARTIES												
47 UNDER-UTILISATION												
59 TOTAL PROFIT /LOSS/												

SOURCE   BREL

FIGURE 16.4   *Form sent by Works Managers to BREL HQ every 4 weeks together with a commentary on major variances from budget*

Only in the production centres is direct work for the customer carried out (except for minor specialised jobs in maintenance centres). The costs of the other types of cost centre have therefore to be levied on each individual production centre on a basis that fairly charges each with a proportion of their cost.

WORKS AND COMPANY BUDGETS

The budget calculation is an annual event for the following calendar year. The railway regions determine their requirements for repairs and BR HQ indicates the load for new vehicles, major modifications and refurbishment programmes. Loads are allocated to individual works, which assess the load in terms of capacity and manpower availability. It is fundamental to the process that labour, physical capacity and workload are properly balanced.

Pricing of the main budget workload is as follows:

(a) Repairs A standard price for all works for each type of repair to rolling stock, based on an average of individual unit costs of repair from all works;

(b) New construction Based on the original supply committee contract price, plus index-linked price variation and authorised modification.

From these an output budget of repaired and new vehicles and manpower budgets are prepared, which are then evaluated in financial terms to produce a works and ultimately a company budget. The financial budget consists therefore of forecast expenditure detailed by individual items of expense and forecast sales levels by activities, such as new vehicles and repairs to locomotives.

In compiling budgets the works produce individual cost centre budgets so as to review every item of expense. This also provides the most effective financial control during the year and enables the actual expenditure to be compared to the budget at the management level responsible for incurring the expense. The budget is in effect the total company policy expressed in financial terms. Actual expenditure and sales levels achieved are compared to the budget, so as to identify the causes of variation, in order that management action can be taken to correct any adverse trends. Each Works Manager submits his budget, which is appraised individually by BREL HQ officers to ensure that realism and financial stringency have been observed. Similarly the Managing Director of BREL is appraised by BRB for the company budget. Once agreed the budget becomes the company's or works' commitment and acts as a yardstick against which performance is measured on a 4-weekly basis.

For charging arrangements each of the main areas of activity is dealt with separately, as follows:

(1) Repairs to locomotives and rolling stock;
(2) Modifications to locomotives and rolling stock in service;
(3) Major refurbishment/life extension of BR stock;
(4) New construction of stock;
(5) Other work for BR;
(6) Other costs.

The procedures are complex and varied, for they have to cope with a wide variety of activities and have evolved over the years with changing circumstances.

RECORDS

The Rolling Stock Library located in Derby has a highly important function in maintaining close contact with all departments and depots involved with rolling stock, including BREL works and the Director of Supply, to ensure that all information regarding new builds, modifications, withdrawals and disposals is put through the system as early as possible. For accounting purposes records for each vehicle contain the historic building cost, year built, year entered service and book life. Each vehicle also has a status code which puts it into one of the following categories:

(1) Authorised for building or conversion;
(2) Built/converted and certified as accepted;
(3) In revenue-earning use;
(4) In use as a service vehicle;
(5) Withdrawn revenue vehicle now used as a service vehicle;
(6) Authorised for withdrawal;
(7) Withdrawn awaiting disposal;
(8) Disposed of.

These important records form the basis for the entries in the board's capital accounts for all rolling stock assets, associated depreciation and current cost accounting calculations. They also provide the statistical information regarding rolling stock published within the board's annual accounts.

Functional responsibility comes under the Director of Mechanical and Electrical Engineering; but the financial work is the responsibility of the BR Chief Accountant, subject to the control of the main BR Board, and it is customary for the Chairman of BREL to be a member of the BR Board.

17 Towards AD 2000

Much has happened since those pioneering and epoch-making days when the first public railway, the Stockton & Darlington, was opened in 1825 for coal carrying and the second, the Liverpool & Manchester Railway, was opened in 1830 mainly for passenger carrying. Whereas the railways gradually replaced most of the canal traffic, the motorways – all built since the second world war – have taken over a massive proportion of former rail traffic.

Debate about the relative contributions of road, rail, air and water transport to the national economy is likely to remain relevant for transport in the twenty-first century. As long ago as 1939 a deputation of chairmen of the four railway companies waited upon the Minister of Transport, the Rt Hon. Leslie Burgin, on 23 November for the initial presentation of the case for the railways. The deputation consisted of Lord Stamp (LMS), Mr K. Holland-Martin (SR), Lord Palmer (GWR) and Sir Ronald W. Matthews (LNER). The railway companies' case for equal treatment with the road industry at the hands of Parliament had received extensive publicity in the press, and the justice of their claim appeared to be widely recognised.

At nationalisation in 1948 British Railways employed a total staff of 450 000. It carried 996 050 000 passengers and 276 117 million tons of freight. Some 62 000 staff were employed in the main works. There were over 20 000 locomotives, over 40 000 carriages and well over a million wagons. Current figures present a very different picture. Most of the lost traffic has transferred to the roads and the remainder to air transport.

The British Transport Commission in 1954 launched BR's 15-year modernisation and re-equipment plan at a cost of £1500 million. This provided, inter alia, for all steam locomotives to be withdrawn and replaced by diesel-electric locomotives and diesel or electric railcars. This fundamental change meant much less work for the main works because a significant proportion of the locomotives and other power units would have to be purchased from outside.

In 1962 Dr Richard Beeching (later Lord Beeching) succeeded Lord Robertson as Chairman and within a relatively short time reduced the railway network by eliminating all duplication of services, such as retaining the Euston–Birmingham and closing the Paddington–Birmingham line, as well as shutting down many branch lines which had virtually closed themselves. This again had a significant effect on the main works.

It is apparent from Figure 17.1 how road transport, both passenger and freight, has multiplied, to the detriment of BR and with far-reaching effects on the volume of work arising in the main works. The totals since 1976 are not shown because they have been compiled on a different basis and are not comparable. (For further details see Appendix.) They do, however, indicate a steady rise in the number of vehicles each year, and in the case of goods vehicles it should also be borne in mind that appreciably heavier loads per

211

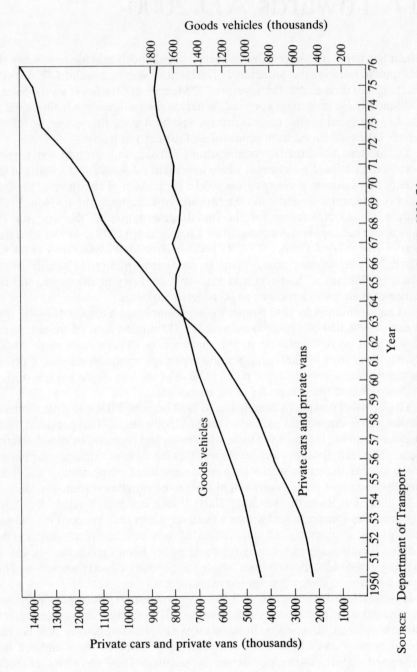

Goods vehicles (thousands)

Private cars and private vans (thousands)

Year

Goods vehicles

Private cars and private vans

SOURCE   Department of Transport

FIGURE 17.1   *Road motor vehicles licensed in Great Britain, 1950–76*

vehicle have been authorised throughout the UK, in line with the rest of the EEC, and are now commonplace from and to Europe. The 1982 official total of all classes of road vehicles licensed in Great Britain was little short of 20 million, a rise of 2 per cent on the 1981 total. The number of cars on the roads was projected by the British Road Federation in 1984 to increase by almost a third in the period to the year 2000. Cars on the roads in 1984 totalled 15·5 million compared with 5·5 million in 1960.

There are some years when not a single passenger is killed on BR, and in general the railways have maintained a very high safety standard and achieved an outstanding safety record. At one time there was even a saying that the safest place in the world was the interior of a GWR carriage, which arose from the fact that this much respected company had no fatal accident involving a passenger between 1895 and 1941. One of the safest means of transport in the UK is still on a British Rail train, not least because of the high quality of engineering and maintenance throughout the railway workshops. In 1983 the Department of Transport reported that 1982 was the safest year in the history of the railways in Britain and further stated that, for the fourth time in the previous seven years, not a single passenger was killed in a train collision, derailment or fire. Sadly the annual death toll and injuries which occur on the roads (see Appendix) can only be described as appalling and their continuance on such a scale quite unacceptable. The total number of road casualties in 1981 was 324 840 and of these no fewer than 5846 were killed, well over 100 each week. Road accidents were estimated in 1984 to be costing some £2370 million a year. These revealing figures give food for thought – and action!

The introduction of diesel and electric traction in the 1960s has resulted in higher acceleration and faster journey times, so important to those who wish to travel or who have bulk freight to move. It is undeniable that rail travel and facilities still have a great deal to offer. It would make life more pleasant for most of us if the trend towards the transfer of heavy freight from rail to road were reversed and if fewer new major roads, taking up hundreds of acres of our ever-contracting countryside, were undertaken. But instead successive British Governments have given preference to building new roads, which has meant decreasing traffic for the railways.

It is perhaps a moot point whether the full cost of building and maintaining the new motorways and trunk roads is adequately evaluated in calculating the fees for road fund and drivers' licences. In addition to the construction of new roads, many sizeable road repairs have to be undertaken each year, and all this work by contractors adds up to a very considerable amount of taxpayers' money. According to figures issued by the Department of Transport in 1984 major repairs to motorways were costing an average of £2.5 million a mile, or £600 000 a mile if work could be confined to a new coat of hot-rolled asphalt. The cost of repairs in 1984 totalled £150 million, consisting of £93 million for main repairs, £41 million for less extensive work, and £16 million for routine work such as verge maintenance, sweeping, gully-cleaning, snow-clearing and salting.

All these figures certainly call for close examination and official comment. By and large the Serpell Review of 1982/3 – which resulted from a commission set up by the Secretary of State for Transport to examine possible ways of improving railway finances and operations – was regarded by a majority of MPs, the BR Board, BREL management and the trade unions as leaving too much wide open. A fair comparison of the true costs of building and maintaining the roads and bridges and the relevant costs of the hospital casualty wards and the police, as well as the effect on the environment, evaluated by a high-level committee comprising railway management, road users, the Home Office, the Department of the Environment, the Department of Transport and the Department of Health and Social Security, with a High Court judge as chairman, would certainly be very revealing, if the opportunity were to arise for a further committee of inquiry. It can reasonably be accepted that the motor car, the bus, the coach and the tradesman's van have come to stay, but the heavy goods lorries with their ever-increasing loads are a different matter and call for a most searching review.

As a result of such competition the importance of the railway since nationalisation in 1948 has much declined. The receipts of the four large group companies which operated from 1923 to 1947 averaged 70 per cent freight and 30 per cent passenger traffic. Today the situation is roughly reversed and the total receipts, despite inflation, are greatly reduced. In 1980 the railway carried only about 54 per cent (by weight) of the freight it did in 1950; and while total passenger travel (by rail, bus and car) nearly trebled between 1950 and 1980, rail passenger miles decreased marginally. The Appendix carries a wealth of information on these changes since nationalisation and on results in 1980.

Although BREL cannot influence the receipts, it can continue to carry out new building and maintenance work as efficiently as possible. In 1981 vehicle maintenance and repairs of the entire fleet carried out by BREL cost £266 million, representing 55 per cent of all maintenance expenditure. The cost of day-to-day maintenance in the many motive power running sheds and carriage and wagon outdoor depots distributed throughout the country, together with the civil engineering, signal and telecommunications departments and ancillary departments, comprised the remainder. Diesel locomotives averaged 42 000 miles per annum, electric locomotives 92 000 miles per annum and diesel multiple units and electric multiple units 70 000 miles per annum. If utilisation were increased by improved scheduling in service, say by 10 per cent, it would lead to a saving of some £15 million a year; and if productivity could be improved throughout each of the main works, further substantial savings could be effected.

The size of the BR workforce generally, as well as that of BREL, has contracted very substantially in recent years (see Tables 17.1 and 17.2). Staff reductions within BREL have been necessary in order to tailor the capacity of

TABLE 17.1 *Total staff employed in main works and BREL HQ, 1960–89*

Year	Number	Remarks
1960	60 000	
1966	42 000	} Reorganisation and rationalisation:
1969	38 000	8 closures, 4 reductions
1979	36 000	
1981	35 000	
1982	34 000	2 closures
1983	28 000	
1984	27 000	
1985	27 000	
1986	23 000	
1987*	18 000	
1989*	10 000	

*projected totals

TABLE 17.2 *BR staff 1981–6, excluding BREL*

Year	Total number	Cumulative reduction
1981	170 300	
1982	162 300	8 000
1983	158 300	12 000
1984	155 700	14 600
1985	153 800	16 500
1986	151 300	19 000

the workshops to the amount of work available. A reduction of around one per cent in the wage bill would have improved the railway's overall finances in 1983 by approximately £14 million.

The main workload in the main works is high quality maintenance and there is no comparable organisation in the country. BREL management must be in close daily contact with the operating and motive power departments in order to use the works and the railway to the best advantage. The works are well equipped and have a sound progressive organisation for their special task. BREL safety standards must remain extremely high in the interests of BR customers.

Since the second world war there has been the inflationary ritual of an annual increase in wages for the same output – indeed sometimes for less, where hours of work have been shortened. When the unit cost of a product is correspondingly increased to adjust to the increased wages being paid to the employees, the product may cease to be competititve and there may well be a loss of customers, both at home and abroad, with a resultant likely rise in the level of unemployment. So far as BR is concerned the total passenger and freight receipts to meet these increased costs have tended to fall short of break-even, requiring substantial Government subsidies in recent years. A passenger train carrying only a busload of passengers, or a freight train consisting of only six or eight wagons, can never pay, and if the railways are to survive – as common sense tells most people they should – they will have to be seen to offer a highly competitive alternative to road transport. There is no doubt that Railfreight faces tough competition, and the raising of maximum permitted lorry weights gives an advantage to road haulage competitors, enabling them to reduce their costs.

There is a clear mandate for BREL management and all its employees – whether skilled, semi-skilled or unskilled – to give of their best. The only sound course for them to follow is the ceaseless aim to increase productivity. The individual performance of each employee should be accurately measured in BSI standard minutes at regular intervals, perhaps once a year, for each task carried out, to see whether an improved method involving less manual time per unit, and often less fatigue, can be evolved.

With the high cost of oil fuel the main strategic routes are likely to be electrified before the end of the twentieth century. Following the authorisation in 1984 of the £306 million electrification of the East Coast main inter-city line from London to Leeds and Edinburgh, the Western Region of BR was the only area of the national railway network to remain reliant solely upon oil-powered traction. Table 17.3 shows the forecast use of diesel traction by the year 2000.

In other areas, too, BR continues to break new ground. For example, through passenger traffic between the north and south of England via Kensington in London was introduced in 1986. The proposed Channel Tunnel, which will link BR with the continent, offers a further challenge; not just the immediate cross-channel traffic, but wider links between several UK cities and the major centres of the EEC are in prospect.

TABLE 17.3   *Forecast of diesel traction on BR*

Period	Multiple units	Diesel locomotives	Total
In service 1983	2 984	2 750	5 734
Scrapped by 1990	1 461	778	2 239
New build to 1990	365	323	688
In service 1990	1 888	2 295	4 183
Scrapped 1990–2000	1 523	1 308	2 831
New build 1990–2000	750	790	1 540
In service 2000	1 115	1 777	2 892

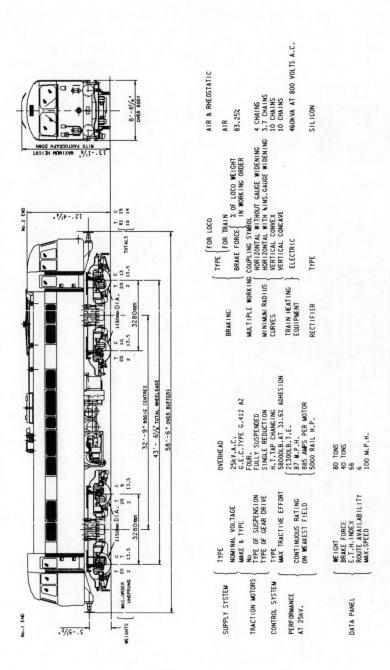

SUPPLY SYSTEM	TYPE	OVERHEAD
	NOMINAL VOLTAGE	25kV.A.C.
	MAKE & TYPE	G.E.C.TYPE G.412 AZ
TRACTION MOTORS	No	FOUR.
	TYPE OF SUSPENSION	FULLY SUSPENDED
	TYPE OF GEAR DRIVE	SINGLE REDUCTION
CONTROL SYSTEM	TYPE	H.T.TAP CHANGING
	MAX TRACTIVE EFFORT	58000LB.AT 31.6% ADHESION
		21300LB.T.E.
PERFORMANCE AT 25kV.	CONTINUOUS RATING ON WEAKEST FIELD	87 M.P.H.
		885 AMPS PER MOTOR
		5000 RAIL H.P.
DATA PANEL	WEIGHT	80 TONS
	BRAKE FORCE	40 TONS
	E.T.H.INDEX	66
	ROUTE AVAILABILITY	6
	MAX.SPEED	100 M.P.H.
BRAKING	TYPE { FOR LOCO	AIR & RHEOSTATIC
	{ FOR TRAIN	AIR
	BRAKE FORCE { % OF LOCO WEIGHT IN WORKING ORDER	83.25%
MULTIPLE WORKING	COUPLING SYMBOL	
MINIMUM RADIUS CURVES	HORIZONTAL WITHOUT GAUGE WIDENING	4 CHAINS
	HORIZONTAL WITH ¾INS.GAUGE WIDENING	3.7 CHAINS
	VERTICAL CONVEX	10 CHAINS
	VERTICAL CONCAVE	10 CHAINS
TRAIN HEATING EQUIPMENT	ELECTRIC	460kVA AT 800 VOLTS A.C.
RECTIFIER	TYPE	SILICON

SOURCE BREL

FIGURE 17.2 *BR B–B AC electric locomotive Class 87/0 (June 1984); see also Plate 17b*

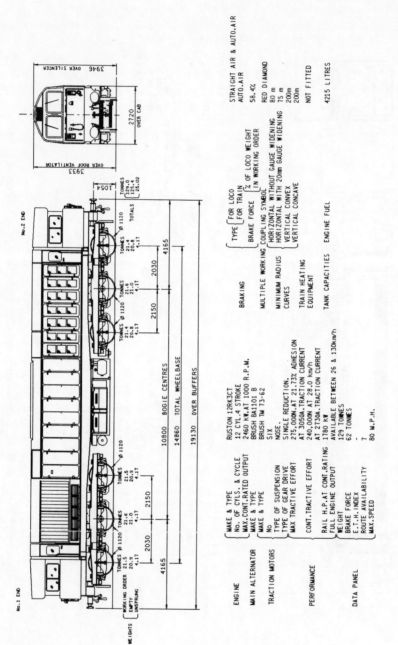

ENGINE	MAKE & TYPE	RUSTON 12RK3CT
	NO. OF CYLS. & CYCLE	12 CYL.4 STROKE
	MAX.CONT.RATED OUTPUT	2460 KW.AT 1000 R.P.M.
MAIN ALTERNATOR	MAKE & TYPE	BRUSH BA1101 B
TRACTION MOTORS	MAKE & TYPE	BRUSH TM 73-62
	No	SIX
	TYPE OF SUSPENSION	NOSE.
	TYPE OF GEAR DRIVE	SINGLE REDUCTION.
	MAX TRACTIVE EFFORT	275,000N.AT 21.73% ADHESION AT 305.0A.TRACTION CURRENT
PERFORMANCE	CONT.TRACTIVE EFFORT	240,000N AT 28.0 km/h AT 273.0A.TRACTION CURRENT
	RAIL H.P.AT CONT.RATING	1780 KW
	FULL ENGINE OUTPUT	AVAILABLE BETWEEN 26 & 130km/h
	WEIGHT	129 TONNES
DATA PANEL	BRAKE FORCE	62 TONNES
	E.T.H.INDEX	-
	ROUTE AVAILABILITY	7
	MAX.SPEED	80 M.P.H.

BRAKING	TYPE ⎧ FOR LOCO ⎩ FOR TRAIN	STRAIGHT AIR & AUTO.AIR AUTO.AIR
	BRAKE FORCE ⎧% OF LOCO WEIGHT ⎩ IN WORKING ORDER	58.4%
MULTIPLE WORKING COUPLING SYMBOL		RED DIAMOND
MINIMUM RADIUS CURVES	HORIZONTAL WITHOUT GAUGE WIDENING	80 m
	HORIZONTAL WITH 20mm GAUGE WIDENING	75 m
	VERTICAL CONVEX	200m
	VERTICAL CONCAVE	200m
TRAIN HEATING EQUIPMENT		NOT FITTED
TANK CAPACITIES	ENGINE FUEL	4215 LITRES

SOURCE BREL

FIGURE 17.3   *BR 2460 kW Co-Co diesel-electric locomotive Class 58 (October 1984)*

British Rail is still BREL's major customer. The introduction in 1984 of new railbuses at a cost of £350 000 each followed seven years of intensive development work by BR, BREL and British Leyland. Other orders included 50 new medium-weight diesel multiple units worth £22 million and 15 heavy freight locomotives worth £14·7 million. Developments such as new electrification and the Channel Tunnel will also contribute to the workload of the workshops.

Yet the world railway export market has become of major importance for BREL as a complement to domestic demand. BREL has already made a significant impact on the world export market, having supplied products totalling over £300 million to 34 countries. Its revolutionary international coach, embodying video-screens and reclining seats and designed for a life of 10–15 years at a cost per coach of about £250 000, can be built to suit the lengths, heights and widths of any railway system in the world. BREL's capability to manufacture non-railway engineering products is also likely to be a feature of its domestic and export output in future decades. BREL opened a £250 000 centre at Derby Litchurch Lane Works in 1986 to exhibit its full range of international products to prospective customers and to provide conference facilities.

During the 1980s, in addition to the transfer of Eastleigh, Wolverton, Glasgow and Doncaster activities to the newly-formed British Rail Maintenance Ltd (1987), the divestment of BREL from the public sector has also emerged as a distinct probability, as part of the Government's privatisation programme. This was confirmed in 1987, when the Secretary of State for Transport announced that the remaining four BREL works – Crewe, Derby Locomotive, Derby Carriage and York – would be offered for sale as a single business. The sale of Horwich Foundry would be considered under separate arrangements. Offers for the BREL company would be invited with a view to its sale during 1988. The Executive Directors of BREL expressed confidence in the future capability, growth potential and long-term success of the company, and declared their intention to proceed with a bid for BREL, which it was hoped would include both management and employee participation, and association with other major organisations.

Whatever the future may hold, the past contribution of the railway works to Britain's social history and the advancement of mechanical and electrical engineering has been immense. The generations of workshop staff concerned can be justifiably proud of their unique contribution. Their high technology and products take second place to none among the great railways of the world.

Appendix:
Statistical Information

Appendix

TABLE A.1   *Order in which the main works were built*

Order in which built	Year built	Location of works	Owning company in 1923	Class of work undertaken
1	1833	Shildon	LNER	Wagons
2	1838	Wolverton	LMS	Carriages
3	1840	Brighton	SR	Locomotives
4	1840	Bromsgrove	LMS	Wagons
5	1840	Derby	LMS	Locomotives
6	1842	Cowlairs	LNER	Locomotives, Carriages and Wagons
7	1842	Swindon	GWR	Locomotives
8	1843	Crewe	LMS	Locomotives
9	1846	Barrow-in-Furness	LMS	Locomotives
10	1847	Ashford	SR	Locomotives
11	1847	Stratford	LNER	Locomotives
12	1847	Stratford	LNER	Carriages
13	1849	Gorton	LNER	Locomotives
14	1850	Ashford	SR	Wagons
15	1850	Bow	LMS	Locomotives
16	1853	Doncaster	LNER	Locomotives
17	1853	Doncaster	LNER	Carriages
18	1853	Earlestown	LMS	Wagons
19	1855	Wolverhampton	GWR	Locomotives
20	1856	St Rollox	LMS	Locomotives
21	1856	St Rollox	LMS	Carriages
22	1856	Kilmarnock	LMS	Locomotives
23	1863	Darlington	LNER	Locomotives
24	1864	Stoke-on-Trent	LMS	Locomotives, Carriages and Wagons
25	1865	York	LNER	Wagons
26	1869	Swindon	GWR	Carriages and Wagons
27	1876	Derby L.L.	LMS	Carriages and Wagons
28	1876	Newton Heath	LMS	Carriages and Wagons
29	1881	Gorton	LNER	Carriages and Wagons
30	1884	York	LNER	Carriages
31	1887	Horwich	LMS	Locomotives
32	1888	Lancing	SR	Carriages
33	1889	Doncaster	LNER	Wagons
34	1891	Eastleigh	SR	Carriages
35	1896	Temple Mills	LNER	Wagons
36	1899	Caerphilly	GWR	Locomotives
37	1901	Barassie	LMS	Wagons
38	1901	Caerphilly	GWR	Carriages and Wagons
39	1902	Walkergate	LNER	Carriages and Wagons

TABLE A.1 *Continued*

Order in which built	Year built	Location of works	Owning company in 1923	Class of work undertaken
40	1903	Inverurie	LNER	Locomotives, Carriages and Wagons
41	1909	Eastleigh	SR	Locomotives
42	1923	Faverdale	LNER	Wagons

TABLE A.2 *Railway companies and trade unions who were parties to Industrial Court Award No. 728 of 8 July 1922*

Railway companies
Alexandra Docks Railway;
Barry Railway;
Cardiff Railway;
Great Eastern Railway;
Great Western Railway;
Hull & Barnsley Railway;
London & North-Western Railway;
Lancashire & Yorkshire Railway;
London & South-Western Railway;
Maryport & Carlisle Railway;
Midland Railway;
North-Eastern Railway;
North Staffordshire Railway;
Rhymney Railway;
South-Eastern & Chatham Railway;
Taff Vale Railway.

Trade unions
National Union of Railwaymen;
Federation of Engineering and Shipbuilding Trades, comprising: Associated Black-
   smiths' and Ironworkers' Society of Great Britain and Ireland; United Society of
   Boilermakers and Iron and Steel Shipbuilders; National Society of Brass Workers
   and Metal Mechanics; London Society of Amalgamated Brass Workers; London
   United Brass Founders' Society; National Union of Sheet Metal Workers and
   Braziers; National Society of Coppersmiths, Braziers and Metal Workers; Dock,
   Wharf, Riverside and General Workers' Union of Great Britain and Ireland;
   National Amalgamated Union of Enginemen, Firemen, Mechanics, Motormen and
   Electrical Workers; Electrical Trades Union; Amalgamated Society of Farriers and
   Blacksmiths; National Amalgamated Furnishing Trades Association; National
   Union of General Workers; National Union of Operative Heating and Domestic
   Engineers; General Iron Fitters' Association; Iron, Steel and Metal Dressers' Trade
   Society; National Amalgamated Union of Labour; National Union of Stove, Grate,
   Fender and General Light Metal Workers; Birmingham Operative Tinplate, Sheet
   Metal Workers' and Braziers' Society; National Amalgamated Society of Operative
   House and Ship Painters and Decorators; United Patternmakers' Association;
   United Operative Plumbers' and Domestic Engineers' Association of Great Britain
   and Ireland; Amalgamated Society of Railway Vehicle Builders, Wheelwrights,
   Carpenters and Mechanics; Ship Constructors' and Shipwrights' Association;
   Amalgamated Union of Upholsterers; National Union of Vehicle Builders;
   Amalgamated Wheelwrights', Smiths' and Kindred Trades Union; Amalgamated
   Society of Woodcutting Machinists of Great Britain and Ireland; Amalgamated
   Society of Woodworkers;
National Federation of Building Trades Operatives;
National Federation of General Workers, comprising: National Union of General
   Workers; National Amalgamated Union of Labour Workers' Union.

TABLE A.3 *Railway companies amalgamated to form the four main-line companies in 1923*

Great Western Railway Company

Constituent companies (7)
The Barry Railway Company;
The Cambrian Railway Company;
The Cardiff Railway Company;
The Great Western Railway Company;
The Rhymney Railway Company;
The Taff Vale Railway Company;
The Alexandra (Newport & South Wales) Docks & Railway Company.

Subsidiary companies (26)
The Brecon & Merthyr Tydfil Junction Railway Company;
The Burry Port & Gwendreath Valley Railway Company;
The Cleobury Mortimer & Ditton Priors Light Railway Company;
The Didcot, Newbury & Southampton Railway Company;
The Exeter Railway Company;
The Forest of Dean Central Railway Company;
The Gwendreath Valleys Railway Company;
The Lampeter, Aberayron & New Quay Light Railway Company;
The Liskeard & Looe Railway Company;
The Llanelly & Mynydd Mawr Railway Company;
The Mawddy Railway Company;
The Midland & South-Western Junction Railway Company;
The Neath & Brecon Railway Company;
The Penarth Extension Railway Company;
The Penarth Harbour, Dock & Railway Company;
The Port Talbot Railway & Docks Company;
The Princetown Railway Company;
The Rhondda & Swansea Bay Railway Company;
The Ross & Monmouth Railway Company;
The South Wales Mineral Railway Company;
The Teign Valley Railway Company;
The Vale of Glamorgan Railway Company;
The Van Railway Company;
The Welshpool & Llanfair Light Railway Company;
The West Somerset Railway Company;
The Wrexham & Ellesmere Railway Company.

London Midland and Scottish Railway Company

Constituent companies (8)
The Caledonian Railway Company;
The Furness Railway Company;
The Glasgow & South-Western Railway Company;
The Highland Railway Company;

TABLE A.3   *Continued*

The Lancashire & Yorkshire Railway Company;
The London & North-Western Railway Company;
The Midland Railway Company;
The North Staffordshire Railway Company.

Subsidiary companies (27)
The Arbroath & Forfar Railway Company;
The Brechin & Edzell District Railway Company;
The Callander & Oban Railway Company;
The Cathcart District Railway Company;
The Charnwood Forest Railway Company;
The Cleator & Workington Junction Railway Company;
The Cockermouth, Keswick & Penrith Railway Company;
The Dearne Valley Railway Company;
The Dornoch Light Railway Company;
The Dundee & Newtyle Railway Company;
The Harborne Railway Company;
The Killin Railway Company;
The Knott End Railway Company;
The Lanarkshire & Ayrshire Railway Company;
The Leek & Manifold Valley Light Railway Company;
The Maryport & Carlisle Railway Company;
The Mold & Denbigh Junction Railway Company;
The North & South-Western Junction Railway Company;
The North London Railway Company;
The Portpatrick & Wigtownshire Joint Committee;
The Shropshire Union Railways & Canal Company;
The Solway Junction Railway Company;
The Stratford-upon-Avon & Midland Junction Railway Company;
The Tottenham & Forest Gate Railway Company;
The Wick & Lybster Light Railway Company;
The Wirral Railway Company;
The Yorkshire Dales Railway (Skipton to Grassington) Company.

London and North-Eastern Railway Company

Constituent companies (7)
The Great Central Railway Company;
The Great Eastern Railway Company;
The Great Northern Railway Company;
The Great North of Scotland Railway Company;
The Hull & Barnsley Railway Company;
The North British Railway Company;
The North-Eastern Railway Company.

Subsidiary companies (26)
The Brackenhill Light Railway Company;
The Colne Valley & Halstead Railway Company;

TABLE A.3 *Continued*

The East & West Yorkshire Union Railway Company;
The East Lincolnshire Railway Company;
The Edinburgh & Bathgate Railway Company;
The Forcett Railway Company;
The Forth & Clyde Junction Railway Company;
The Gifford & Garvald Railway Company;
The Great North of England, Clarence & Hartlepool Junction Railway Company;
The Horncastle Railway Company;
The Humber Commercial Railway & Dock Company;
The Kilsyth & Bonnybridge Railway Company;
The Lauder Light Railway Company;
The London & Blackwall Railway Company;
The Mansfield Railway Company;
The Mid-Suffolk Light Railway Company;
The Newburgh & North Fife Railway Company;
The North Lindsey Light Railways Company;
The Nottingham & Grantham Railway & Canal Company;
The Nottingham Joint Station Committee;
The Nottingham Suburban Railway Company;
The Seaford & Sefton Junction Railway Company;
The Sheffield District Railway Company;
The South Yorkshire Junction Railway Company;
The Stamford & Essendine Railway Company;
The West Riding Railway Committee.

Southern Railway Company

Constituent companies (5)
The London & South-Western Railway Company;
The London Brighton & South Coast Railway Company;
The London Chatham & Dover Railway Company;
The South-Eastern Railway Company;
The South-Eastern and Chatham Railway Companies Managing Committee.

Subsidiary companies (14)
The Bridgwater Railway Company;
The Brighton & Dyke Railway Company;
The Freshwater Yarmouth & Newport (Isle of Wight) Railway Company;
The Hayling Railways Company;
The Isle of Wight Railway Company;
The Isle of Wight Central Railway Company;
The Lee-on-the-Solent Railway Company;
The London & Greenwich Railway Company;
The Mid-Kent Railway (Bromley to St Mary Cray) Company;
The North Cornwall Railway Company;
The Plymouth & Dartmoor Railway Company;
The Plymouth Devonport & South-Western Junction Railway Company;
The Sidmouth Railway Company;
The Victoria Station & Pimlico Railway Company.

TABLE A.4   *London Midland and Scottish Railway Company statistics, 1924*

The LMS was the largest of the four companies which came into existence in 1923. It represented 40 per cent of the total railway system in England, Scotland, Wales and Northern Ireland, with a total staff of 275 000. The following facts and figures which applied in 1924 – when the railways in the British Isles were approaching their peak – will enable the reader to make his own comparisons with the much smaller British Railways in 1982 (Table A.29). Sums of money should be multiplied by approximately 20 to give the 1982 equivalent.

	£
Financial statistics	
Capital	398 929 175
Gross receipts	86 515 433
including:	
Railway	80 587 891
Steamboats	1 572 165
Canals	153 004
Docks	690 360
Hotels, refreshment rooms and dining cars	3 430 472

Mileage open for traffic	
Railway lines – Great Britain	7 214
– Ireland	320
Total	7 534
Canals	549

Stations etc.	
(including those joint with other companies)	
Stations – passenger	2 598
– goods	2 403
Private sidings	4 365

Passenger traffic	
No. of passengers carried	
(excluding season ticket holders)	357 607 262
No. of season ticket holders	301 391
Parcels and packages of luggage in advance	30 742 483

	tons
Freight traffic	
Merchandise	34 039 893
Coal, coke and patent fuel	90 144 191
Other minerals	34 284 565
Total	158 468 649

TABLE A.4   *Continued*

Livestock carried

Horses	55 654
Cattle	2 049 806
Calves	232 046
Sheep	6 346 155
Pigs	1 175 190
Miscellaneous	9 836
Total	9 868 687

Net ton miles

General merchandise	2 318 506 335
Coal, coke and patent fuel	4 023 852 862
Other minerals	1 671 083 024
Total	8 013 442 221

Engine mileage

Train miles – coaching	89 099 429
– freight	61 805 018
Shunting and other miles	80 406 457
Total	231 310 904

Steamship services

Regular Irish and continental steamship services (daily)	14
Nautical miles run between England and Ireland (approx.)	450 000
Nautical miles run between England and the continent	450 000

Steamships owned

East Coast: sailing between Goole and Hull and continental ports (Amsterdam, Antwerp, Ghent, Hamburg, Rotterdam, Copenhagen, Dunkirk)	25
West Coast: sailing between England and Ireland	
Holyhead and Kingstown	3
Holyhead and North Wall, Dublin (cargo)	7
Holyhead and Greenore	3
Fleetwood and Belfast	3
Heysham, Belfast and Douglas	4
Liverpool and Drogheda	2
Stranraer and Larne	2
Miscellaneous	5
Lake steamers	
Windermere	5
Coniston	2
Loch Tay	3
Loch Awe	1
Loch Lomond (joint with LNER)	6
Firth of Clyde	11
Tilbury and Gravesend ferry	6
Total	88

TABLE A.4   *Continued*

Locomotives and rolling stock

Locomotives – steam	10 246
– electric	2
Electric motor vehicles (with seating capacity for 15 828 persons)	272
Rail motor cars (with seating capacity for 1461 persons)	28
Passenger carriages (with seating capacity for 1 002 384 persons)	19 025
Restaurant cars (with seating capacity for 6177 persons)	204
Sleeping cars (with berths for 1427 persons)	113
Post Office vans	110
Luggage, parcel and brake vans	2 563
Horse boxes	1 594
Carriage trucks	1 649
Other passenger train vehicles	1 543
Wagon stock exclusive of service vehicles (with a total carrying capacity of 3 029 219 tons)	302 868

Main works
As described in Chapter 3.

Hotels

Owned and managed by the LMS: 32

Ayr	Station Hotel
Belfast	Midland Station Hotel
Birmingham	Queen's Hotel
Bletchley	Station Hotel
Bradford	Midland Hotel
Crewe	Crewe Arms
Derby	Midland Hotel
Dornoch	Dornoch Hotel
Dumfries	Station Hotel
Edinburgh (Princes St)	Caledonian Hotel
Furness Abbey	Furness Abbey Hotel
Glasgow	Central Hotel, St Enoch Hotel
Gleneagles	Gleneagles Hotel
Greenore	Greenore Hotel
Holyhead	Station Hotel
Inverness	Station Hotel
Keighley	Station Hotel
Kyle of Lochalsh	Station Hotel
Larne	Laharna Hotel
Leeds	Queen's Hotel
Liverpool	North-Western Hotel, Exchange Station Hotel, Midland Adelphi Hotel
London	Euston Hotel, St Pancras Midland, Grand Hotel
Manchester	Midland Hotel
Morecambe	Midland Hotel
Portrush	Northern Counties Hotel

TABLE A.4   *Continued*

Preston	Park Hotel	
Strathpeffer	Highland Hotel	
Turnberry	Turnberry Hotel	
Refreshment rooms at stations		116

Docks, harbours and wharves

Docks, harbours and wharves owned	31
Total length of quay (feet)	101 293

Other property

Houses	25 613

Road vehicles and horses

Horse-drawn vehicles	19 259
Motor vehicles, tramcars and omnibuses	1 372
Horses	10 221

Coal

Consumption for all purposes (tons)	6 780 840

Staff

Number of staff employed (approx.)	274 523

TABLE A.5   *London and North-Eastern Railway Company statistics, 1930*

Track mileage	
Owned	6 294
Share of joint lines	75
Leased or worked	11
Leased or worked jointly	—
Total, 1st track	6 381
Total, 2nd track	3 953
Total, 3rd track	472
Total, 4th track	356
Over 4 tracks	302
Total length of single track (including sidings)	16 732
Authorised but not open for traffic	12
Mileage run over by company's locomotives	
Owned	6 294
Party owned	360
Leased or worked	11
Leased or worked jointly	156
Total	6 821
Rolling stock	
Locomotives – steam	7 316
– electric	13
– petrol shunting	2
Road motor vehicles	
Steam	85
Electric	87
Petrol	1
Petrol electric	2
Electric trailer cars	55
Passenger carriages	
Uniform class	10 108
Composite	2 951
Restaurant cars	223
Sleeping cars	112
Post Office vans	64
Luggage, parcels, miscellaneous	45
Total coaching stock	13 503
Open wagons	121 844
Covered wagons	33 351
Mineral wagons	88 826
Special wagons	3 382
Cattle trucks	7 290
Rail and timber trucks	13 687
Brake vans	4 670
Total merchandise and mineral stock	273 050

TABLE A.5 *Continued*

Service vehicles		15 030
Departmental locomotives		18
Road traffic equipment		
Road motors for goods and parcels		798
Road motors for passenger traffic		40
Horse wagons and carts		8 801
Miscellaneous		88
Horses for road vehicles		5 113
Horses for shunting		328
Houses and dwellings		
Labouring class dwellings		2 460
Houses and cottages for staff		9 491
Other houses and cottages		6 167

Traffic carried

	Total	*Originating on LNER*
No. of passengers	205 716 944	192 513 638
No. of season tickets	183 409	158 014
Goods tonnage		
Merchandise (excl. Classes 1–6)	24 848 403	18 696 516
Minerals and merchandise (Classes 1–6)	26 801 174	21 807 496
Coal, coke and patent fuel	87 569 499	76 146 423
Totals	139 219 076	116 650 435
Head of livestock	6 836 808	5 582 938

Train Mileage

Steam coaching	63 650 514
Steam goods	47 871 270
Total	111 521 784
Electric coaching	1 295 645
Electric goods	65 898
Steam rail motors	2 410 950
Petrol etc.	58 566
Shunting miles – coaching	4 113 237
– goods	34 665 369
Assisting and light mileage	16 393 850
Total engine miles	170 525 299

Revenue

	Gross receipts £	*Expenditure* £	*Net receipts* £
Railway	52 390 710	41 863 042	10 527 668
Road transport	111 047	108 869	3 078
Total	52 501 757	41 971 911	10 530 746

TABLE A.5 *Continued*

The gross receipts (railway) were made up of:	£
Passenger train traffic	18 368 344
Goods train traffic	33 584 082
Miscellaneous receipts	438 284
Railway expenditure included, e.g.:	
Maintenance and renewal of rolling stock	8 343 953
Locomotive running expenses	10 203 902
Staff	
Total staff at 8 March 1930	195 030

TABLE A.6 *Total expenditure by the four main-line companies on locomotive repairs and partial renewals, total mileage and cost per mile, 1928–47*

Year	Expenditure £	Total mileage	Average cost per mile d
1928	10 388 884	538 854 068	4.63
1929	10 247 724	549 262 136	4.48
1930	9 843 664	537 122 647	4.40
1931	8 907 535	512 378 164	4.17
1932	8 186 276	495 578 856	3.97
1933	7 950 247	494 567 790	3.86
1934	8 557 256	516 075 271	3.97
1935	8 391 165	521 204 047	3.86
1936	8 492 684	537 450 063	3.79
1937	8 623 546	550 259 958	3.76
1938	8 931 447	533 400 415	4.02
1939	8 904 367	512 179 630	4.17
1940	9 795 620	498 945 416	4.68
1941	10 839 038	497 145 038	5.21
1942	13 107 393	505 121 801	6.23
1943	16 187 367	509 684 753	7.63
1944	17 688 053	508 605 689	8.35
1945	18 409 165	496 565 263	8.90
1946	20 129 057	500 804 139	9.65
1947	22 483 150	479 193 500	11.26

SOURCE British Rail

TABLE A.7   *Total expenditure on carriage and wagon repairs and partial renewals by each of the four main-line companies, 1928 and 1947*

	1928 £	1947 £
Carriage expenditure		
GWR	765 552	1 460 689
LMS	1 591 501	2 862 673
LNER	1 473 456	2 931 943
SR	968 345	1 541 861
Total	4 798 854	8 797 166
Wagon expenditure		
GWR	556 221	1 095 206
LMS	1 409 031	3 716 657
LNER	1 836 679	3 493 274
SR	207 033	610 107
Total	4 008 964	8 915 244
Carriage and wagon total	8 807 818	17 712 410

SOURCE   British Rail

TABLE A.8   *Locomotive output, 1947*

Output of repaired locomotives (MOT classification)
12 Heavy repairs – number
13 Heavy repairs – light weight of engines
14 Heavy repairs – light weight of tenders
15 Heavy repairs – light weight of engines and tenders
16 Light repairs –   number
17 Light repairs –   light weight of engines
18 Light repairs –   light weight of tenders
19 Light repairs –   light weight of engines and tenders
20 Mileage run by maintained stock during 1947
21 Total miles made good

Works & reference no.	12 No.	13 Tons	14 Tons	15 Tons	16 No.	17 Tons	18 Tons
GWR							
1 Swindon	717	42 480	9 521	52 001	287	17 544	3 324
2 Wolverhampton	178	8 653	1 010	9 663	68	3 652	470
3 Caerphilly	184	9 042	—	9 042	40	2 289	—
Totals	1 079	60 175	10 531	70 706	395	23 485	3 794
LMS							
4 Crewe	779	50 568	16 364	66 932	714	47 442	14 525
5 Derby	768	36 494	11 059	47 553	280	14 994	4 018
6 Horwich	440	21 976	6 182	28 158	228	12 197	2 937
7 St Rollox	354	18 433	6 138	24 571	239	13 981	4 683
8 Bow	102	47 725	876	5 601	91	4 545	718
9 Kilmarnock	77	3 414	1 242	4 656	111	5 145	1 576
Totals	2 520	135 610	41 861	177 471	1 663	98 304	28 457
LNER							
10 Darlington	567	29 150	7 113	36 263	121	7 132	2 041
11 Doncaster	582	37 373	10 683	48 056	156	10 853	3 334
12 Gorton	547	30 819	9 623	40 442	92	5 440	1 825
13 Cowlairs	393	19 337	5 474	24 811	189	10 873	3 408
14 Stratford	390	18 638	4 718	23 356	354	17 511	3 545
15 Inverurie	118	5 093	1 880	6 973	76	3 845	1 340
Totals	2 597	140 410	39 491	179 901	988	55 654	15 493
SR							
16 Eastleigh	327	18 803	5 268	24 071	124	7 621	2 364
17 Ashford	276	12 884	3 377	16 261	89	4 440	1 282
18 Brighton	—	—	—	—	—	—	—
Totals	603	31 687	8 645	40 332	213	12 061	3 646

TABLE A.8 *Locomotive output, 1947*

Output of new locomotives
22 New locomotives – number
23 New locomotives – light weight of engines
24 New locomotives – light weight of tenders
25 New locomotives – light weight of engines and tenders

19 Tons	20 Miles	21 Miles	22 No.	23 Tons	24 Tons	25 Tons
20 868	—	—	60	3 285	663	3 948
4 122	—	—		No new engine building		
2 289	—	—		No new engine building		
27 279	88 922 962	90 258 000	60	3 285	663	3 948
61 967	—	75 754 283	36	2 169	896	3 065
19 012	—	51 854 580	49	3 322	—	3 322
15 134	—	31 484 382	28	1 807	732	2 539
18 664	—	36 524 366		No new engine building		
5 263	Included under Derby			No new engine building		
6 721	Included under St Rollox			No new engine building		
126 761	193 291 833	195 617 611	113	7 298	1 628	8 926
9 173	—	—	25	1 600	634	2 234
14 187	—	—	7	650	204	854
7 265	—	—		No new engine building		
14 281	—	—		No new engine building		
21 056	—	—		No new engine building		
5 185	—	—		No new engine building		
71 147	152 697 200	165 036 791	32	2 250	838	3 088
9 985	23 029 204	26 144 769		All works pooled		
5 722	16 507 755	17 831 833		for new engine		
—	651 896	—		building		
15 707	40 188 855	43 976 602	18	1 386	311	1 697

SOURCE British Rail

Notes:
(a) Cols 12–19 for LMS exclude repairs to 107 Austerity locomotives for the MOT and 28 on loan from the LNER.
(b) Cols 12–19 for SR include under Eastleigh and Ashford some locomotives which were normally repaired there, although during 1947 they were actually repaired at Brighton. No locomotives allocated to Brighton for maintenance were repaired at Brighton during 1947.
(c) Cols 16–19 for LNER Stratford include 149 shed repairs, many of which would not be comparable with ordinary shop light repairs.

TABLE A.9   *Repair output of subsidiary locomotive works, 1947*

Works	Average no. of locomotives on works	Classified output		Other activities
		Heavy	Light	
GWR				
Barry	10.5	9	115	
Bristol, Bath Road	2.0	—	48	unclassified repairs;
Newport, Ebbw Jct.	5.6	—	65	divisional outdoor
Newton Abbot	14.4	—	195	machinery
Old Oak Common	6.1	—	53	maintenance
Tyseley	7.4	—	54	
Worcester	10.5	3	87	
Total	56.5	12	617	
LMS*				
Bristol	3.0	—	21	
Inverness	3.5	15	28	
Leeds	5.6	5	108	nil
Rugby	10.3	25	126	
Total	22.4	45	283	
LNER				
Gateshead	13.0	—	238	unclassified repairs; grease factory; outdoor machinery maintenance
SR				
Bournemouth	0.5	1	9	
Bricklayers' Arms	4.8	9	28	
Eastleigh	1.2	—	9	
Exmouth Jct.	1.3	1	5	unclassified
Feltham	0.9	—	4	running shed
Guildford	1.4	2	19	maintenance
Hither Green	0.9	—	4	
New Cross Gate	5.8	7	15	
Nine Elms	1.5	2	25	
Salisbury	0.5	1	6	
Stewarts Lane	5.3	7	41	
Total	24.1	30	165	

*Between 1923 and 1947 the LMS closed six of its subsidiary locomotive works, at Belle Vue (Manchester), Carlisle, Kentish Town, Leeds, Saltley (Birmingham) and Grimesthorpe (Sheffield).

TABLE A.10 *Carriage and wagon output, 1949*

Works and reference no.	No. of artisan staff employed	No. of classified repairs*						New rolling stock*		
		Carriages		Wagons		Containers		Carriages	Wagons	Containers
		Heavy	Light	Heavy	Light	Heavy	Light			
Eastern and North-Eastern Regions										
1 York C&W	2 977	924	3 264	5 891	7 072	246	849	188	—	—
2 Shildon Wagon	2 573	4	13	3 979	25 898	—	13	—	4 032	—
3 Doncaster C&W	1 968	1 002	1 941	2 849	19 593	460	519	19	—	—
4 Stratford C&W	1 417	1 090	4 608	2 025	18 023	—	1 408	—	—	—
5 Faverdale Wagon	539	17	2	1 793	2 048	976	372	—	1 588	295
6 Gorton C&W	503	39	254	4 211	20 050	10	567	—	—	—
7 Walkergate C&W	482	66	788	1 924	16 952	—	—	—	—	—
Regional totals	10 459	3 142	10 870	22 672	109 636	1 692	3 728	207	5 620	295
London Midland Region										
8 Derby C&W	4 748	2 971	460	8 050	4 978	—	—	261	3 674	—
9 Wolverton C&W	3 687	2 973	502	12	52	—	—	303	3 050	50
10 Earlestown Wagon	1 691	21	2	12 816	2 079	1 737	—	—	—	1 966
11 Bromsgrove Wagon	366	—	—	4 853	2 088	973	—	—	—	—
Regional totals	10 492	5 965	964	25 731	9 197	2 710	—	564	6 724	2 016
Scottish Region										
12 Cowlairs C&W	1 207	443	2 367	5 005	3 812	148	353	—	—	—
13 St Rollox Carriage	876	1 171	1 091	—	—	—	—	—	—	—
14 Barassie Wagon	714	—	—	7 575	955	209	20	—	—	—
15 Germiston Wagon	403	—	—	3 094	861	209	—	—	—	—
16 Inverurie C&W	229	259	753	853	6 160	1	414	—	—	—
Regional totals	3 429	1 873	4 211	16 527	11 788	358	787	—	—	—

TABLE A.10 *Continued*

Works and reference no.	No. of artisan staff employed	No. of classified repairs*						New rolling stock*		
		Carriages		Wagons		Containers		Carriages	Wagons	Containers
		Heavy	Light	Heavy	Light	Heavy	Light			
Southern Region										
17 Eastleigh C&W	1 722	15	1 130	2 362	2 451	281	280	370†	—	242
18 Lancing Carriage	1 692	538	2 088	—	1	—	—	18	140‡	60
19 Ashford Wagon	789	—	—	2 889	3 703	—	—	—	2 756	—
Regional totals	4 203	553	3 218	5 251	6 155	281	280	388	2 896	302
Western Region										
20 Swindon C&W	4 221	1 567	1 622	4 995	7 983	1 130	280	153	1 368	97
21 Caerphilly Carriage	97	101	228	—	—	—	—	—	—	—
Regional totals	4 318	1 668	1 850	4 995	7 983	1 130	280	153	1 368	97
Totals: all regions	32 901	13 201	21 113	75 176	144 759	6 161	5 075	1 312	16 608	2 710

SOURCE British Rail

Notes:

*The repair figures are in accordance with the differing classifications used by the various regions in 1949. A given number of carriage heavy repairs, for example, may not represent the same amount of work on different regions. The figures for new rolling stock are also not directly comparable, not only on account of the variety of vehicles built but also because of the varying extent to which components and assemblies were purchased from the trade.

†Underframes built or converted at Lancing.

‡Underframes built at Ashford.

Journeys	Total all regions			London Midland Region		Western Region		Southern Region		Eastern Region		North-Eastern Region		Scottish Region	
	000s	Percentage of total %	Increase or (Decrease) on 1947 journeys 000s	000s	Increase or (Decrease) on 1947 journeys 000s	000s	Increase or (Decrease) on 1947 journeys 000s	000s	Increase or (Decrease) on 1947 journeys 000s	000s	Increase or (Decrease) on 1947 journeys 000s	000s	Increase or (Decrease) on 1947 journeys 000s	000s	Increase or (Decrease) on 1947 journeys 000s
Analysis by fare categories															
Ordinary fares	69 314	6·96	(6 518) (8·60%)	18 243	(2 557) (12·30%)	9 032	(1 498) (14·22%)	24 720	(1 285) (4·94%)	10 362	309 3·07%	2 238	(889) (28·44%)	4 719	(598) (11·25%)
Monthly return	252 034	25·30	(50 998) (16·83%)	83 064	(16 303) (16·41%)	26 091	(9 910) (27·53%)	94 119	(8 956) (8·69%)	25 649	(5 509) (17·68%)	7 899	(6 588) (45·48%)	15 212	(3 732) (19·70%)
Excursion, weekend, cheap day, etc.	84 686	8·50	50 136 145·11%	25 642	15 419 150·83%	14 615	8 618 143·69%	23 624	13 765 139·61%	7 643	4 807 169·51%	7 017	3 320 89·82%	6 145	4 207 217·07%
Workmen	229 784	23·07	(3 325) (1·43%)	87 626	(1 407) (1·58%)	21 576	(1 571) (6·79%)	75 188	3 195 4·44%	22 513	(1 351) (5·66%)	11 283	(1 731) (13·30%)	11 598	(460) (3·82%)
Other descriptions	64 514	6·48	(12 935) (16·70%)	16 999	(3 005) (15·02%)	11 079	(2 574) (18·86%)	18 395	(3 783) (17·06%)	8 365	(1 172) (12·29%)	4 325	(1 409) (24·57%)	5 351	(992) (15·64%)
Season tickets	295 718	29·69	(56 977) (16·15%)	73 314	(16 256) (18·15%)	29 968	(7 754) (20·56%)	132 255	(17 506) (11·69%)	27 383	(7 235) (20·90%)	9 597	(2 416) (20·11%)	23 201	(5 810) (20·03%)
Total	996 050	100	(80 617) (7·49%)	304 888	(24 109) (7·33%)	112 361	(14 689) (11·56%)	368 301	(14 570) (3·81%)	101 915	(10 151) (9·05%)	42 359	(9 713) (18·65%)	66 226	(7 385) (10·03%)
Analysis by class of travel															
First class – journeys	29 290	2·94	(3 826) (11·55%)	11 048	(1 246) (10·13%)	2 913	(219) (7·00%)	7 178	(1 104) (13·33%)	2 595	(157) (5·69%)	1 148	(140) (10·86%)	4 408	(960) (17·89%)
– takings	£15 597	12·39	£729 4·90%	—	—	—	—	—	—	—	—	—	—	—	—
Second class – journeys	617	0·06	(3) (0·58%)	—	—	—	—	485	(19) (3·82%)	132	16 13·54%	—	—	—	—
– takings	£1 744	1·39	£119 7·37%	—	—	—	—	—	—	16	—	—	—	—	—
Third class – journeys	736 359	73·93	(73 463) (9·07%)	206 214	(21 456) (9·42%)	87 872	(12 899) (12·80%)	285 450	(16 642) (5·51%)	76 675	(8 659) (10·15%)	29 928	(7 842) (20·76%)	50 220	(5 965) (10·62%)
– takings	£102 055	81·09	£3 488 3·54%	—	—	—	—	—	—	—	—	—	—	—	—
Workmen – journeys	229 784	23·07	(3 325) (1·43%)	87 626	(1 407) (1·58%)	21 576	(1 571) (6·79%)	75 188	3 195 4·44%	22 513	(1 351) (5·66%)	11 283	(1 731) (13·30%)	11 598	(460) (3·82%)
– takings	£6 457	5·13	£839 14·93%	—	—	—	—	—	—	—	—	—	—	—	—

SOURCE British Rail

Notes:

(a) Passenger journeys represent the number of passengers carried by BR except where the journey began on London Transport and ended on the BR system. Figures shown in respect of a region are the passenger journeys originating in that region; they do not include journeys terminating or passing through that region which originated in another region. Through booked continental, Channel Islands and Irish traffic is included, with certain minor exceptions, as originating in the region of the port of entry.

(b) Children for whom tickets are issued are treated as adults, but infants in arms are ignored. Return tickets are counted as two journeys and journeys by season ticket holders computed on the basis of 600 journeys per annum. 'Ordinary fares' are the standard or full fares applicable to the ordinary travelling public, including children. 'Other descriptions' covers all bookings at fares lower than those applicable to the ordinary travelling public, except those which are shown separately. Examples are commercial travellers' weekend tickets, privilege tickets, services duty and furlough tickets, warrants, etc.

TABLE A.12   *Freight train traffic originating, 1948*

Freight type	Total all regions — Percentage of total %	Total all regions — tons 000s	Total all regions — Increase or (Decrease) on 1947	London Midland Region — tons 000s	London Midland Region — Increase or (Decrease) on 1947	Western Region — tons 000s	Western Region — Increase or (Decrease) on 1947	Southern Region — tons 000s	Southern Region — Increase or (Decrease) on 1947	Eastern Region — tons 000s	Eastern Region — Increase or (Decrease) on 1947	North-Eastern Region — tons 000s	North-Eastern Region — Increase or (Decrease) on 1947	Scottish Region — tons 000s	Scottish Region — Increase or (Decrease) on 1947
Merchandise	19.84	54 780	(568) (1·03%)	18 494	143 0·78%	9 955	(307) (2·99%)	3 704	(1) (0·02%)	7 261	(311) (4·11%)	7 481	300 4·18%	7 885	(392) (4·74%)
Minerals	21.47	59 280	6 783 12·92%	21 075	1 816 9·43%	8 249	1 114 15·61%	1 631	81 5·28%	9 562	657 7·38%	10 724	1 802 20·19%	8 039	1 313 19·52%
Coal and coke	58.36	161 145	11 862 7·95%	56 587	3 523 6·64%	24 194	1 359 5·95%	3 457	160 4·84%	25 558	2 716 11·89%	30 429	3 196 11·74%	20 920	908 4·54%
Livestock	0.33	912	(46) (4·82%)	201	(1) (0·42%)	153	3 2·42%	45	2 4·16%	78	(16) (17·58%)	92	(1) (0·92%)	343	(33) (8·84%)
Total	100	276 117	18 031 6·99%	96 357	5 481 6·03%	42 551	2 169 5·37%	8 837	242 2·82%	42 459	3 046 7·73%	48 726	5 297 12·20%	37 187	1 796 5·07%

SOURCE British Rail

Notes: (a) Tonnage figures for each region represent the total volume of freight traffic originating in the region and do not include traffic terminating, or passing through, which has originated in another region.. Continental, Channel Islands and Irish traffic invoiced to BR is treated as originating at the port of entry. In total, therefore, the figures represent the tonnage of revenue-earning traffic conveyed. Free hauled traffic, which includes railway service materials conveyed without charge on revenue-earning trains, is excluded.
(b) Traffic is classified as follows: 'Merchandise' includes all freight train traffic except 'Coal and Coke', 'Livestock' and traffic in Classes 1 to 6 of the General Railway Classification. 'Minerals' comprises all traffic in Classes 1 to 6 of the General Railway Classification, e.g., bricks, iron ore, lime, limestone, pig iron, roadstone and stone in the rough. 'Coal and coke' includes coal, coke, patent fuels, slack, smudge, cannel and coal cinders for fuel. 'Livestock' consists of the tonnage equivalent of the number of horses, cattle, sheep, pigs, etc., computed on a standard basis.

TABLE A.13 *Design offices involved in post-nationalisation BR Standard locomotive design*

Type of locomotive	Parent office for design	Detail design offices								
		Wheels and axles	Motion	Frames	Bogie complete	Pony truck complete	Brake gear	Boiler	Standard boiler fittings	Tender complete
0–6–0 diesel-electric shunting with EE power equipment	Derby	Derby	Derby	Derby			Derby			
0–6–0 diesel-electric shunting with Crompton Parkinson, GEC or BTH power equipment	Doncaster	Doncaster	Doncaster	Doncaster			Doncaster			
Class 8, 4–6–2 passenger tender	Derby	Derby	Derby	Derby	Derby	Derby	Brighton	Derby	Swindon	Derby
Class 7, 4–6–2 mixed traffic tender	Derby	Derby	Doncaster	Derby	Derby	Derby	Brighton	Derby	Swindon	Derby
Class 6, 4–6–2 mixed traffic tender	Derby	Derby	Doncaster	Derby	Derby	Derby	Brighton	Derby	Swindon	Derby
Class 5, 4–6–0 mixed traffic tender	Doncaster	Derby	Doncaster	Doncaster	Derby		Brighton	Doncaster	Swindon	Derby
Class 4, 4–6–0 mixed traffic tender	Brighton	Derby	Doncaster	Brighton	Derby		Brighton	Brighton	Swindon	Derby
Class 4, 2–6–0 mixed traffic tender	Doncaster	Derby	Doncaster	Doncaster		Derby	Brighton	Doncaster	Swindon	Derby
Class 3, 2–6–0 mixed traffic tender	Swindon	Swindon	Doncaster	Swindon		Derby	Brighton	Swindon	Swindon	Derby
Class 2, 2–6–0 mixed traffic tender	Derby	Derby	Derby	Derby		Derby	Brighton	Derby	Swindon	Derby
Class 4, 2–6–4 mixed traffic tank	Brighton	Derby	Doncaster	Brighton	Derby	Derby	Brighton	Brighton	Swindon	
Class 3, 2–6–2 mixed traffic tank	Swindon	Swindon	Doncaster	Swindon		Derby	Brighton	Swindon	Swindon	
Class 2, 2–6–2 mixed traffic tank	Derby	Derby	Derby	Derby		Derby	Brighton	Derby	Swindon	
Class 9, 2–10–0 freight tender	Brighton	Derby	Doncaster	Brighton		Derby	Brighton	Brighton	Swindon	Derby

SOURCE British Rail

TABLE A.14 *Building of the first BR Standard locomotives, 1954*

Type of locomotive		Building allocation	
		Number	*Region/works*
2–10–0	Class 9	67	LM/Crewe
4–6–2	Class 6	15	LM/Crewe
4–6–0	Class 5	15	LM/Derby
4–6–0	Class 4	10	W/Swindon
2–6–4T	Class 4	15	S/Brighton
2–6–0	Class 4	30	E/NE/Doncaster
2–6–0	Class 3	5	W/Swindon
2–6–2T	Class 3	18	W/Swindon
2–6–0	Class 2	10	E/NE/Darlington
0–6–0T	16xx	20	W/Swindon
350 HP diesel-electric		{ 45	LM/Derby
		{ 40	E/NE/Darlington

SOURCE British Rail

TABLE A.15 *BR stock levels, 1948–64*

Year	Locomotives			Multiple-unit vehicles power cars and trailers		Coaching vehicles		
	Steam	*Electric*	*Diesel and diesel-electric*	*Electric*	*Diesel and diesel-electric*	*Passenger carriages*	*Seating and berth capacity*	*Non-passenger vehicles (parcels vans, etc.)*
1948	20 211	17	69	4 235	40	40 351	2 417 000	15 315
1949	19 790	17	102	4 606	39	41 192	2 464 000	15 226
1950	19 598	10	128	4 597	39	42 218	2 506 000	16 004
1951	19 103	33	148	4 560	36	42 087	2 501 000	15 902
1952	18 859	58	211	4 597	36	41 881	2 482 000	15 791
1953	18 584	65	260	4 571	39	41 762	2 468 000	15 529
1954	18 420	71	320	4 638	72	41 917	2 480 000	15 847
1955	17 955	71	456	4 685	181	41 715	2 459 000	15 687
1956	17 522	71	609	4 948	455	41 522	2 438 000	15 163
1957	16 954	71	803	5 013	1 351	41 827	2 446 000	14 994
1958	16 103	72	1 201	5 270	2 422	42 003	2 446 000	14 926
1959	14 452	85	1 800	5 854	3 252	40 537	2 361 000	14 271
1960	13 271	135	2 550	6 442	3 833	40 091	2 331 000	14 871
1961	11 687	158	3 179	6 916	4 011	37 849	2 203 000	14 551
1962	8 764	178	3 683	6 982	4 087	33 607	1 953 000	12 482
1963	7 047	194	4 060	7 021	4 145	31 598	1 809 000	11 521
1964	4 970	198	4 462	7 004	4 120	26 678	1 546 000	10 725

SOURCE British Rail

TABLE A.16   *BREL statistics, 1979*

	£000s
Turnover – year 1979	
Repairs and modifications to BR rolling stock	186 083
New rolling stock production for BR	109 161
Services and material issues to BR	68 529
Work for private parties	31 349
Total	395 122
Book Value of Capital Employed 31.12.79	£234.5m
Position at 31.12.79	
Number of workshops	13
Number of staff	
Salaried	5 776
Wages paid	30 460
Total	36 236
Output of repaired rolling stock in 1979	
Locomotives	1 562
HST power cars	88
HST trailer cars	330
Locomotive-hauled carriages	6 463
Diesel multiple units	1 349
Electric multiple units	2 066
Wagons	33 118
Containers	55

SOURCE   BREL

Table A.17   *Total output of BREL workshops, year ending 31 December 1981*

New construction for BR	No. built
High Speed Train power cars	36
Class 56 diesel main-line locomotives	14
High Speed Train coaches	32
Mark III sleeping cars	27
EMUs – Class 315	95
EMUs – Class 317	71
Diesel-electric multiple units – prototype	3
BREL/Leyland rail-bus	1
Steel-carrying wagons – BBA	12
Steel-carrying wagons – BBD conversion	90
Steel-carrying wagons – BPA conversion	30
Steel-carrying wagons – BRA conversion	146
Service wagons – 'Seacow'	186
Service wagons – skip storage	22
Service wagons – bogie hopper ballast	6
47-ton mineral wagons – HAA	655
40-foot container carrying vehicle	1
44-ton 2-axle van – VGA	1
Open wagons – OCA	265
PVC/nylon wagon sheets	1 063

New construction for private parties		
Customer	Description	No. built
Tanzania	First-class couchette cars	14
	Buffet cars	10
	Bogie covered goods wagons	112
	Crew vans	8
Bangladesh	Broad-gauge wagons	128
Blue Circle Cement Ltd	Cement tank wagons	60
Ministry of Defence	'Warflat' wagons	26
British Petroleum Oil Co.	Tank conversions	220

			Classified		
Repair work	General	Inter.	Light	Total	Unclassified
High Speed Train power cars	–	40	66	106	3
Diesel-engined main-line locomotives	98	159	98	355	356
Electric-engined main-line locomotives	45	6	42	93	46
Diesel-electric shunting locomotives	32	18	–	50	61
Traction motors – armatures				7 555	
Traction motors – carcases				7 094	
Generators – armatures				783	
Generators – carcases				778	

TABLE A.17   *Continued*

Repair work (contd)		C1R	C1/C2	C3	C3T	C4	C4X	C6	Total	C5
					Classified					
Loco-hauled coaching stock										
High Speed Train trailer				151		294			445	24
Passenger-carrying – special			3	98		261			362	58
– ord'y			191	742	324	1 810			3 067	269
Non-passenger-carrying										
Bogie repairs			58	388		494			940	113
DMUs		157	59	829		58			1 103	86
EMUs		248	659	938		85	152	4	2 086	35

	GR	IR/L	IR/W	IR	Total
		Classified			
Traffic wagons	2 858	238	2 917	8 818	14 831
PVC/nylon wagon sheets					5 219

	Engines	Gearboxes	Final drives	Torque converters
DMU components	2 252	2 334	1 488	59

TABLE A.18　*Unit cost of BREL new builds, 1977 and 1981*

1982 prices	1977 £000	1981 £000	% change
Locomotive	913	856	− 6
HST power	671	652	− 3
HST trailer	152	156	+ 3
Loco-hauled coach	142	288	+103
EMU	194	218	+ 12
Freight wagon	20.5	25.3	+ 23

SOURCE　BREL

TABLE A.19　*Maintenance costs per unit, 1981*

	Number in fleet	1981 outturn maintenance cost £m	1981 outturn cost per vehicle £
Diesel locomotives	2 054	106	51 600
Electric locomotives	267	12	44 940
Shunting locomotives	803	5	6 230
HST power cars	181	35	199 370
DMUs	3 105	71	22 870
EMUs	7 365	91	12 350
LHCVs	7 734	61	7 890
Freight wagons	84 568	57	675

SOURCE　BREL

TABLE A.20　*Staff employed in BR Engineering and in BREL, 1982*

	Number of employees (approx.)		
		Region/Workshops	
Function	Headquarters	Salaried	Wage earning
CE	210	7 080	27 300
S&TE	160	2 570	7 100
M&EE	1 600	3 700	17 600
BREL	350	5 500	28 800

SOURCE　BREL

Appendix

TABLE A.21   *BR traffic, 1980*

Freight	Million tonnes
Coal and coke	94
Iron and steel	13
Oil and chemicals	18
Building materials	19
Mixed traffic	2
Freightliners	8
	154
Total revenue	£610 m
Passenger	
Journeys	760 m
Revenue	£954 m

SOURCE   British Rail

TABLE A.22   *BR financial results, 1980*

Where the money came from	£m	Totals £m
Railway		
Passenger, freight and parcels	1 564.5	
Contract payments	633.6	2 198.1
Shipping		
Ships	196.3	
Harbours	24.1	220.4
Hotels		42.0
Catering		
Station	45.5	
Train	21.2	66.7
Property		
Operational letting	35.7	
Non-operational letting	13.7	49.4
Others		
Rail workshop sales	39.6	
Freightliners	69.0	
Hovercraft	13.1	
Transmark (consultancy services)	6.1	
Other	14.7	142.5
Total income		2 719.1
Where the money went		
Staff costs		1 547.9
Materials, supplies and services		858.6
Fuel and power		191.3
Interest on borrowing		69.7
Depreciation on assets		128.5
Total outgoings		2 796.0

SOURCE   British Rail

Note:
As this shows, BR made a loss of £76.9 m. After taking into account additional provision for replacement of assets owing to inflation, there was an overall loss of £163 m.

TABLE A.23   *Changes in method of BR freight movement, 1970–81*

Method	1970 million tonnes	1974 million tonnes	1979 million tonnes	1981 million tonnes
Trainload	106	133	145	137
Wagonload	93	43	24	17

SOURCE   British Rail

TABLE A.24   *Analysis of BR freight carryings, 1970–81*

Commodity	1970 million tonnes	1974 million tonnes	1979 million tonnes	1981 million tonnes
Coal & coke	114	88	94	95
Iron & steel	40	31	25	18
Petroleum/chemicals	23	23	21	16
Aggregates/building materials	18	22	19	16

SOURCE   British Rail

TABLE A.25   *BR freight carryings by commodity, 1981*

Commodity	Million tonnes	% share of total rail freight by weight	Tonne miles	% share of total rail freight by tonne miles
Coal & coke	95	62	3 929	34
Iron & steel	18	12	1 366	12
Petroleum/chemicals	16	10	1 960	17
Aggregates/building materials	16	10	1 485	13
Other	9	6	2 690	24

SOURCE   British Rail

TABLE A.26   *BR passenger miles, revenue, costs and grant 1975–82*

1982 prices	1975	1976	1977	1978	1979	1980	1981	1982
Passenger miles (millions)	18 800	17 700	18 200	19 100	19 900	19 700	19 100	17 000
Revenue (pence) per passenger mile	5.2	5.7	5.8	5.9	5.7	5.8	5.8	5.4
Costs (pence) per passenger mile	9.2	9.4	9.2	9.5	9.4	9.8	10.5	11.3
Grant (pence) per passenger mile	3.9	3.8	3.6	3.7	3.9	3.9	4.7	5.4

SOURCE   British Rail

TABLE A.27   *BR freight and parcels business results, 1975–82*

1982 prices	1975 £m	1976 £m	1977 £m	1978 £m	1979 £m	1980 £m	1981 £m	1982 £m
Revenue	805	861	863	847	848	752	715	616
Costs	940	891	860	830	826	788	698	605

SOURCE   British Rail

TABLE A.28   *BR financial results, 1975–82*

1982 prices	1975 £m	1976 £m	1977 £m	1978 £m	1979 £m	1980 £m	1981 £m	1982 £m
Revenue: passenger	1 031	1 045	1 090	1 154	1 149	1 167	1 126	927
freight	604	664	667	654	661	585	586	522
parcels	201	197	197	193	187	170	130	94
Total revenue	1 836	1 906	1 954	2 001	1 997	1 919	1 841	1 543
Costs	2 663	2 554	2 533	2 648	2 701	2 723	2 700	2 567

SOURCE   British Rail

TABLE A.29 *BR five-year statistical summary, 1978–82*

		1978	1979	1980	1981	1982
Passenger receipts and traffic						
Receipts	£m	701.8	799.7	954.0	1 022.8	924.1
Passenger journeys	millions	734.0	748.0	760.0	718.5	630.1
Passenger miles (estimated)	millions	19 100	19 900	19 700	19 100	17 000
Freight and parcels receipts and traffic						
Freight train – receipts	£m	384.5	432.1	459.8	503.7	478.2
– traffic	tonnes, m	171.0	169.0	153.0	154.2	141.9
– net tonne miles						
(trainload and wagonload)	millions	12 416	12 361	10 961	10 877	9 867
Parcels – receipts	£m	119.4	130.8	141.2	119.4	92.2
– traffic	tonnes, m	1.2	1.2	1.2	0.9	0.7
Operations						
Loaded train miles – coaching	millions	208.0	207.0	214.0	208.9	185.2
freight	millions	38.0	36.0	32.0	30.4	27.0
Traction hours in						
traffic – coaching	millions	9.3	9.1	9.2	8.9	7.9
– freight	millions	5.7	5.5	4.8	4.3	3.7
Loaded wagons forwarded	millions	7.0	6.7	5.9	5.7	5.0
Loaded wagon miles	millions	590.0	565.0	483.0	444.8	381.2
Assets at end of year						
Locomotives – diesel		3 268	3 261	3 078	2 864	2 750
– electric		312	310	301	267	266
APT – power cars		2	5	6	6	6
– passenger carriages		6	15	30	30	30
HST – power cars		109	136	142	181	197
passenger carriages		421	533	630	664	709
Coaching vehicles		21 031	20 963	20 408	18 268	16 889
Freight vehicles (excluding						
brake vans)		150 371	137 589	119 507	88 327	71 452
Stations		2 837	2 821	2 787	2 742	2 711
Route open for traffic	miles	11 123	11 020	10 964	10 831	10 706
Staff at end of year		182 198	182 031	178 059	170 397	161 407

SOURCE British Rail

TABLE A.30　*BR overall performance, 1979–83*

		1979	1980	1981	1982	1983
Total receipts per train mile	£	7.41	6.97	6.89	6.62	6.83
Train service (operating) expenses per train mile	£		2.30	2.36	2.39	2.31
Train service (maintenance) expenses per train mile	£		1.97	1.94	2.13	1.90
Terminal expenses per train mile	£		1.17	1.10	1.12	1.06
Infrastructure expenses per train mile	£		2.60	2.58	2.02	2.72
Administration costs per train mile	£	1.36	1.33	1.41	1.49	1.35
Train miles per member of staff (total staff productivity)	miles	1 521	1 570	1 597	1 495	1 688
Revenue per £1000 gross paybill costs	£	1 537	1 459	1 394	1 256	1 400
Train miles per train crew member (train crew productivity)	miles	7 099	7 244	7 478	6 947	7 898
Track maintenance costs per single track mile	£	9 621	9 539	9 523	9 475	10 010
Signal renewal and maintenance costs per single track mile	£	6 379	6 342	6 284	5 982	6 000
Signal operating costs per single track mile	£	4 625	4 547	4 655	4 463	4 506
Train miles per single track mile	000s	12.6	12.8	12.6	11.3	12.5
Train miles per locomotive/HST set	000s	51.7	53.4	55.2	51.1	57.1
PSO grants per passenger mile	pence	3.89	4.0	4.80	5.52	4.98
PSO grants as percentage of passenger receipts	%	65.3	66.3	78.9	95.9	81.4
Passenger receipts per loaded train mile	£	6.05	5.86	5.78	5.51	5.93
Receipts per passenger mile	pence	5.96	6.04	6.08	5.76	6.12
Passenger miles per loaded train mile (average trainload)	passengers	102	97	95	96	97
Loaded train miles per passenger vehicle	miles	11 416	11 937	12 417	11 580	13 076
Passenger trains arriving within 5 mins of booked time	%	87	89	90	88	90
Passenger trains cancelled	%	3.1	1.4	1.1	1.3	1.0
Train catering services cancelled	%		4.7	3.2	3.5	3.6
Freight operating surplus as percentage of receipts	%				0.4	1.5
Freight receipts per train mile	Index	103	100	104	105	105
Freight receipts per net tonne mile	Index	102	100	100	98	93
Tonne miles per loaded freight train mile (average trainload)	tonnes	343	338	358	366	377
Train miles per freight wagon	miles	303	308	385	408	525
Parcels operating surplus as percentage of receipts	%				8.9	14.1

SOURCE　British Rail

Table A.31   *BR stock levels, 1949 and 1981*

Classification	1949	1981	Reduction %
Locomotives	19 909	3 131	84
Coaches	58 222	19 149	67
Freight vehicles	1 141 925	119 128	90
Containers	25 536	125	99
Total	1 245 592	141 533	89

Note: Allowance must be made for the introduction of much larger freight vehicles in recent years.

Table A.32   *BR locomotive stock on 1 January 1983*

Class of locomotive	Number
Main-line diesel-electric	2 005
Diesel-electric shunters	745
AC electric	219
DC electric	47
Steam	3
Total stock	3 019

Note: The three steam locomotives were built for the narrow-gauge Vale of Rheidol Light Railway, built in 1902 and becoming part of the GWR at the 1923 amalgamation. It only operates during the summer months. No. 9 ('Prince of Wales') was built in 1902 and Nos 7 and 8 ('Owen Glendower' and 'Llewellen') in 1923.

TABLE A.33   *Road motor vehicles licensed in Great Britain, 1903–80*

Year	Private cars and private vans	Motor cycles scooters and mopeds	Public transport vehicles	Goods	Agri- cultural tractors	Other vehicles	Crown and exempt vehicles	All vehicles
			Figures in thousands					
1903	8		5	4				17
1930	1 056	712	101	349	15	15	24	2 272
1940	1 423	278	81	444	50	2	47	2 325
1950	2 258	729	136	895	296	26	68	4 408
1960	5 526	1 796	93	1 397	443	72	113	9 440
1970	11 515	1 048	103	1 616	434	99	135	14 950
1980	15 073	1 372	110	1 761	397	100	397	19 210

SOURCE   Department of Transport

TABLE A.34   *Road accidents in Great Britain by type of area, class of road and severity, 1981*

Location	Fatal	Serious	Slight	All accidents
Built-up areas	2 814	44 189	142 172	189 175
Non-built-up areas	2 541	20 788	35 762	59 091
Main roads*	3 309	31 604	88 312	123 225
Minor roads†	2 046	33 376	89 628	125 050
All areas/all roads‡	5 355	64 980	177 941	248 276

SOURCE   Department of Transport

Notes:
The severity of a road accident is defined as 'the severity of the most seriously injured casualty in the accident'.
* motorways, A(M) and A roads (i.e. motorways, trunk and principal roads)
† B, C and unclassified roads (i.e. other roads)
‡ includes unknown road type

TABLE A.35   *Road casualties in Great Britain by class of road user, 1978–81*

Year	Pedestrians All ages	Children only	Pedal cyclists	Motor cyclists and moped riders	Car users	Other vehicle users	Total casualties	Motor traffic (thousand million kilometres)
1978	70 295	28 909	22 201	69 733	157 875	29 691	349 795	274.2
1979	66 714	26 379	23 645	67 155	149 511	27 488	334 513	275.8
1980	63 299	24 931	24 788	70 838	143 517	24 290	328 600*	283.1
1981	60 750	23 722	25 306	69 129	146 317	23 338	324 840	277.7

*Adjusted for additional accidents not analysed in detail
SOURCE   Department of Transport

TABLE A.36   *Road casualties in Great Britain by class of road user, type of area and severity, 1981*

	Casualties by severity			
	Killed	*Seriously injured*	*Slightly injured*	*Total of all casualties*
Pedestrians				
Children	318	6 229	17 175	23 722
Adults – 15–59 years	605	6 353	17 148	24 106
– 60 and over	947	3 912	6 334	11 193
Age not reported	4	119	1 606	1 729
Total casualties	1 874	16 613	42 263	60 750
Pedal cyclists				
Children	86	2 010	7 262	9 358
Adults	224	3 169	12 177	15 570
Age not reported	—	15	363	378
Total casualties	310	5 194	19 802	25 306
Two-wheeled motor vehicle users				
Moped	81	2 873	7 597	10 551
Motor scooter	18	559	1 600	2 177
Motor cycle	1 032	17 766	37 603	56 401
Total casualties	1 131	21 198	46 800	69 129
Other vehicle users				
Car	2 287	31 338	112 692	146 317
Bus and coach	20	941	8 925	9 886
Goods vehicle	203	2 688	9 264	12 155
Other vehicle	21	287	989	1 297
Total casualties	2 531	35 254	131 870	169 655
All road users				
Children	504	9 853	34 036	44 393
Adults – 15–59 years	3 782	59 119	178 950	241 851
– 60 and over	1 554	8 845	23 091	33 490
Age not reported	6	442	4 658	5 106
Total casualties	5 846	78 259	240 735	324 840
Type of area				
Built-up (30–40 m.p.h.)	2 940	49 707	179 617	232 264
Non-built-up (50–70 m.p.h.)	2 906	28 549	61 107	92 562
Area not reported	—	3	11	14
Total casualties	5 846	78 259	240 735	324 840

SOURCE   Department of Transport

Notes: The statistics refer to personal injury accidents reported to the police. Figures for deaths refer to persons who died within 30 days of the accident. This is the usual international definition and differs from that used in other contexts by the Registrars General.

TABLE A.37 *Senior railway engineers who have held the office of President of the Institution of Mechanical Engineers since it was founded in 1847 and up to 1986*

	Period of office
George Stephenson	1847–8
Robert Stephenson, FRS	1849–53
John R. Ramsbottom	1870–1
Joseph Tomlinson	1890–1
Samuel Waite Johnson	1898
Sir John A.F. Aspinall	1909–10
Sir Vincent L. Raven, KBE	1925
Sir Henry Fowler, KBE	1927
Sir Nigel Gresley, CBE	1936
Sir William A. Stanier, FRS	1941
Oliver V.S. Bulleid, CBE	1946
Roland C. Bond	1963

Bibliography

Ahrons, E. L., 'Histories of Famous Locomotive Builders', series of articles in *The Engineer*, vols 129–36.

Allen, C. J., *The London and North Eastern Railway* (Ian Allan).

Bagnell, P. S., *The History of the National Union of Railwaymen* (George Allen & Unwin, 1963).

Berdrow, W., *The Krupps, 1787–1937* (Verlag für Sozialpolitik, Wirtschaft und Statistik, 1937).

Bonavia, M. R., *The Economics of Transport* (Nisbet/Cambridge University Press, 1936).

Bonavia, M. R., *The Organisation of British Railways* (Ian Allan, 1971).

Bonavia, M. R., *The Birth of British Rail* (George Allen & Unwin, 1979).

Bonavia, M. R., *The Four Great Railways* (David & Charles, 1980).

Bonavia, M. R., *British Rail: The First 25 Years* (David & Charles, 1981).

Bonavia, M. R., *Railway Policy Between the Wars* (Manchester University Press, 1981).

Bonavia, M. R., *The History of the LNER*, vols 1 and 2 (George Allen & Unwin, 1982); vol. 3 (George Allen & Unwin, 1983).

Bond, R. C., *A Lifetime with Locomotives* (Goose & Son, 1975).

Brown, F. A. S., *Sir Nigel Gresley, Locomotive Engineer* (Ian Allan, 1962).

Bulleid, H. A. V., *Master Builders of Steam* (Ian Allan, 1983).

Cox, E. S., *Locomotive Panorama*, 2 vols (Ian Allan, 1965).

Cox, E. S., *British Railways Standard Steam Locomotives* (Ian Allan, 1966).

Darwin, B., *A Century of Medical Service: The Swindon Medical Fund Society* (Swindon Press, 1947).

Doughan, D., *Sir William Armstrong – The Great Gunmaker* (Frank Graham, Newcastle-upon-Tyne, 1970).

Gale, W. K. V., *Iron and Steel* (The Moorland Publishing Co., Ashbourne, 1977).

Hume, K. J., *History of Engineering Metrology* (Mechanical Engineering Publications, 1980).

Johnson, J., and R. A. Long, *British Railways Engineering, 1948–80* (Mechanical Engineering Publications, 1981).

Kelley, T., *George Birkbeck: The Creator of the Mechanics Institutes* (Liverpool University Press, 1957).

Larkin, E. J., *Works Organization and Management* (Pitman, 1st edn 1940; 2nd edn 1945).

Larkin, E. J., *The Elements of Workshop Training* (Pitman, 1st edn 1945; reprinted 1946; 2nd edn 1947).

Larkin, E. J., *Memoirs of a Railway Engineer* (Mechanical Engineering Publications, 1979).

Low, R. C. S., 'The Re-organisation of British Railways Workshops', *Journal of Institution of Locomotive Engineers*, 1967.

Lowe, J. W., *British Steam Locomotive Builders* (Goose & Son, 1975)

Mountford, E., *Caerphilly Works, 1901–1964* (Roundhouse Books, 1965).

Nock, O. S., *Sir William Stanier, An Engineering Biography* (Ian Allan, 1966).

Nock, O. S., *History of the Great Western Railway* (Ian Allan, 1964).

Nock, O. S., *Two Miles a Minute* (Patrick Stephens, 1980).

Nock, O. S., (gen. ed.) *Encyclopaedia of Railways* (Octopus, 1977).

Peck, A. S., *The Great Western at Swindon Works* (Oxford Publishing Company, 1983).

Radford, J. B., *Derby Works and Midland Locomotives* (Ian Allan, 1971).

Reed, B., *Crewe Locomotive Works and its Men* (David & Charles, 1982).

Rogers, H. C. B., *The Last Steam Locomotive Engineer* (George Allen & Unwin, 1970).

Rogers, H. C. B., *Riddles and the '9Fs'* (Ian Allan, 1982).

Round the Works of Our Great Railways (Arnold, 1893).

Skeat, W. O., *George Stephenson and His Letters* (Mechanical Engineering Publications, 1973).

Smith, S. A. S., 'The British Railways Mechanised Iron Foundry, Horwich', *Journal of Institution of Locomotive Engineers*, 1955.

Thomas, J., *The Springburn Story: The History of the Scottish Railway Metropolis* (David & Charles, 1964).

Warder, S. B., 'Electric Traction in the British Railways Modernisation Plan,' *Journal of Institution of Civil Engineers*, vol. 18, 1961.

Warren, J. G. H., *A Century of Locomotive Building, Robert Stephenson & Company, 1823–1923* (Andrew Reid & Co., 1923).

Wilson, R. B., *Sir Daniel Gooch: Memoirs and Diary* (David & Charles, 1972).

Wilson and Reader, *Men and Machines: History of D. Napier and Son, 1808–1958* (Weidenfeld & Nicolson, 1958).

Young, R., *Timothy Hackworth* (Shildon 'Stockton & Darlington Railway' Jubilee Committee, Shildon Town Council Office, County Durham, 1975).

Index

Index